P9-DHN-883

A Teacher's Guide to

GEOMETRY

A Teacher's Guide to

GEOMETRY

Harold R. Jacobs

W. H. FREEMAN AND COMPANY
San Francisco

The cover illustration is a lithograph titled <u>Ascending and Descending</u>

by Maurits Escher. Reproduced by permission of the Escher Foundation,

Haags Gemeentemuseum, The Hague.

Copyright © 1974 by W. H. Freeman and Company

No part of this book may be reproduced by any mechanical,
photographic, or electronic process, or in the form of
a phonographic recording, nor may it be stored in a retrieval
system, transmitted, or otherwise copied for public or
private use, without the written permission of the publisher.

Printed in the United States of America

ISBN 0-7167-0460-9

9 8 7 6 5 4 3 2

Contents

Introductory Comments

Several years ago, Dr. Morris Kline wrote in The Mathematics Teacher:

I believe that the chief problem in teaching mathematics is motivation. It is difficult for beginners in mathematics...to see just why one should study the subject.... Vague answers, such as that scientists and engineers use it...or that it is needed to get into college, don't help at all. The motivation was sadly deficient in the traditional curriculum, and is entirely absent in the modern mathematics curriculum. By utilizing real problems chosen from the world in which the student lives and involving phenomena which he himself experiences we may be able to motivate the study of mathematics....

The method recommended to supply motivation...gives meaning to mathematics. We would all agree that we want our subject to make sense to the students. The road to making sense is through the senses, and this means physical problems and situations....*

As is probably evident from my geometry textbook, I am in complete agreement with Dr. Kline. The purpose of this teacher's guide is to provide you with additional ideas on how to motivate your students to want to learn geometry and on how to help them enjoy the subject. In addition to many practical applications and historical anecdotes, I have included puzzles with surprising answers and problems that are merely whimsical in nature. I have found that most students do

---

*Morris Kline, "A Proposal for the High School Mathematics Curriculum," The Mathematics Teacher, April 1966, pp. 329-330.

not judge the value of what they are learning by the immediate practical use they may see in it, but by whether it is interesting to them. Students who are enjoying what they are learning do not continually ask why they have to learn it or what good it is.

First, a comment about the textbook itself. I am aware of the problems of students who are poor readers and have tried, in writing my book, to present the material in a way that will help such students improve their reading skills. I feel that every high school course for college-bound students should provide this opportunity. I think that the difficulty with many mathematics textbooks is that they are either so dull or so condescending that many students do not want to read them and become too dependent upon their teachers. I hope that your students will find the anecdotes and illustrations sufficiently entertaining that they will be encouraged to read the lessons. I have made every effort to present geometry in such a way that students will be able to teach themselves any lessons they have missed.

I have tried to include sufficient detail in the lesson plans in this guide to give a clear picture of what I do in my own classroom. The presentation of lessons, including questions that I might use, are interspersed with comments to you explaining what I am doing. However, what works well for me may not for you, just as I might have difficulty in succeeding with some of the things that you do in your classroom. If you are a beginning teacher, you may be tempted to try to follow these lesson plans rigidly. If so, I urge you not to take them too seriously. I am a firm believer in continually trying out new ideas and in modifying or discarding those that don't turn out well.

It is expected that most classes will ordinarily cover one lesson each day. You will note in a few of the plans, however, that some of them may take two days. You may decide that more than one day should be devoted to some of the other lessons as well. Some teachers provide their students with a complete list of assignments and due dates at the beginning of a course. I think this is very unwise. It is better to be flexible and to modify one's plans whenever the students seem to be finding the work especially difficult. You may want to devote some days to laboratory activities or to algebra review or to doing an assignment together in small groups in class. If you compare the number of lesson plans in this guide with the number of days on your school calendar, you should find that you have a reasonable number of spare days in which to do these things.

For most classes, the normal assignment might consist of all of the exercises in Sets I and II. Ordinarily, but not always, the exercises in Set I are the easiest and emphasize the basic ideas of the lesson. For slow classes, it is best not to assign all of the exercises in Set II. The Set III exercises are meant to be optional and I count the work of those students who do them correctly as extra credit. I have tried to make the Set III exercises sufficiently interesting that the brighter students will want to do them; although some of them are fairly easy, others are quite challenging.

As you have probably noted, the answers to many of the exercises are provided at the end of the textbook. Even though some students may be tempted to misuse them, I see no reason not to make most answers readily available to students. Answers to almost all of the exercises in the chapter reviews are provided so that the students can check their work. I often assign them as classwork on the day immediately preceding the test on the chapter; therefore there is not always enough time to discuss all of them in class.

All of the answers to exercises that are not provided in the text are given in the answer section of this guide. This primarily includes the Set II proofs and the Set III exercises, since I feel it would be demoralizing to provide these kinds of answers to the student. Calculations for many of the numerical exercises answered in the textbook are also included in this guide and are denoted by asterisks.

References are made throughout the lesson plans to a series of overhead transparencies and student worksheets. These are available from the publisher in book form. The perforated pages can be removed and a Thermofax machine can be used to make whichever ones you choose into projection transparencies and duplicator masters. I have found that the overhead projector makes it possible to present ideas much more easily and efficiently than can be done using just a blackboard.

A set of tests for the sixteen chapters, together with midyear and final examinations, is also available from the publisher. Each test is in two forms and can be made into duplicator masters or merely used as a source of ideas for test questions.

Harold R. Jacobs

Recommended Books

Coxeter, H. S. M. Introduction to Geometry, second edition. John Wiley and Sons, 1969.

Coxeter, H. S. M., and S. L. Greitzer. Geometry Revisited. Random House, 1967.

Cundy, H. Martyn, and A. P. Rollett. Mathematical Models, second edition. Oxford University Press, 1961.

Eves, Howard W. In Mathematical Circles (in two volumes). Prindle, Weber and Schmidt, 1969.

Eves, Howard W. Mathematical Circles Revisited. Prindle, Weber and Schmidt, 1971.

Eves, Howard W. Mathematical Circles Squared. Prindle, Weber and Schmidt, 1972.

Fremont, Herbert. How to Teach Mathematics in Secondary Schools. W. B. Saunders Company, 1969.

Gardner, Martin. The Scientific American Book of Mathematical Puzzles and Diversions. Simon and Schuster, 1959.

Gardner, Martin. The Second Scientific American Book of Mathematical Puzzles and Diversions. Simon and Schuster, 1961.

Gardner, Martin. Martin Gardner's New Mathematical Diversions from Scientific American. Simon and Schuster, 1966.

Gardner, Martin. The Unexpected Hanging and Other Mathematical Diversions. Simon and Schuster, 1969.

Gardner, Martin. Martin Gardner's Sixth Book of Mathematical Games from Scientific American. W. H. Freeman and Company, 1971.

Holden, Alan. Shapes, Space, and Symmetry. Columbia University Press, 1971.

Kline, Morris. Mathematics and the Physical World. Thomas Y. Crowell, 1959.

Kline, Morris. Mathematics in Western Culture. Oxford University Press, 1953.

Ogilvy, C. Stanley. Excursions in Geometry. Oxford University Press, 1969.

Steinhaus, H. Mathematical Snapshots, third edition. Oxford University Press, 1969.

Valens, Evans G. The Number of Things: Pythagoras, Geometry and Humming Strings. E. P. Dutton and Co., 1964.

Wenninger, Magnus J. Polyhedron Models. Cambridge University Press, 1971.

Geometry in the Mathematics Curriculum. Thirty-sixth Yearbook, National Council of Teachers of Mathematics, 1973.

A Teacher's Guide to

GEOMETRY

LESSON PLANS

Euclid, the Surfer, and the Spotter

The introductory section includes a brief commentary on Euclid and the Elements, the construction of an equilateral triangle, and the puzzles of the surfer and the spotter. Although this material could be assigned as homework, it is intended to be completed and discussed in class. You will probably need to provide your students with rulers and compasses.

In essence, the puzzle of the spotter is to find the location of the point inside or on an equilateral triangle for which the sum of the distances from that point to the vertices of the triangle is a minimum. After some experimentation, your students should conclude that this point is at the "center" of the triangle. Someone might explain how they think the center of the triangle might be accurately located. The three paths from the center to the vertices would have the same length; their sum is about 20.8 km. The worst place on the island for the spotter to locate is at the point for which the sum of its distances to the vertices of the triangle is a maximum. There are actually three of these points—namely, the vertices themselves. The sum of the lengths of the paths from one vertex to the other two is 24.0 km.

The surfer's puzzle consists of trying to find the location of the point inside or on an equilateral triangle for which the sum of the distances from that point to the sides of the triangle is a minimum. Before they try any points, your students will probably assume that the answer to this puzzle is the same as before. It is a remarkable fact, however, that the sum of the three distances is the same for every point either inside or on the triangle! It is about 10.4 km. Hence there is no best or worst place for the surfer to locate.

My students are generally content with their analysis of the spotter's puzzle. Although they haven't proved why the center is the best place and the corners are the worst, these answers seem reasonable.

The result of the surfer's puzzle, on the other hand, is surprising and hence disconcerting. Why should the sum of the three distances be independent of the position of the point? Certainly no amount of experimentation is capable of either proving or explaining this claim. This realization suggests that, to be confident of the conclusions that we may draw in geometry, we must have some basis for understanding them and for convincing others that they are correct. Deductive reasoning provides this basis and it is the subject of the first unit of the course.

Transparencies 0-1, 0-2, 0-3, and 0-4 are for use in presenting the introductory lesson.

The spotter's puzzle is a special case of a problem proposed by Pierre Fermat; its solution can be explained by means of transformations. The solution to the surfer's puzzle can be understood by means of the theory of area. Both puzzles will be reconsidered later in the course.

Chapter **1**

THE NATURE OF
DEDUCTIVE REASONING

Lesson 1
Drawing Conclusions

The purpose of this lesson is to reveal how
difficult it is to draw conclusions with cer-
tainty from passages of ordinary English.
It needs very little introduction. You might
introduce it by showing Transparency 1-1
and mentioning that the headline of this ad
is written so as to fool the reader into
drawing an incorrect conclusion. Since that
conclusion is surprising, he is enticed into
reading the rest of the ad, in which a different conclusion is revealed.

You may wish to have a couple of your
students read the passages in Set I aloud and
then let the class answer the accompanying
exercises orally. Avoid the temptation of
telling the students that their answers are
"right" or "wrong." There will probably be
many differences of opinion; if everyone is
encouraged to defend his views, it will be
easier to appreciate more fully that we need
to have a common basis for drawing conclusions with which we can all agree. Our
study throughout the rest of this unit of the
nature of deductive reasoning will help provide this basis.

Lesson 2
Conditional Statements

Dr. Banesh Hoffman has written an interesting book titled The Tyranny of Testing
(Crowell-Collier Press, 1962). In it, he
points out that it is difficult to construct
multiple-choice questions that are completely unambiguous. Transparency 1-2 shows a
subtle ambiguity in a sample question from
an early version of a test on critical thinking. Because of this ambiguity, the question
was later revised.

The person taking the test was supposed
"to decide for each assumption whether it
necessarily is taken for granted in the
statement." It was claimed that assumptions
1 and 2 were made whereas assumption 3 was
not. The answer for assumption 2 was justi-
fied by saying that "in order to save time by
plane, it must be possible to go by plane."
Although this is certainly true, it may not be
possible to go by plane to our destination.
Perhaps we can fly most of the way and drive
a car the remaining distance.

Can you think of how the second assumption might be easily reworded to remove
this ambiguity? (After your students have

had time to think about this, add the overlay to Transparency 1-2, which shows how the test-makers revised the question.) If even test-makers sometimes have difficulty in stating questions from which definite conclusions can be drawn, it is evident that we will always need to be on guard for hidden or unjustified assumptions in our study of geometry.

To introduce the new lesson, you might show Transparency 1-3 (this ad is also on page 12 of the text) and point out that its headline is an example of a conditional statement. Advertisements having conditional-statement headlines are surprisingly common—a bulletin board covered with such ads would provide an impressive display of the wide use of these statements to persuade people to draw specific conclusions. Explain that, since conditional statements are also used very frequently in mathematics, we will take time to consider their structure. Use Transparency 1-4 to show how an ad's headline can be illustrated by an Euler diagram. Be sure to generalize, so that the students understand the meaning of the symbols a → b.

Lesson 3
Equivalent Statements

Ask if anyone knows who is pictured on the U.S. fifty dollar bill and then show Transparency 1-5.

Since grants are used to support all sorts of educational enterprises, we will use one to support today's geometry lesson. Consider the following statement:

If something is a U.S. $50 bill, then it has a picture of Grant on it.

(Have students draw an Euler diagram to illustrate it.)

Does the following statement say the same thing?

If something has a picture of Grant on it, then it is a U.S. $50 bill.

Add overlay to Transparency 1-5 to reveal photograph of portrait of Grant hanging on a wall.

The first statement seems to be true whereas the second one is obviously false. Identify it as the converse of the first and

have your students draw an appropriate diagram to illustrate it.

Consider the statement

If something is not a U.S. $50 bill, then it does not have a picture of Grant on it.

Is this true or false? Show how the diagram illustrating the converse also illustrates this and identify it as the inverse of the original statement.

Finally, consider the statement

If something does not have a picture of Grant on it, then it is not a U.S. $50 bill,

and identify it as the contrapositive of the original statement.

For additional practice, show Transparency 1-6 and have your students state the converse, inverse, and contrapositive of the slogan "When it rains, it pours."

Lesson 4
Valid and Invalid Deductions

A problem about pelicans

Problems comparable to the following one are included in the mathematics section of the S.A.T. (Scholastic Aptitude Test). (Show Transparency 1-7.)

If all pelicans have enormous beaks, which of the following must be true?
   a) All birds that are not pelicans do not have enormous beaks.
   b) All birds with enormous beaks are pelicans.
   c) All birds that do not have enormous beaks are not pelicans.
   d) No birds that have enormous beaks are not pelicans.

Can you figure out which answer is correct? (Statement c is the contrapositive of the statement "If a bird is a pelican, it has an enormous beak," so it must be true.)

Transparency 1-8 will be useful in discussing the exercises in Set II of Lesson 3. A model of the electric circuit shown in the photograph is fairly easy to build. You might ask your school's physics teacher if one of his students would be willing to make one for the math department.

To introduce the new lesson, you might show Transparency 1-9, one of the first ads in the Avis "We're only No. 2" campaign. (Chapter 2 of the book The New Advertising by Robert Glatzer, Citadel Press, 1970, contains a comprehensive history of this amusing campaign and the reaction of the Hertz company to it.)

One of the most unusual advertising campaigns in recent history has been that of the Avis Rent a Car System. The theme of the campaign is "If you're not the biggest, you have to try harder." Draw an Euler diagram to illustrate this statement.

Show Transparency 1-10 and add Overlay A:

If you're not the biggest, you have to try harder. Avis is No. 2.

What can we conclude from these two statements? (Avis has to try harder.) We might represent this argument symbolically as:

$$a \rightarrow b$$
$$\underline{a}$$
$$\text{Therefore, b.}$$

Replace Overlay A with Overlay B:

If you're not the biggest, you have to try harder. Avis has to try harder.

Can any conclusion be drawn from these two statements? (Use the Euler diagram to show why not.) It seems appropriate to say that someone who assumes that from the statements

$$a \rightarrow b$$
$$b$$

we can conclude a is making the converse error. That is, it does not follow from $a \rightarrow b$ that $b \rightarrow a$.

Replace Overlay B with Overlay C:

If you're not the biggest, you have to try harder. Hertz is No. 1.

Can any conclusion be drawn from these statements? (Again show, using the Euler diagram, why not.) Someone who assumes that from the statements

$$a \rightarrow b$$
$$\text{not a}$$

we can conclude not b is making the inverse error. It does not follow from $a \rightarrow b$ that not a $\rightarrow$ not b.

Finally, replace Overlay C with Overlay D:

If you're not the biggest, you have to try harder. Hertz doesn't have to try harder.

In this case, a conclusion can be drawn.

What is it? (Hertz is not not the biggest; i.e., Hertz is the biggest.) Verify this with the Euler diagram.

An argument of the form:

$$a \rightarrow b$$
$$\underline{\text{not b}}$$
$$\text{Therefore, not a}$$

is valid, because if $a \rightarrow b$, then not b $\rightarrow$ not a.

Lesson 5
Arguments with Two Premises

A few years ago, the increasing popularity of diet soft drinks inspired the sugar producers to advertise in order to fight back. An ad similar to one they used is shown on Transparency 1-11.

This ad says that Annie "needs a sugarless, powerless soft drink like a moose needs a hat rack." How does a moose need a hat rack? The analogy implies that "if a soft drink does not contain sugar, then Annie does not need it."

Consider the following argument (Transparency 1-12 with Overlay A):

If a soft drink does not contain sugar, then you do not need it. Crummy Cola contains no sugar. Therefore, you do not need it.

Is this logical? Does the conclusion follow? Replace Overlay A with Overlay B:

If a soft drink does not contain sugar, then you do not need it. Sparkle Soda contains lots of sugar. Therefore, you need it.

Does this argument make sense?

You might follow this analysis with a discussion of the Volkswagen ad in Set III of Lesson 4. It also suggests a conclusion that requires assuming the inverse of what the ad has previously stated.

To introduce the new lesson dealing with arguments with two premises, you might make up a set of examples comparable to the following.

Draw an Euler diagram to represent the statement "All Grant students are teenagers." Add a circle to the same diagram so that it also represents the statement "All teenagers were born after 1950." Now cross out the circle that represents "all teenagers." What conditional statement do the two remaining circles illustrate?

Putting the three statements together, we have a short argument consisting of two premises and a conclusion. Such arguments are sometimes called syllogisms.

All Grant students are teenagers.
All teenagers were born after 1950.
Therefore, all Grant students were born after 1950.

Notice that the pattern of this argument is

$$a \rightarrow b$$
$$b \rightarrow c$$
Therefore, $a \rightarrow c$.

Any argument of this form is valid, even though one or both of its premises are false. Now consider this argument.

All Grant students are teenagers.
All teenagers have driver's licenses.
Therefore, all Grant students have driver's licenses.

Is it valid? Why is the conclusion false?

Additional arguments worth considering are:

All Grant students are teenagers.
All Grant students live in southern California.
Therefore, ...

All Grant students are teenagers.
All 16-year-olds are teenagers.
Therefore, ...

All Grant students are teenagers.
All the members of this class are Grant students.
Therefore, ...

Lesson 6
Undefined Terms and Definitions

A proof that a cow has nine legs

Show Transparency 1-13.

A cow has four legs more than no cow.
No cow has five legs.
Therefore, a cow has nine legs.

This argument is similar to the one comparing breadcrumbs and steak in Set III of Lesson 5. The way in which it has been worded implies that it is of the form

$$a \rightarrow b$$
$$b \rightarrow c$$
Therefore, $a \rightarrow c$,

and hence valid. Yet the premises are true and the conclusion is false. Actually, the conclusion of the first premise is not the same as the hypothesis of the second. This is evident when they are restated in "if-then" form.

If (an animal is) a cow, then it has four legs more than no cow.
If (an animal is) a cow, it does not have five legs.

The form of the argument is actually

$$a \rightarrow b$$
$$a \rightarrow c.$$

If a poll of mathematicians was made to determine their favorite author, Lewis Carroll would probably be near the top. Here are two more passages from his work Through the Looking Glass. They are conversations between Alice and the White King and the king and one of his messengers. (Show Transparencies 1-14 and 1-15.)

"Just look along the road, and tell me if you can see either of them."

"I see nobody on the road," said Alice.

"I only wish I had such eyes," the king remarked in a fretful tone. "To be able to see Nobody! And at that distance too! Why, it's as much as I can do to see real people, by this light!"

"Who did you pass on the road?" the King went on...

"Nobody," said the Messenger.

"Quite right," said the King: "this young lady saw him too. So of course Nobody walks slower than you."

"I do my best," the Messenger said in a sullen tone. "I'm sure nobody walks much faster than I do!"

"He can't do that," said the King, "or else he'd have been here first."

What makes these dialogues amusing is the fact that the word "nobody" does not mean the same thing to the king that it does to Alice and the messenger. Although a word may have several meanings, we can usually tell from the context in which it is being used which meaning is intended. Consider the word "fuzzy" and its meanings in the following sentences (show Transparency 1-16, revealing one line at a time):

The kitten is fuzzy.
The photograph is fuzzy.
The meaning is fuzzy.

To prevent any possibility of confusion, it might seem reasonable to define every geometric term that we will use. Here is a list of some of these terms. (Show Transparency 1-17.) The term "angle," for example, can be defined by means of the terms "ray" and "line." The term "ray" can be defined

Some basic
geometric terms

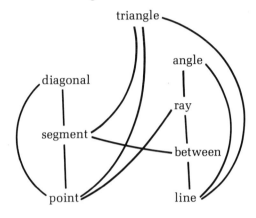

by means of the terms "point" and "between," and so forth. Notice that it is impossible to define every term by means of simpler terms. If you do not understand any of the words in the list, then they are useless in helping you understand yet other words. On the other hand, if you know what a few key words mean, they can be used in definitions to enable you to understand the others. A great German physicist, Max Born, tells a story that illustrates this fact:

I was going for a walk with a French friend and we got thirsty. By and by we came to a farm and I said: "Let's buy a glass of milk here." "What's milk?" "Oh, you don't know what milk is? It's the white liquid that...!" "What's white?" "White? You don't know what that is either? Well the swan...!" "What's swan?" "Swan, the big bird with the bent neck." "What's bent?" "Bent? Good heavens, don't you know that? Here, look at my arm! When I put it so, it's bent!" "Oh, that's bent, is it? Now I know what milk is!"*

*Max Born, The Restless Universe (Harper, 1936).

Lesson 7
More on Definitions

A definition of a klutz for those who don't know

Leo Rosten, the author of The Education of Hyman Kaplan, has written an entertaining book of Jewish humor titled The Joys of Yiddish. In it, he defines a "klutz" as "a clod; a clumsy, slow-witted...person; an inept blockhead."*

Draw an Euler diagram to represent the conditional statement

> If you are a klutz, you are an inept blockhead.

(Show Transparency 1-18.) Since, by its very nature, the definition of a term and the term itself have the same meaning, they are interchangeable. Hence, since the word "klutz" and the phrase "inept blockhead" mean the same thing, they may be interchanged to form the statement

> If you are an inept blockhead, you are a klutz.

(Add overlay.) What relationship does this statement have to the previous one? This illustrates the fact that the converse of a definition is always true. To make this clearer, we might replace the two diagrams for the definition of "klutz" with the following one. (Show Transparency 1-19.)

We can also combine the two statements into one:

> You are a klutz if and only if you are an inept blockhead.

(You may prefer either to elaborate on this further or else to leave it to your students to explore in the Set II exercises of Lesson 7.)

Lesson 8
Postulates about the Undefined Terms

Geometry wins an Academy Award

Norton Juster, author of The Phantom Tollbooth, has written an amusing book titled The Dot and The Line: A Romance in Lower Mathematics (Random House, 1963) about a line who fell in love with a point. It has

*Leo Rosten, The Joys of Yiddish (McGraw-Hill, 1968).

been made into an animated film by M. G. M. and won an Academy Award for best short subject: cartoon in 1965. The book is short enough that it could easily be made into a set of overhead transparencies to show and read to your class.

To introduce the new lesson you might show the class a rule book for some sport and use it to develop the analogy between reasoning in geometry and playing a game.

Lesson 9
Direct Proof: Arguments with Several Premises

The presidents in a single line

A drawing of George Washington on a horse followed by every succeeding U.S. president through Lyndon Johnson was once published in The Saturday Evening Post (October 31, 1964). Created by Oscar Berger, it consisted of "one unbroken line" and is reproduced as Transparency 1-20.

After asking your students why such a figure is not considered to be a "line" in geometry (it is not straight and does not extend without end), you might review how these properties seem to be implied by Postulate 1.

Transparencies 1-21 and 1-22 are for use in discussing the Set III exercises of Lesson 8. Let your students explain their own method for answering Exercise 3 before developing the general formula

$$\ell = \frac{n(n-1)}{2}$$

where ℓ is the number of lines and n is the number of points.

Lesson 10
Indirect Proof

A deduction by Sherlock Holmes

Read the following section from the beginning of Sir Arthur Conan Doyle's Sherlock Holmes story "The Adventure of the Dancing Men."

Holmes had been seated for some hours in silence, with his long, thin back curved over a chemical vessel in which he was brewing a particularly malodorous product. His head was sunk upon his breast, and he looked from my point of view like a strange, lank bird, with dull gray plumage and a black topknot.

"So, Watson," said he, suddenly, "you do not propose to invest in South African securities?"

I gave a start of astonishment. Accustomed as I was to Holmes' curious faculties, this sudden intrusion into my most intimate thoughts was utterly inexplicable.

"How on earth do you know that?" I asked.

He wheeled round upon his stool, with a steaming testtube in his hand and a gleam of amusement in his deep-set eyes.

"Now, Watson, confess yourself utterly taken aback," said he.

"I am."

"I ought to make you sign a paper to that effect."

"Why?"

"Because in five minutes you will say that it is all so absurdly simple."

"I am sure that I shall say nothing of the kind."

"You see, my dear Watson"—he propped his testtube in the rack and began to lecture with the air of a professor addressing his class—"it is not really difficult to construct a series of inferences, each dependent upon its predecessor and each simple in itself. If, after doing so, one simply knocks out all the central inferences and presents one's audience with the starting-point and the conclusion, one may produce a startling, though possibly a meretricious, effect. Now, it was not really difficult, by an inspection of the groove between your left forefinger and thumb, to feel sure that you did not propose to invest your small capital in the gold fields."

"I see no connection."

"Very likely not; but I can quickly show you a close connection. Here are the missing links of the very simple chain: 1. You had chalk between your left finger and thumb when you returned from the club last night. 2. You put chalk there when you play billiards to steady the cue. 3. You never play billiards except with Thurston. 4. You told me four weeks ago that Thurston had an option on some South African property which would expire in a month, and which he desired you to share with him. 5. Your check book is locked in my drawer, and you have not asked for the key. 6. You do not propose to invest your money in this manner."

"How absurdly simple!" I cried.

"Quite so!" said he, a little nettled. "Every problem becomes very childish when once it is explained to you."

(Show Transparency 1-23.) Holmes' reference to "a series of inferences, each dependent upon its predecessor" is a description of the form of a simple direct proof. He also says, "after doing so, one simply knocks out all the central inferences and presents one's audience with the starting-point and the conclusion." The "starting-point and conclusion" constitute the theorem being proved.

These observations make a natural preface to a discussion of Lesson 9.

After the discussion, you might use the following part of Holmes' argument to introduce the idea of an indirect proof. He has concluded that Watson does not plan to invest his money in South African securities by reasoning in the following fashion.

Suppose Watson does plan to invest his money in this way. Then he would need his checkbook. Since it is locked in Holmes' drawer, he would have asked for the key. But this contradicts the fact that he has not asked for the key. Therefore, the supposition that Watson plans to buy South African securities is false. So he does not intend to invest in them.

Emphasize that this method of reasoning is based upon eliminating what you want to disprove by showing that, if it is assumed to be true, it leads to a contradiction.

The puzzle about Emerson, Lake, and Palmer in Lesson 10 (stated on Transparency 1-24) can be used as another example of how this method works.

Lesson 11
Some Theorem Proofs

A puzzle about three golfers

Show Transparency 1-25 and, after everyone has had time to think about the puzzle, ask a volunteer to explain how he has figured it out. The most straightforward method is first to determine which one is Tom, since he is the only one who can be counted upon to tell the truth. Neither the first nor second man can be Tom because he would be lying if he said what they are saying. Since he is the third, Harry is in the middle. That

leaves Dick (who is not telling the truth this time) for the first man.

Transparencies 1-26 and 1-27 will be useful in discussing Lesson 10.

Show Transparency 1-28 to introduce Lesson 11. The purpose of the lesson is to illustrate how a few simple postulates can be used to prove some theorems. Although the postulates should be committed to memory, it is not intended that the students memorize either the theorems or their proofs. Use Transparency 1-29 to develop the proof outlined on page 63 of the text.

Review of Chapter 1

Mr. Green and Mr. White own a bowling alley. When it was built, they couldn't agree upon what color the pins should be. Mr. Green felt that they should be green and Mr. White insisted that they be white. Finally the two men compromised by deciding that they would buy some of each color and arrange them at random on each lane.

Transparency 1-30 shows some of the arrangements. After studying these patterns for a long time, Mr. Green noticed something. In every arrangement, at least three pins of the same color are located at the corners of an equilateral triangle. (Verify this for several arrangements.) Mr. Green decided that an arrangement that does not contain such a pattern must be impossible. He suggested to Mr. White that they offer a prize of $1000 to anyone who bowled at their alley and observed such an arrangement. Mr. Green thought that this would be a good way to increase their business without any cost, since he was certain that no one would win the prize. Mr. White, however, wasn't convinced that this was a good idea.

Distribute Worksheet 1 and let your students try to discover an arrangement in which three pins of the same color are not located at the corners of an equilateral triangle.

After some experimenting, Mr. Green finally figured out a way to prove by means of deductive reasoning that such an arrangement is impossible. Here is his proof.

The pin in the center is either green or white. Suppose it is green. Pins 2, 7, and 8 are located at the corners of an equilateral triangle so at least one of them must be green. Suppose it is pin 2 (the choice makes no difference since all three occupy equivalent positions: each is next to a corner of the array). Pins 3 and 5 must be white, so pin 9 is green. Therefore, pins 8 and 7 are also white. Since 3 and 7 are white, 4 must be green. But this means that pins 2, 4, and 9 are green, and they are located at the corners of an equilateral triangle.

If we assume at the beginning that the center pin is white, the same argument (with the colors reversed) can be repeated.

After Mr. White saw this proof, he decided to offer a prize of a million dollars to any customer whose pin arrangement did not contain such a triangle. The bowling alley has been doing very well ever since!

(This problem is adapted from one presented in Martin Gardner's "Mathematical Games," Scientific American, February 1962, p. 152.)

Chapter 2

FUNDAMENTAL IDEAS: LINES AND ANGLES

Lesson 1
The Distance Between Two Points

If you have access to a U.S. Geological Survey map of your region, you can use its contour lines to determine the elevation of your school above sea level with an accuracy of just a few feet. Quadrangle maps cost 75¢ each and may be ordered from the following addresses:

> If you live west of the Mississippi River:
> United States Geological Survey
> Denver Distribution Section
> Building 41, Denver Federal Center
> Denver, Colorado 80225.

> If you live east of the Mississippi River:
> United States Geological Survey
> Washington Distribution Section
> 1200 South Eads St.
> Arlington, Virginia 22202.

Have your students estimate the height of the ceiling of your classroom and then, instead of revealing the actual height directly, tell them the elevations of the floor and ceiling. For example, the floor and ceiling of my second-floor room are 689 feet and 703 feet above sea level, respectively. You might make a transparency comparable to Transparency 2-1 to illustrate this.

This approach leads easily into a discussion of what is meant by the distance between two points and how it is measured by coordinatizing the line determined by the points.

Lesson 2
Betweenness of Points

The signs by the side of the road

A very famous and long-lived advertising campaign (beginning in 1927 and ending in 1963) consisted of a series of jingles painted on signs located alongside a highway.* Each jingle consisted of six lines, each line painted on a separate sign. They became so well known that some of them didn't even

---

*An amusing book by Frank Rowsome, Jr., titled The Verse by the Side of the Road, tells the history of this campaign. It is published by the Stephen Greene Press in Brattleboro, Vermont.

mention the product they advertised. (Show Transparency 2-2.) For example, one jingle went:

> If You
> Don't Know
> Whose Signs
> These Are
> You Can't Have
> Driven Very Far.

The jingles advertised a shaving cream named Burma-Shave and many of them were quite amusing. Some more examples:

> Does Your Husband/Misbehave/Grunt and Grumble/Rant and Rave/Shoot the Brute/Some Burma-Shave.
> Little Bo-Peep/Has Lost Her Jeep/It Struck/A Truck/When She Went to Sleep/Burma-Shave.
> Slow Down, Pa/Sakes Alive/Ma Missed Signs/Four/And Five/Burma-Shave.

The six signs on which each jingle was painted were spaced equal distances apart. If this distance was 50 yards, how far do you think it would be from the first to the last sign? (250 yards.) Is it possible that the signs could be spaced 50 yards apart, but that the last sign was less than 250 yards from the first one? (Yes. If the signs are arranged along a curve rather than being collinear.) Could the last sign be more than 250 yards from the first one? (No.)

This sign-post model provides a nice way to introduce the new lesson dealing with the concept of betweenness of points. For example, you might show Transparency 2-3, which represents six signs arranged along a curve. Explain that, although it is natural to say that signs B, C, D, and E are "between" signs A and F, the word "between" is used in a somewhat different way in geometry. Illustrate some points that are between A and F.

Lesson 3
Rays and Angles

Hilo, Lanai City, and Waikiki

(Show Transparency 2-4.) Hilo, Lanai City, and Waikiki are "collinear," but not necessarily in that order. Hilo is 140 miles from Lanai City, which is 70 miles from Waikiki.

1. Which city is NOT between the other two? (Hilo.)
2. What could be the distance between Hilo and Waikiki? (210 miles or 70 miles.)

Your students will be interested in seeing Transparency 2-5, a map showing the actual relationship of the locations of the three cities. The map reveals that Lanai City is between Hilo and Waikiki, so that the latter two cities are 210 miles apart.

Transparency 2-6 and its overlay can be used to develop Lesson 3 on rays if you use the laser-beam model discussed in the text. Although the notion of a ray is very simple, its formal definition in terms of betweenness is not immediately obvious to all students.

Lesson 4
Angle Measurement

How many angles?

Show Transparency 2-7, which illustrates a set of 60 rays having a common endpoint. When your students realize that it contains many angles other than those formed by two consecutive rays, they will readily agree that it would be very difficult and confusing to try to count all of the angles without using a systematic procedure. To develop such a procedure, we might count the numbers of angles in some comparable figures that consist of just a few rays. Have your students construct a table showing the numbers of angles formed by 1, 2, 3, 4, and 5 rays.

Number of rays	1	2	3	4	5
Number of angles	0	1	3	6	10

After someone has noticed that the differences between consecutive pairs of numbers on the second line are 1, 2, 3, and 4, respectively, you might rewrite the table as shown below.

Number of rays	Number of angles
1	0
2	0 + 1
3	0 + 1 + 2
4	0 + 1 + 2 + 3
5	0 + 1 + 2 + 3 + 4

This suggests that the figure consisting of 60 rays contains

$$0 + 1 + 2 + 3 + \ldots + 56 + 57 + 58 + 59$$

angles. Adding pairs of numbers from the

ends of this row toward its center, we get
$$0 + 59 = 59, \quad 1 + 58 = 59, \quad 2 + 57 = 59,$$
and so forth. Since there are 30 <u>pairs</u> of numbers to be added, the figure consists of
$$30 \cdot 59 = 1770 \text{ angles}.$$

Transparency 2-8 will be useful in developing the new lesson on angle measurement. The terms "rotation of rays" and "half-rotation of rays" are introduced merely to facilitate the statement of the Protractor Postulate and do not merit much emphasis. The point to be made is that, if we wish to measure angles in the same sort of way that we measure segments, we need to establish a one-to-one correspondence between a set of rays and a set of numbers just as we establish a one-to-one correspondence between the points on a line and the real numbers. To do this, we limit the set of rays to those in a "half-rotation" and the set of numbers to those real numbers between 0 and 180 inclusive.

Lesson 5
Complementary and Supplementary Angles

An exercise in estimation

Show Transparency 2-9 and ask your students to estimate the measure of each angle to the nearest 5°. Then let someone measure the angles with a plastic protractor so that the class can watch.

Someone who has guessed how the protractor pictured on page 91 works might show how it could be used to measure some of the same angles correctly. (Make Transparency 2-10 and cut out the protractor.)

Transparencies 2-11 and 2-12 can be used to introduce Lesson 5. The first of these shows the title page of an early edition of Isaak Walton's famous book on fishing, The Compleat Angler, published in 1676.

Lesson 6
Betweenness of Rays

Doublemintary angles

An amateur mathematician named Wrigley once decided to "invent" a new angle rela-

tionship. If the measure of one angle is twice that of another, then, according to Wrigley, the larger angle is the "doublemint" of the smaller and the angles are said to be "doublemintary."

Can you solve the following problem about doublemintary angles? (Show Transparency 2-13 with Overlay A.)

1. What is the measure of an angle whose complement and doublemint are equal?
$$90 - x = 2x, \quad \text{so } x = 30°.$$

How about this problem? (Replace Overlay A with Overlay B.)

2. Can you find an angle whose supplement is the doublemint of its complement?
$$180 - x = 2(90 - x), \quad \text{so } x = 0.$$
There is no such angle.

Lesson 7
Some Consequences of the Ruler and Protractor Postulates

Angles and visual perception

Show Transparency 2-14.

This picture, adapted from a drawing by Paul Klee titled One Man Figuring, was used in an experiment designed to determine how human beings look at, and later learn to recognize, unfamiliar objects.* As a person studies something he has never seen before, his eyes move from one part of it to another.

(Add overlay.) The jagged path shows the way in which one person viewed this picture for the first time. In experiments of this type, it has been discovered that, when someone looks at a simple line drawing, it is the angles in the drawing that most strongly attract the eye and that they are the main features stored by the brain to make later recognition of the drawing possible. An illustration that supports this conclusion is shown on Transparency 2-15. Although this drawing consists entirely of line segments that meet to form angles of various sizes, it is easy to recognize it as a picture of a sleeping cat.

---

*David Noton and Lawrence Stark, "Eye Movements and Visual Perception," Scientific American, June 1971, pp. 34-43.

What type of angle do the majority of the angles in the figure seem to be? (Obtuse.) Can you find any examples of linear pairs in the figure? (It seems to contain four linear pairs.) Any vertical angles? (No.) A set of three rays in which one is between the other two? (Nose, chin, and arm.)

Review of Chapter 2

From here to Mars

The earth is about 93 million miles from the sun and Mars is about 142 million miles from the sun. Can you figure out how far it is from the earth to Mars? (Those students who say that the distance is 49 million miles have assumed that the sun, the earth, and Mars are collinear with the earth between.) Is it correct to assume that the sun, the earth, and Mars are always collinear? (No.) That they are always coplanar? (Yes.) What is the greatest distance apart that the earth and Mars might be? (235 million miles, if they are collinear with the sun between.)

Show Transparency 2-16. This diagram shows side views of the orbits of the earth and of Mars about the sun. The orbits of the two planets are actually very close to being coplanar, so that the actual angle between them is only about 2°. Since they are not, however, it is easy to assume from the diagram that the sun, the earth, and Mars can never be collinear. Do you think this assumption is correct? (Two-dimensional representations of three-dimensional relationships can sometimes be misleading. The answer to the question is no, as Transparency 2-17 reveals.)

Chapter **3**

SOME BASIC POSTULATES
AND THEOREMS

Lesson 1
Postulates of Equality

The following puzzle is from Puzzle-Math by George Gamow and Marvin Stern (Viking Press, 1963) and makes a nice introduction to the first lesson.

Suppose a set of dominoes is placed in a stack so that each domino is offset with respect to the one below it. (Illustrate with some actual dominoes as shown in the first figure on Transparency 3-1.) How far can the stack lean without toppling over? Can the dominoes be arranged so that the total offset is more than the length of one domino? If the individual offsets are not equal, but vary as shown in the second figure on Transparency 3-1, the answer to this question is yes. In fact, it is possible to prove that the total offset can be made as large as you please.

Instead of doing this, we will prove that a simple relationship must exist between each pair of successive dominoes in the stack: the distance between their left ends must be equal to the distance between their right ends. (Show how this may be done by presenting a proof comparable to the "sticks" example on page 114 of the text. The final steps of the proof make it evident that we will need some postulates dealing with equality in addition to the geometric ones that we have already considered.)

Lesson 2
Two Bisection Theorems

A "proof" that 1 = 2

The following algebraic proof is based upon the postulates of equality considered in the preceding lesson. Can you identify the postulate used in each step?

If $a = b$, then $a^2 = ab$.
If $a^2 = ab$, then $a^2 - b^2 = ab - b^2$.
If $a^2 - b^2 = ab - b^2$, then $(a + b)(a - b) = b(a - b)$.
If $(a + b)(a - b) = b(a - b)$, then $a + b = b$.
If $a + b = b$, then $2b = b$.
If $2b = b$, then $2 = 1$.
If $2 = 1$, then $1 = 2$.

Since we have arrived at a false conclusion, at least one of the statements in our proof must be incorrect. Which one is it? (In the fourth step, we divided both members of the first equation by $a - b$ to get the second. But, by hypothesis, $a = b$. Hence $a - b = 0$ and we have misused the division postulate, which does not permit division by zero.)

To introduce the new lesson, you might hand a meter stick to someone and ask him to try to find its midpoint while his eyes are closed. He will probably locate the point by trying to balance the meter stick on one finger. A surprisingly easy way to do this is to place one finger under each end of the stick and then slide them together until they meet. The fingers need not be placed at equal distances from the midpoint of the stick in order for this to work.

Transparency 3-2 can be used to present a proof of Theorem 1.

Lesson 3
Some Angle Relationship Theorems

Someone can ordinarily tell whether his body is in a vertical or tilted position by means of two clues: from feeling the force of gravity and from looking at his surroundings. Which of these clues is more important? If this classroom were tilted very slowly through an angle of 15°, do you think you would notice it? During one hour, this actually happens because of the earth's rotation about its axis; we do not sense this because the direction in which gravity acts upon us is also rotating.

Some psychologists once devised an experiment to determine how someone would react if gravitational and visual clues to which way is up conflicted with each other.* (Show Transparency 3-3.) This photograph shows a small room that can be tilted to the left or right. The subject is seated in a chair that can also be tilted. If both the room and chair are tilted by the same amount and the subject does not realize this, then observations of his surroundings are

more important than the feel of gravity in deciding which direction is vertical.

The psychologists discovered that some people were fooled by the room-tilting far more than others; in other words, people differ in the degree to which they are influenced by visual clues in judging which way is up.

Show Transparency 3-4 with the overlay positioned on it so that the axes coincide. Turn the overlay through about 15° and have your students identify some pairs of complementary angles. Label three consecutive angles 1, 2, and 3 and point out that, although $\angle 1$ is complementary to $\angle 2$ and $\angle 2$ is complementary to $\angle 3$, $\angle 1$ is not complementary to $\angle 3$. Instead, they are equal. This suggests the theorem that complements of the same angle are equal. Since the proof of this (the complements of equal angles version) is an exercise in Lesson 3, it is probably best to present the proof of the supplements theorem in class instead. This theorem, along with the vertical angles theorem, may also be illustrated with Transparency 3-4 and its overlay.

Lesson 4
Theorems about Right Angles

Another experiment in perception

Show Transparency 3-5 and ask your students to describe what they see.* (Most will probably interpret the figure as being flat, consisting of two overlapping "diamonds" whose bottom corners are joined.) Rotate the figure 45° counterclockwise and ask for another description. (Many people will now see the figure as three-dimensional —consisting of two opposite faces of a cube joined by an edge.) If we assume that the drawing represents a figure made of rods, the number of right angles that the rods seem to determine depends upon which version of the figure we see. How many are there in each case? (Flat version: 16—4 in each diamond and 4 at each overlapping point; solid version: 10—4 in each face and 2 in perspective. Stick models of the two versions might be helpful.)

---

*Herman A. Witkin, "The Perception of the Upright," Scientific American, February 1959, pp. 50-56.

*This figure is from an article titled "Pictorial Perception and Culture," by Jan B. Deregowski, Scientific American, November 1972, pp. 82-88.

These observations provide a way to introduce Lesson 4 with its definition of perpendicular lines and three theorems on right angles. Note that the proofs of all three theorems are included in the exercises.

Transparency 3-6 will be useful in discussing the Set III exercise of Lesson 3.

Lesson 5
Some Original Proofs

First Day

The only national flag in the world that is not rectangular in shape is that of the country of Nepal. (Show Transparency 3-7.) One of your students may recognize that the symbols on this flag represent the sun and moon. Point out that one of the goals of studying geometry is to learn how to write original deductive proofs. As an example of how to create a proof, we will make a couple of assumptions about the shape of the Nepal flag and show how they imply that something else about it is true. (Show Transparency 3-8 and have your students write the proof with your guidance.)

Proof for Nepal exercise.
1. $\angle$ N and $\angle$ L are complementary. (Given.)
2. $\angle$ N + $\angle$ L = 90°. (If two angles are complementary, the sum of their measures is 90°.)
3. $\overline{NE} \perp \overline{EP}$. (Given.)
4. $\angle$ E is a right angle. (If two lines are perpendicular, they form right angles.)
5. $\angle$ E = 90°. (A right angle has a measure of 90°.)
6. $\angle$ N + $\angle$ L = $\angle$ E. (Substitution.)
7. $\angle$ N = $\angle$ E - $\angle$ L. (Subtraction.)

Unless you have a very good class, it is probably wise to spend two days on this lesson. The assignment for the first day might include reading the lesson and completing Set I and Exercises 1 and 2 of Set II. The remainder of the lesson might be assigned on the second day. This will enable the students to do more of the assignment in class and should help them develop confidence in their ability to write proofs on their own.

Beginning with this lesson, a "par" is given for each original proof. These pars should not be taken too seriously. Their purpose is to indicate to a student that he may have omitted some important ideas or that he may have included more than is necessary. Each statement in the given information that is set off by a semicolon is counted as a single step in determining the par.

Second Day

The ability to see plays such an important role in understanding geometry that it would seem that a blind person would be unable to learn it. Yet blind students have not only taken geometry but also excelled in it.

To put yourself in the position of such a student, consider the following problem. (Show Transparency 3-9.) Can you imagine what a figure that fits the given conditions would look like? Draw it. What simple relationships do you observe in the figure that are not explicitly stated in the given conditions? (Points A, O, and C are collinear with A-O-C; $\overrightarrow{OB}$ is between $\overrightarrow{OA}$ and $\overrightarrow{OC}$; $\angle$ AOB and $\angle$ BOC are a linear pair, etc.) Develop a proof with your students such as the following:

1. $\overrightarrow{OA}$ and $\overrightarrow{OC}$ are opposite rays. (Given.)
2. $\angle$ AOB and $\angle$ BOC are a linear pair; $\angle$ AOD and $\angle$ DOC are a linear pair. (If two angles have a common side and their other sides are opposite rays, they are a linear pair.)
3. $\angle$ AOB and $\angle$ BOC are supplementary; $\angle$ AOD and $\angle$ DOC are supplementary. (If two angles are a linear pair, they are supplementary.)
4. $\overrightarrow{OA}$ bisects $\angle$ BOD. (Given.)
5. $\angle$ AOB = $\angle$ AOD. (If an angle is bisected, it is divided into two equal angles.)
6. $\angle$ BOC = $\angle$ DOC. (Supplements of equal angles are equal.)

After the proof is complete, ask which steps seem to be most strongly supported by the figure. (Steps 2 and 5 in the proof shown.) With detailed descriptions of what may be assumed in each proof, we could do all of geometry without any figures. This exercise reveals, however, how challenging it would be. For simplicity, we will consistently assume collinearity and betweenness relationships from the figures illustrating the proofs; we will never assume that segments or angles are equal, however, or that they have certain measures. To emphasize this, you might show Transparency 3-10 and ask your students which of the statements below the figure may be assumed from looking at it. (Statements 2, 4, and 7.)

Review of Chapter 3

Show Transparency 3-11 and ask which fishpole caught the fish. (This version of a well-known optical illusion is adapted from an illustration in a clever little puzzle book published by Hallmark Cards titled Challenge by Charlie Rice.) Although fishpole B seems to be the one to which the fish is attached, it is actually A, as you can verify for your class by means of a straightedge. The illusion is easy to draw. Have your students draw two vertical segments intersected by parts of one line as shown on Transparency 3-12. (I suggest drawing the figure along with the students, rather than showing a finished copy of the transparency.) Number the angles as indicated and point out that, if we assume that $\angle 1 = \angle 3$, it is very easy to prove that $\angle 2 = \angle 4$. After giving everyone a chance to think about it, ask someone to explain how. (Since $\angle 1$ and $\angle 2$ are a linear pair, as are $\angle 3$ and $\angle 4$, they are supplementary. Supplements of equal angles are equal.)

Chapter 4

CONGRUENT TRIANGLES

Lesson 1
Triangles

Show Transparency 4-1. Although this figure seems to contain several curves, it consists entirely of straight line segments. These line segments are the sides of six sets of equilateral triangles: the successive triangles in each set spiral inward as they become progressively smaller.

Since the lesson presents a large amount of basic vocabulary, it may be easiest to assign it for individual study rather than trying to present every term in class. If possible, make a ditto master or electronic stencil of Worksheet 2, print it on heavy-weight colored paper (Gestetner cover stock is especially suitable for this purpose), cut the sheets in half along the line, and give one set of the polyiamond patterns to each student who wants to do the Set III exercise.

Lesson 2
Congruent Triangles

How many triangles?

Ripley's "Believe It or Not!" books contain many mathematical puzzles. One of them consists of a cross that is subdivided into a set of small triangles. (Show Transparency 4-2.) The problem is to determine how many triangles the figure contains. This is harder to do than it might first seem; in fact, Ripley's answer, 104 triangles, is wrong. Your students may enjoy working together to find the correct answer.

Every triangle in the figure is both isosceles and right. Letting one of the smallest triangles be one "unit," the figure contains the following numbers of triangles:

Number of "units" in triangle	Number of triangles
1	40
2	28
4	24
8	12
9	8
16	4
18	4
	120

Transparency 4-3 can be used, along with a set of student-made polyiamonds, to discuss the Set III exercise of Lesson 1.

Escher incorporated the reptile mosaic shown on page 148 of the text in one of his most intriguing works, a woodcut titled Metamorphosis II, which is reproduced in the book The World of M. C. Escher, edited by J. L. Locher (Abrams, 1971), pp. 111-112. An authorized full-size reproduction is available for $20 from Phoenix Gallery Editions, 257 Grant Ave, San Francisco, Calif. 94108. The picture is almost 8 inches high and slightly more than 13 feet long! Mounted on plywood, it would make a handsome addition to one of the walls of your classroom.

The overhead projector is very helpful in explaining the concepts of correspondence and congruence. Transparency 4-4 and its overlay can be used to illustrate the examples on page 149 of the text.

Lesson 3
Some Congruence Postulates

Show your students a model of a polyhedron made from drinking straws threaded together. This photograph shows a great

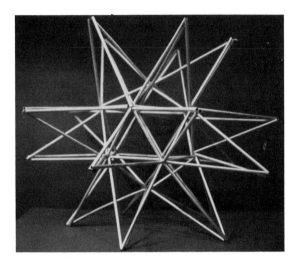

stellated dodecahedron that I made in this way; a simpler model that you might use is the icosahedron. These solids are quite complex, yet each is rigid. Do you think a model of a cube could be constructed in this way? Show one to your class and everyone will immediately see that it will not hold its shape at all. What is the significant difference in the structure of these solids that accounts for the fact that one is rigid and one is not?

Drinking straw models of a triangle and quadrilateral like those shown at the top of page 155 of the text will be helpful in introducing the S.S.S. Congruence Postulate. To make the other postulates seem reasonable, you might have your students use a ruler and protractor to draw a triangle, given two sides and the included angle or two angles and the included side.

Students interested in geodesic domes will enjoy looking at the book Domebook 2 published by Pacific Domes in 1971 and distributed by Random House.

Transparency 4-5 and its overlay are for use in discussing the Set III exercise of Lesson 2. I suggest reproducing the overlay on 3M Type 529 film (black image on green background) and cutting the figure out.

Lesson 4
Proving Triangles Congruent

(Show Transparency 4-6.) This photograph seems to show a drink so potent that it itself is tipsy! Can you explain it? (Since gravity acts upon a liquid in an open container so as to keep its surface level, the pitcher and glass were evidently fastened to the table and the camera and table were tilted.)

What do we mean when we say that something is level? (That it is horizontal; that is, perpendicular to the vertical.) A simple device invented thousands of years ago to determine whether a surface is horizontal is the plumb level. (If possible, show one to the class.) It consists of a wooden frame in the shape of an isosceles triangle. A string with a weight on it is suspended from its vertex. (Show Transparency 4-7.) Can you explain how it is used and why it works? (When the frame is placed so that the weight hangs over the midpoint of $\overline{AB}$, $\overline{AB}$ is horizontal. Since $\triangle ACD \cong \triangle BCD$ (S.S.S.), $\angle ADC = \angle BDC$. Hence $\overline{AB} \perp \overline{CD}$. Since $\overline{CD}$ is vertical—it is the plumb line—$\overline{AB}$ is horizontal.)

Lesson 5
More Congruence Proofs

Thales, a Greek mathematician of the sixth century B.C., is said to have used congruent triangles to measure the distance of a ship from the shore. He may have used a method comparable to the one described in Lesson 5 for finding the distance to the drive-in. Transparency 4-8 and its overlays can be used to present it to your class.

I recommend reproducing the original transparency on 3M Type 588 film (black) and then adding the two-way arrow and question mark representing the distance as they are shown in the composite in permanent red ink. Use 3M Type 888 film (green or blue) to make each overlay.

Lesson 6
The Isosceles Triangle Theorem

Richard L. Gregory, a professor of bionics at the University of Edinburgh, has written a fascinating book on human perception titled The Intelligent Eye (McGraw-Hill, 1970). In it he includes a drawing of a "Penrose triangle." (Show Transparency 4-9.) Can such an object as this exist? The answer to this is yes, as the photograph on Transparency 4-10 reveals. (This may remind your students of the photograph of the "impossible crate" on page 131 of the text.) The photograph, of a wooden model of a Penrose triangle, has not been retouched in any way. It is the position of the camera with respect to the model that creates the illusion. The same model, photographed from the opposite side, is shown on the overlay for Transparency 4-10. (An actual model, slowly rotated in front of the class, would be helpful in further explaining the illusion.)

The model of the Penrose triangle changes radically in appearance if it is viewed from the "other side." Drawings of a few ordinary triangles are shown in Transparency 4-11. (Make two copies of this transparency and first place them on the projector so that they coincide.) How would these triangles appear if viewed from the "other side"? (Turn the top copy over and place it on the other so that the reversed images are at the right of the others.) Which triangle looks exactly the same? Why? This suggests that a congruence correspondence exists between the vertices of an isosceles triangle and its reflection that does not exist for scalene triangles. We can use this correspondence to prove that if two sides of a triangle are equal, the angles opposite them are equal. (Letter the vertices of the bottom pair of triangles and use them to develop the proof of the Isosceles Triangle Theorem that is on page 170 of the text. This proof is attributed to Pappus, an Alexandrian geometer who lived several centuries after Euclid.)

Transparency 4-12 is for use in discussing the Set III exercise of Lesson 5.

Lesson 7
Overlapping Triangles

(Show Transparency 4-13.) This picture is a detail from a painting by the modern artist Salvador Dali. It shows two nuns standing before an open archway; several people are gathered beside them. Here is the complete painting of which this scene is a part (show Transparency 4-14). Look closely and you may see something else where the nuns were standing. (The painting is titled Slave Market with the Disappearing Bust of Voltaire. The heads of the nuns become the eyes of Voltaire.) This is a rather dramatic example of a picture whose parts may be perceived in more than one relationship. The ability to see a variety of relationships in geometric figures is of great importance in developing proofs about them.

Show the top part of Transparency 4-15 (the figure only) and ask your students to name some pairs of triangles in it that look as if they might be congruent. Reveal the rest of the transparency and ask them to try to find a pair that can be proved congruent on the basis of this information. (All of this is developed on page 174 of the text but is probably best considered as a class exercise.)

Transparency 4-16 can be used to help your students to see both of the ladies in the picture. An amusing way to do this is to draw glasses and lipstick on one version and then the other.

If you have a fairly slow class, you may find it desirable to spend two days on this lesson. In this case, assign Set I and the first proof in Set II for the first day. The second day's assignment could include the remaining two proofs in Set II and the Set III exercise.

Another interesting picture that can be interpreted in two ways is on the jacket of the first record album of the rock group Santana. It was drawn by Lee Conklin and is reproduced on Transparency 4-17.

Some rather challenging proofs that make good class exercises are reproduced on Transparencies 4-18, 4-19, 4-20, and 4-21.

Lesson 8
Some Straightedge and Compass Constructions

The pyramids of Giza in Egypt were built so that their sides face directly north, south, east and west. (Show the top half of Transparency 4-22.) How did the ancient Egyptians determine these directions so accurately? They had observed that the sun's shadow at noon, the shortest shadow of the day, pointed toward the point in the sky about which the stars revolve at night, the direction called north. (Show the bottom half of

Transparency 4-22.) A method that they are thought to have used to find this direction is based upon this observation. A vertical pole was placed on some leveled ground and a circle was traced on the ground with the base of the pole as its center. During the day, the shadow of the pole would change in length as the sun moved through the sky, being smallest at noon when the sun was at its highest position. Once in the forenoon and once again in the afternoon the tip of the shadow would touch the circle. These two positions of the shadow form the angle labeled ∡ AOB in the figure. The bisector of this angle pointed north.

Have your students illustrate the method by marking a point on a piece of paper to represent the base of the pole, drawing a circle with a compass, and choosing two points on it to represent the tips of the equal morning and afternoon shadows. Draw the angle and show how, by drawing equal intersecting arcs centered at these two points, it may be bisected.

Transparency 4-23 and its overlay are intended for use in discussing the Set III exercise of Lesson 7.

Review of Chapter 4

One day in August 1931, the United Press sent out a story announcing that a famous problem in geometry had been solved for the first time. A Dr. Callahan, the president of an eastern university, claimed that he had discovered a way to trisect an angle using just a straightedge and compass. What made this accomplishment so amazing was the fact that people had been trying to figure out how to do it for more than two thousand years without success.

When the story appeared in the newspapers, other mathematicians immediately claimed that whatever Dr. Callahan had discovered must be incorrect. They refused to believe that the problem had been solved, not because they were stubborn or jealous, but because they knew that it had been proved nearly a century before that the problem could not be solved.

After Dr. Callahan's method was published, it was discovered that, instead of trisecting a given angle, he had, in effect,

tripled it. That is, he had constructed an angle with three times the measure of the given angle. (Have your students draw a fairly acute angle and try to do this.) Since it is so easy to triple an angle with just a straightedge and compass, it is no wonder that someone might think it should also be possible to trisect an angle with these tools. If you have studied the Set III exercise of Lesson 8, you know of a method that many people think of. Illustrate it with Transparency 4-24 and its overlay. Curious students will be interested in reading the article on angle trisection by Martin Gardner cited on page 184 of the text. Another good reference is the booklet The Impossible in Mathematics, by Irving Adler (John Day, 1967).

A Supplementary Lesson

A class experiment: models of some tetrahedra

Show your class a model of a regular tetrahedron and ask someone to try to describe it. Explain that it can be made from a flat sheet of paper by constructing a pattern of four equilateral triangles, cutting it out, and folding it together. Provide each student with a pair of scissors (also with rulers and compasses if necessary) so that he can make such a model. A convenient length for each edge is 5 cm.

The faces of a tetrahedron need not be equilateral triangles. Patterns for the following tetrahedra are successively more challenging to design:

A tetrahedron having one equilateral face and three isosceles faces that are not equilateral.

A tetrahedron having one equilateral face and its other three edges of different lengths.

A tetrahedron having four scalene faces that are congruent: each face having sides of lengths 4 cm, 5 cm, and 6 cm.

If you want to collect the results, print copies of Worksheet 3 and have your students glue the central face of each pattern to the appropriate place on the paper so that the tetrahedra can be formed by folding the other faces upward.

Chapter 5

TRANSFORMATIONS

Lesson 1
The Reflection of a Point

(Show Transparency 5-1, which is a photograph of Lake Mathieson in New Zealand.) There is something peculiar about this picture. Can you guess what it is? (As a clue, you might show the cartoon on Transparency 5-2.) The photograph is upside-down! We were fooled by the almost perfect reflection of the landscape and sky in the water into mistaking their images for them. (Turn the picture rightside-up.) The edge of the lake divides the picture into two parts in which most of the points above the edge have image points below it. (Draw a line along the lake's edge and mark several such pairs of points on the picture at various distances from the line. Include one point on the line. Your students should note that the reflection line is the perpendicular bisector of the segments joining the points to their image points.) On the basis of these observations, we will build a "mathematical model" of reflection.

Develop the rest of Lesson 1, including the method for locating the reflection of a point through a line by means of straight-edge and compass. If possible, provide each student with a mirror and allow time to complete the Set I exercises in class. Especially suitable for this purpose are the 10 cm x 10 cm mirrors available from the Edmund Scientific Company (Edscorp Building, Barrington, New Jersey 08807) for 35¢ each (Catalog No. 60,246). You should point out that most physical mirrors are "one-sided" (that is, they reflect in only one direction), whereas a line of reflection is always "two-sided" (it reflects in both directions).

Lesson 2
More on Reflections

Several years ago Universal Pictures released a film titled Journey to the Far Side of the Sun. In it a new planet has supposedly been discovered that travels about the sun in the same orbit as the earth. This planet is always on the opposite side of the sun, which is why it had gone undetected for so long. A spaceship sets out for this planet and, upon landing, the crew discovers that it is exactly like the earth in every way but one! (Show Transparency 5-3.) Can you guess the one difference from this picture of it? (The planet and everything on it are a mirror image of the earth; everything is reversed left and right.) The crew of the spaceship does not realize this at first and, from a comparison of these two photographs (show only the top half of Transparency 5-4), it is easy to see why. Unless you are familiar with the region in which the picture was taken, there is no way to tell which is the actual image and which is the reflected one. The only clues that would make the reversal obvious are man-made ones; can you think of any? (Printed words would probably be the most noticeable; show the lower half of Transparency 5-4. An intriguing article on this subject is "On Telling Left from Right" by Michael C. Corballis and Ivan S. Beale, Scientific American, March 1971.)

A discussion of Lesson 1 should precede the new lesson in which the reflection of a set of points through a line is considered. Transparency 5-5 is for use in discussing the Set III exercise.

To introduce the new lesson, have your students draw a capital L and mark and label four points on it as shown on Transparency 5-6. Then find the reflections of the points through the vertical and slanted lines and use them to sketch the reflections of the letter itself through these lines. (Add the overlay after the students have done this.) Notice that the results imply that, if a set of points is reflected through a line, several properties of that set of points are preserved: collinearity, betweenness, distance, and angle measure. Connecting the ends of the L and its two reflections to form three triangles also suggests that a triangle and its reflection through a line are congruent. Orientation, however, is reversed.

Again a mirror is recommended for use in the Set I exercises.

Lesson 3
Line Symmetry

Some mirror monkey business

Martin Gardner, in his book The Ambidextrous Universe, tells of the varying levels of behavior of different animals manifested by their reactions to mirrors:

A parakeet...is endlessly fascinated by what it sees in the reflecting toys placed inside its cage...the parakeet's behavior suggests that it thinks it is seeing another bird. Dogs and cats are more intelligent. They lose interest in mirrors as soon as they learn that the images are not substantial. Chimpanzees also learn quickly that mirror images are illusory, but their high intelligence makes them intensely curious about what they are seeing. A chimp will play for hours with a pocket mirror. He makes faces at himself. He uses the mirror for looking at things in back of him. He will study the way an object looks when seen directly, then compare it with how the same object looks in a mirror. *

Suppose a chimpanzee has a mirror with which he studies the reflections of the letters of the word MONKEY when the mirror is held in various positions. (Show Transparency 5-7.) Can you figure out what he might notice? (You may want to distribute mirrors, have your students print the word MONKEY in block capitals as shown on the transparency, and then have them observe the reflections of the letters for various positions of the mirror. They should recognize that, if the O is circular, every reflection of it looks the same. The letters M and Y look the same as their reflection if the mirror is placed vertically on either side of them or through their centers; the letters K and E look the same as their reflections if the mirror is placed horizontally above or below them or through their centers. Every reflection of the letter N looks different from the letter itself.)

These observations lead naturally to a discussion of line symmetry (Lesson 3) and the Set III exercise of Lesson 2.

Lesson 4
Translations

Canadians, after much debate, adopted a new flag in 1965. (Show Transparency 5-8.) The emblem in its center is supposed to represent a maple leaf. While the flag was being considered, however, some people noticed that this emblem could be interpreted in a different way. Concentrate on the white background above the leaf and you may discover what they saw. (It looks like two people in profile; their foreheads touch and they look as if they are angry with each other.) The Canadian flag possesses line

*Martin Gardner, The Ambidextrous Universe (Basic Books, 1964), p. 1.

symmetry. The line of symmetry is rather obvious. (Draw it.) What are some simple ways to determine whether a figure has line symmetry? (Hold a mirror along the line and see if the reflected part in the mirror matches the part behind the mirror. Fold the figure along the line and see if the two halves coincide.) What does our definition of line symmetry say? (A set of points has line symmetry if there is a line such that the reflection through that line of every point of the set is also a point of the set.)

The article cited as the source of the introduction to Lesson 4 appeared in the October 1971 issue of Scientific American. The psychologists who designed the experiment feel that it confirms the hypothesis that a young infant does not realize that a stationary object may be the same object as an object he later sees in motion. The child's strange behavior seems to indicate that he does not follow the train from one place to another but instead perceives it as alternately appearing and disappearing in different places.

Transparency 5-9 and its overlays can be used to compare the translation and reflection transformations; Overlay C prepares the student for our definition of a translation as the composite of two reflections through parallel lines. (Show as Original, Original + A, Original + B, and Original + C.) Transparency 5-10 and its overlays provide another example of a translation. (Show as Original, Original + A, and Original + A + B.)

Lesson 5
Rotations

An interesting model that can be used for several purposes consists of two plane front-surface mirrors mounted on a wooden base so that they form a dihedral right angle. The Edmund Scientific Company (Edscorp Building, Barrington, New Jersey 08007) sells mirrors of this type, 6.75"x 7.75", for $5.00 each (Catalog No. 41,405). Set up such a model in the front of the room and write the following on the blackboard before class:

"Before class, take a good look at yourself in the mirror in the front of the room. Wink your right eye and see which eye winks back."

This mirror arrangement is remarkable

in that it permits you to see yourself as others see you. Unlike reflections in a single mirror, the reflections in this mirror do not reverse left and right. To see why this is so, hand out dittoed copies of Transparency 5-11 to your students and ask them to sketch, in the figure at the left, the reflection of $\triangle ABC$ through line l. Recall that such a transformation reverses orientation. This figure represents the reflection of an object in an ordinary mirror.

Next, have your students sketch, in the figure at the right, the reflection of $\triangle ABC$ through line l_1 and the reflection of the resulting image through line l_2. Label the corresponding points of the two images. This figure represents the reflection of an object in two perpendicular mirrors. The image at the top (the one we observe) is not a reflection of the triangle at the bottom; it is a rotation image of it. Why does the word "rotation" seem an appropriate name for this transformation? (Because the original triangle seems to have been rotated 180° about the point in which l_1 and l_2 intersect.) Note that $l_1 \perp l_2$. What would happen if the lines were not perpendicular?

Use Transparency 5-12 and its overlays to show that the resulting transformation still seems to be a "rotation," but through less than 180°. (Show as Original, Original + A, Original + A + B. Make a third overlay duplicating the original, position it so that the two copies of $\triangle ABC$ coincide, mark the point of intersection of l_1 and l_2, and rotate the overlay so that $\triangle ABC$ falls on $\triangle GHI$.)

Transparencies 5-13 and 5-14 contain the solutions for the Set II exercises of Lesson 4.

A pair of small mirrors, preferably hinged together, is needed for Exercises 2 and 3 of Lesson 5, Set I.

Lesson 6
Point Symmetry

A picture that is its own negative

In ordinary photography, the camera produces a "negative" from which a "positive" of the picture is made. (Show Transparency 5-15.) The picture and its negative look entirely different; whatever is black in one is white in the other. Is it possible that a photograph could be its own negative? Could a picture in which black and white have been reversed be identical to itself? The answer to this question is yes! Here is an example of such a picture. (Show the top half of Transparency 5-16. This picture is from an article by L. S. Penrose titled "Self-reproducing Machines" in Scientific American, June 1959.) Notice that the picture is changed into its negative by turning it upside-down. A figure that looks exactly the same when it is turned upside-down is said to have point symmetry.

Show the figure on the bottom half of Transparency 5-16 and mark its center of symmetry. Mark several pairs of corresponding points on the figure and join each pair with a line segment. Use the results to explain what is meant by "the reflection of a point through a point" and "point symmetry."

Show Transparency 5-17. This is a photograph of an apple that has been sliced in half in the way that an orange is usually cut. Notice the pattern of the core. Does it possess point symmetry? (No.) It does possess a more general type of symmetry called rotational symmetry. Through what angle do you think it could be rotated so that it would seem to be in the same relative position? ($\frac{360^o}{5} = 72^o$.)

Transparencies 5-18 and 5-19 contain the solutions for the Set II exercises of Lesson 5.

A pair of hinged mirrors is needed for Exercise 1 of Lesson 6, Set II.

Review of Chapter 5

A game with a winning strategy based upon symmetry

Show Transparency 5-20. Here is a simple game for two players that can be played with several pennies. The players alternately place pennies inside this rectangle, one penny in each turn, so that each new penny does not touch any of the pennies previously put down. The player who is able to place the last penny under these conditions wins the game.

Have two students try playing the game in front of the class (about 30 pennies are needed). There is a simple strategy that the player who goes first can use to be sure of winning. Perhaps one of your students can figure out what it is. If not, demonstrate the strategy by playing a game with another student. (The strategy is to place the first penny in the exact center of the rectangle and then reflect each of your opponent's successive moves through the center.) It shouldn't take very many moves before someone can explain what you are doing and why, if you do it carefully, you are certain to win. Observe that the strategy is based upon point symmetry. Could a comparable strategy be based upon line symmetry instead? (No. The center of the rectangle is unique whereas there are many points on each of its two lines of symmetry.) Suppose you begin by again placing a penny at the center and choose one of the two symmetry lines through which to reflect your opponent's moves. As long as he does not place a penny on this line, you can make a matching play. The strategy is ruined, however, when he does place a penny on the line because your move must cover the same point on the line and you are not allowed to place the pennies so they touch.

Transparencies 5-21 and 5-22 can be used to check the first two exercises in Set II of Lesson 6. Have a student fill in the squares on the crossword-puzzle figure.

Chapter 6

INEQUALITIES

Lesson 1
Postulates of Inequality

Show the middle section of Transparency 6-1 (reproduce on 3M Type 590 reverse image film). This picture is of one of the most well known constellations in the northern sky: the Big Dipper (also called Ursa Major, or the Great Bear). The Big Dipper has not always looked as it does now because the eight stars that it contains are not all moving in the same direction. By measuring their apparent speeds and paths, astronomers have determined that fifty thousand years ago the constellation looked like this (reveal the top section of the transparency) and that fifty thousand years from now it will look like this (reveal the bottom section of the transparency). Which stars undergo the greatest change in position? (The star at the end of the handle and the upper-right star in the dipper.) The shape of the Big Dipper is changing because the apparent distances between some of its stars are changing: they are becoming either larger or smaller. Consider the distance between the star at the base of the handle and the upper-right star in the dipper. (Label it a, b, and c in the three diagrams.) To show that a is less than b and that b is less than c, we write $a < b$ and $b < c$. Even without seeing the diagrams, we can conclude that $a < c$.

Now consider the distance between the two stars at the end of the handle. (Label it d, e, and f in the three diagrams.) Notice that $d > e$ and that $e < f$. Is it possible, without seeing the diagrams, to conclude anything about how d and f compare? (No.)

These examples prepare the students for a formal discussion of the postulates of inequality. You may prefer to prove the addition and "whole greater than its part" theorems with your students and have them begin their assignment with Exercise 3 of Set I.

Lesson 2
The Exterior Angle Theorem

(Show Transparency 6-2.) The lengths of the two vertical segments in this figure have been labeled a and b. According to the three possibilities postulate, they must have one of three relationships. What are they? ($a < b$, $a = b$, or $a > b$.) Although the two segments actually have the same length so that $a = b$, one of them gives the illusion of being longer. The psychologist Richard Gregory, in an article in Scientific American (November 1968) titled "Visual Illusions," suggests that "the eye unconsciously interprets the arrow-like figures as three-dimensional skeleton structures, resembling either an outside or inside corner of a physical structure." (Add overlay to Transparency 6-2.) We perceive length a to be smaller than it really is and length b to be larger to adjust for the distortion of perspective.

Transparency 6-3 and its overlay can be used to develop the new lesson on the Exterior Angle Theorem. (The overlay should not be taped to the transparency; it can then be slid across the transparency so that the saucer, point C, moves from right to left along the upper line. After doing this, choose an intermediate position, draw $\overline{AC}$ and $\overline{BC}$, and label the saucer's angles of elevation with respect to the observers 1 and 2.)

Note that the proof of the theorem implicitly assumes that $\overrightarrow{BP}$ lies between $\overrightarrow{BC}$ and $\overrightarrow{BD}$. In defense of doing this, I quote the authors of the S. M. S. G. Geometry, with whom I am in complete agreement:

It is probably true that no kind of mathematics can be effectively presented in a completely rigorous form to a tenth-grade class. We should not feel guilty about teaching tenth-grade students merely as much as they can learn. The betweenness problem here will probably go unnoticed by most students. It should be called to the attention only of very capable and critical students. *

In an article in The Mathematics Teacher (May 1967) titled "Sight Versus Insight," Harry Sitomer makes some interesting comments about the reactions of students of varying ability to having their attention called to the need for proving this betweenness assumption.

Lesson 3
Triangle Side and Angle Inequalities

The "visual cliff"

Everyone knows that it is dangerous to leave a small child where he might fall off a high place without continually watching him. How do little children learn to avoid such accidents? Is it from painful experience or through natural development of their ability to perceive depth? (Show Transparency 6-4.) These photographs illustrate an ex-

periment devised in an attempt to answer this question. A board was placed across the center of a heavy sheet of glass. On one side of the board, a checked material was placed directly under the glass so that it seemed to be solid. On the other side, the material was placed several feet below the glass. A child was placed on the center board as shown in the first photograph. When his mother was on the "shallow" side, the child crawled across it to her as the second photograph shows. When she moved to the "deep" side, the child hesitated at its edge (the third photograph) and, in spite of having felt that it was solid, was afraid to crawl across it to his mother (the fourth photograph). This experiment shows that a small child can recognize depth as soon as he is able to crawl. *

This diagram represents a side view of the visual cliff (Transparency 6-5). (Add the overlay.) Point E represents the child's eye and the lines shown form the angles that the squares in the pattern on each side of the cliff make with his eye. Notice that these angles are larger on the shallow side. As we move toward the left from the cliff, the consecutive angles, $\angle$ EDC, $\angle$ ECB, $\angle$ EBA, ..., get larger and larger; also, as we move toward the right from the cliff, the consecutive angles, $\angle$ EFG, $\angle$ EGH, $\angle$ EHI, ..., get larger and larger. Can you explain why? (Each successive angle is an exterior angle of a triangle in which the previous angle is a remote interior angle.) It appears that EC = ED. If so, why is $\angle$ ECD = $\angle$ EDC? (If two sides of a triangle are equal, the angles opposite them are equal.)

In $\triangle$EAB, $\overline{EA}$ seems to be longer than $\overline{EB}$. How do the two angles opposite them compare in measure? ($\angle$ EBA looks obtuse and $\angle$ EAB looks acute, so $\angle$ EBA > $\angle$ EAB.) Look at $\triangle$EFG. Which side is shortest? ($\overline{FG}$.) Which is the triangle's smallest angle? ($\angle$ FEG.) These observations prepare the student for Theorem 19 and its proof.

Lesson 4
The Triangle Inequality Theorem

The anteater-path puzzle discussed in Lesson 4 of the text is a classic problem in geometry and is a good exercise for your stu-

---

*School Mathematics Study Group, Geometry: Teacher's Commentary, Part I (Yale University Press, 1961), p. 150.

---

*Eleanor J. Gibson and Richard D. Walk, "The Visual Cliff," Scientific American, April 1960, pp. 64-71.

dents to work on together. I suggest making a ditto master of Transparency 6-6 and printing a copy for each student. Present the problem with books closed and ask each student to draw three different paths and measure the length of each to the nearest millimeter. Then poll the class to determine who has drawn the shortest path. (The actual minimum is about 207 mm.) Place Transparency 6-6 over that student's paper, trace the path, and show it to the rest of the class.

We have found, by trial and error, what may be the shortest path for the anteater. Is there a more direct way to find it? (Yes; develop the rest of the lesson as is done on pp. 245-246 of the text. Note that completion of the proof of the Triangle Inequality Theorem is left to the student as an exercise.)

Exercises 3 and 4 of Lesson 3, Set I, are worth special attention. Transparency 6-7 is for use in discussing them.

Review of Chapter 6

A miniature golf problem

The game of miniature golf was invented in Tennessee almost fifty years ago. Since then thousands of courses have been built all over the country. (Show Transparency 6-8.) Here is a photograph of one of the holes on a miniature golf course and a diagram showing its layout. The player hits the ball from point A. If he strikes it hard enough and in the right direction, it will fly through a small "house" between A and the hole at C. Otherwise, it will roll down a ramp and end up somewhere in the section beside the house. Suppose the ball stops at point B. Some players, observing the corner between B and the hole, might decide to hit the ball twice, first past the corner, and then into the hole. Can you figure out a way to get the ball into the hole in just one shot? (Reflect the hole through the lower edge and hit the ball toward the reflection.) When the ball strikes the lower edge, it behaves just as a ray of light does when it is reflected by a mirror. Can you explain why the angle at which the ball strikes the edge is equal to the angle at which it leaves it? (That the angles are equal follows from the facts that reflection of a set of points through a line preserves angle measure and that vertical angles are equal. This problem is equivalent to Exercise 1 of Lesson 4, Set II.)

Transparency 6-9 is for use in discussing the Set III exercise of Lesson 4.

Chapter 7

PARALLEL LINES

Lesson 1
Parallel Lines

Show Transparency 7-1 and read the dialogue to the class. Peter and Thor, the two characters in this cartoon, disagree about whether parallel lines intersect. In an attempt to settle their argument, they trace what they think are parallel lines on the ground. Although Peter is certain that the lines do not actually meet, it seems from the perspective that they do. How can he prove to Thor that they do not?

Here are two different views of the lines Peter and Thor have traced on the ground. (Show Transparency 7-2.) The first view shows the lines as seen from overhead and the second view shows them as seen from the ground. (Add Overlay A.) In each diagram, we have added a line that intersects line ℓ_1 in point A and line ℓ_2 in point B. This line, labeled t, is called a transversal with respect to the other two lines. Notice that in the overhead view the angles formed by transversal t and the two parallel lines that are numbered 1 and 2 seem to be equal. The same angles have also been labeled in the perspective view. It is easy to prove that, if these angles are indeed equal, then the lines cannot intersect at point C as they seem to in this view. In other words, if $\angle 1 = \angle 2$, then $\ell_1 \parallel \ell_2$. (Write this below the figures on the transparency.) Notice that, if the lines do intersect, they form a triangle, $\triangle ABC$. What relationship does $\angle 2$ have to the triangle? (It is an exterior angle.) What can you conclude about $\angle 1$ and $\angle 2$? ($\angle 2 > \angle 1$.) Since this contradicts our hypothesis

that $\angle 1 = \angle 2$, the assumption that lines ℓ_1 and ℓ_2 intersect must be false; therefore they are parallel. (Add Overlay B.)

We have established a practical way to prove that two lines are parallel: show that they form equal corresponding angles with a transversal. Show Transparency 7-3 and have your students identify the pairs of corresponding angles in the figure. Then consider the alternate interior angles and the interior angles on the same side of the transversal. Note that no attempt has been made in the text to define these angle relationships.

Lesson 2
Perpendicular Lines

Here are sketches of two faces. (Show the upper half of Transparency 7-4.) Does either one seem to be looking at you? (Your students will probably agree that the face on the left seems to be looking upward, whereas the one on the right seems to be looking toward the observer. Reveal the bottom half of Transparency 7-4.) This diagram represents the two faces as seen from overhead: lines a and b show the directions in which they seem to be looking.

The sketches of the faces are from a book on optical illusions. Although they seem to be looking in different directions, the eyes of each face are actually identical. (Cover everything on the transparency except for the eyes at the top.) If this is the case, it seems reasonable to conclude that the eyes are looking in the same direction. (Uncover the transparency and add the overlay.) If ray n points north, then we can state the direction of lines a and c by giving the measure of the angle that each line makes with the ray: the direction of each line is N 50°E. How does it follow from this that the lines are parallel? (They are parallel because they make equal corresponding angles with a transversal.) What other angle relationships can be used to prove two lines parallel? (You might mark additional angles on the figure to illustrate Corollaries 1 and 2 of Theorem 22.)

Transparency 7-5 is for use in discussing the Set III exercise of Lesson 1.

To begin the new lesson on perpendiculars, you might show Escher's Waterfall (Transparency 7-6). It was inspired by the Penrose triangle (discussed in the lesson plan for Chapter 4, Lesson 6). The triangle appears three times in the lithograph, which you can show by placing Overlay A for Transparency 7-6 in the appropriate positions. Remove Overlay A and add Overlay B. Consider line l and points A and B. Through point A, how many lines are there perpendicular to line l? (Infinitely many; two obvious ones lie in the horizontal and vertical planes that contain l.) If we choose a specific plane that contains line l, how many lines are there through point A perpendicular to the line? (Exactly one.) Through point B, how many lines are there perpendicular to line l? (Exactly one; we need not choose a specific plane in order for this to be true because, as some of your students may recall from Chapter 1, Lesson 11, for a line and a point not on the line, there is exactly one plane that contains them.)

The proofs of Theorems 23 and 24 are not very interesting and it is probably unwise to expect your students to remember them. The two parts of Theorem 24, that there is at least one perpendicular and no more than one, are analogous to Theorem 26 and the Parallel Postulate. Transparency 7-7 can be used to develop the proofs of the two theorems.

Lesson 3
The Parallel Postulate

A moiré pattern

According to The American Heritage Dictionary of the English Language, a "moiré effect" is "the effect of superimposing a repetitive design...on the same or a different design to produce a pattern distinct from its components." Make two copies of Transparency 7-8 and place one over the other so that the superimposed segments are nearly parallel. Then slowly rotate one set of segments until they are perpendicular to the segments in the other set. The moiré effect is most noticeable when the two sets of segments intersect at a very small angle. An article on moiré patterns by Gerald Oster and Yasunori Nishijima is in the May 1963 issue of Scientific American. Kits for experimenting with moiré patterns are available from the Edmund Scientific Company.

Before presenting the new lesson, show Transparency 7-7 again to remind your students of the two theorems already proved about lines through a given point that are perpendicular to a given line. Then show Transparency 7-9, in which the word "perpendicular" in each of these theorems has been changed to the word "parallel." After observing that the first "theorem" is false and proving the part of the second theorem that there is at least one parallel, your students will probably be surprised to be told that, on the basis of the postulates and theorems we already know, it is impossible to prove that there is no more than one parallel. Hence, we assume it as the Parallel Postulate.

Transparency 7-10 is for use in discussing the Set III exercise of Lesson 2.

Lesson 4
Some Consequences of the Parallel Postulate

A well-known date in history is 1492, the year Christopher Columbus made the voyage across the Atlantic Ocean that led to the discovery of America. (A good picture of Columbus that you might make into a transparency is on page 50 of the book Age of Exploration by John R. Hale, a volume in the Great Ages of Man series published by Time-Life Books.) The shaded parts of this map (Transparency 7-11) show the extent of the world known to the Europeans before Columbus set out on his journey. Most educated people of the time agreed that the world was round; Columbus thought that by sailing west from Spain, he would travel around the world and arrive at Japan or China. (Show Transparency 7-12 with Overlay A.) He figured the distance would be about 4,000 miles on the mistaken assumption that the circumference of the earth is much less than it actually is. It is no wonder that when he had gone this distance and arrived at Cuba, he thought it was Japan. Columbus believed this, in fact, to his dying day. Not until later did the Europeans realize that the earth is large enough to contain another continent and ocean.

Yet it is a remarkable fact that one of the Greek mathematicians accurately determined the size of the earth more than seventeen centuries before Columbus made his historic voyage. Use Transparencies 7-13 and 7-12 (with Overlay B) to explain the method Eratosthenes used as described on pages 270-271 of the text. Transparency 7-14 and its overlay can be used to develop the proof of Theorem 28. Transparency 7-15 compares Theorems 22 and 28 and their corollaries.

Lesson 5
The Angles of a Triangle

This map of San Francisco (Transparency 7-16) shows the variations in temperature in that city on a certain spring evening. The temperature ranges from 68° in the center of the city to 53° near one edge. In general, areas that have the greatest concentration of large buildings are the warmest. Meteorologists have found that climate is affected not only by the presence of man-made structures such as buildings, but also by the pavement that provides access to them. The weather in a city is usually milder than in the countryside around it.

One reason for this is the difference in the way that sunlight is reflected in a city and in the country. In a city, a ray of light may be reflected from one surface to another so that most of its energy is absorbed in the process. In the country, on the other hand, a light ray may be reflected directly back to the sky before much of its energy has been released.* (Hand out dittoed copies of Transparency 7-17.) Remember that, because the sun is so far away from the earth, its rays are very close to being parallel. The two parallel line segments in the figure at the top represent two light rays hitting the

---

*William P. Lowry, "The Climate of Cities," Scientific American, August 1967, pp. 15-23.

earth. Use your ruler and protractor to draw the paths of the rays after they are reflected from the ground. Assume that the angle at which a light ray strikes a surface is equal to the angle at which it is reflected. What do you notice? (The reflected rays are also parallel.) Now use your ruler and protractor to draw the paths of the light rays after they are reflected from the vertical wall shown in the second figure. Assume that the rays are reflected each time they hit a surface. (After hitting the wall at the right, the rays hit the ground and the wall at the left before being reflected back into space.)

Transparency 7-18 is for use in discussing the Set III exercise of Lesson 4.

To introduce the new lesson, you might take a piece of stiff paper that has been cut in the shape of a large scalene triangle, tear off its corners, and project them on your screen. You know that it is possible for a triangle to have three angles of these sizes because you have just seen the triangle from which they came. Show Transparency 7-19, revealing only the first figure. Do you think the three angles shown here could be the angles of a triangle? (Students who think the answer is yes should try to draw such a triangle.) After your students have considered the other figures, ask if someone can specify a way to tell whether a set of angles may be the angles of a triangle that does not require actually drawing the triangle. Then align the three corners you tore off the paper triangle to verify that the sum of their measures seems to be 180°.

Explain that we can prove this by using the Parallel Postulate and develop the proof (on page 276 of the text) informally. Note that, at best, the manipulation of the angles torn from a physical model of a triangle can only suggest that the sum of their measures is approximately 180°. By drawing the parallel through one vertex, we are in effect arranging the three angles of the triangle at that vertex in the same way: it is now possible, however, to see why the sum of their measures must be <u>exactly</u> 180°.

Lesson 6
Two More Ways to Prove Triangles Congruent

The largest diamond ever discovered was found in South Africa in 1905. It weighed more than one pound before being cut into nine smaller diamonds several years later.

The brilliance of a diamond depends upon the shape into which it has been cut. (Hand out dittoed copies of Transparency 7-20.) These figures represent cross sections of three different diamonds that have been cut symmetrically with respect to the lines shown. This means that the lower part of each cross section is an isosceles triangle; the measures of the vertex angles of these triangles are given.

Now suppose that a ray of light enters each diamond as shown so that it is parallel to the line of symmetry. On the assumption that the ray is reflected each time it hits a leg of the triangle, can you make an accurate sketch of its path in each diamond? For simplicity, we will assume that the ray passes through the top of the diamond rather than being reflected again. (The ray is actually bent as it passes from the diamond into the air.)

Appropriate drawings for the three cases are shown here.

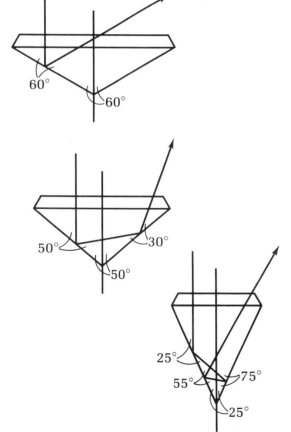

In 1919 a physicist showed, taking into account an aspect of light behavior that we have ignored (its refraction), that the optimum vertex angle for cutting a diamond is about 100°: a diamond reflects the greatest amount of light when it is cut at this angle.

Transparency 7-21 is for use in discussing the Set III exercise of Lesson 5. Ask a student who has found the star to outline it for the rest of the class to see.

I suggest assigning Lesson 6 for individual study rather than presenting it in class.

Review of Chapter 7

One of the seven wonders of the ancient world was a lighthouse at Alexandria in Egypt. Built at about the time of Euclid, it guided ships until as late as the twelfth century. Today more than 10,000 lighthouses mark the shorelines of the world's continents for ships traveling at night.

Here is an example of how the navigator of a ship can use geometry to determine how far the ship is from a lighthouse sighted on the shore. (Show Transparency 7-22.) Suppose the ship is moving along line ℓ when a lighthouse at point L is sighted. As the ship travels along the line, the angle between its course and the line of sight to the lighthouse gets larger and larger. If the navigator measures this angle when the ship is at A and then waits until the ship has moved to a point where the angle has doubled, point B in the figure, he can conclude that the distance from the ship to the lighthouse is equal to the distance the ship has traveled in going from A to B. In other words, if $\angle 2 = 2\angle 1$, then LB = AB. Can you write a brief proof to show why this is so?

Here is such a proof:
1. $\angle 2 = 2\angle 1$. (Given.)
2. $\angle 2 = \angle 1 + \angle L$. (An exterior angle of a triangle is equal in measure to the sum of the measures of the remote interior angles.)
3. $2\angle 1 = \angle 1 + \angle L$. (Substitution.)
4. $\angle 1 = \angle L$. (Subtraction.)
5. LB = AB. (If two angles of a triangle are equal, the sides opposite them are equal.)

Transparency 7-23 is for use in discussing the Set III exercise of Lesson 6.

Chapter 8

QUADRILATERALS

Lesson 1
Quadrilaterals

Show Transparency 8-1 and let your students guess what the photograph is of. It shows cracks in dried mud and is taken from a fascinating book every mathematics teacher should own: Mathematical Snapshots, by H. Steinhaus (Oxford University Press, 1969).

Can you guess which cracks occurred first? (The longest ones.) It is interesting to notice that almost all of the cracks meet at right angles. (There is a physical explanation for this in terms of the laws of mechanics.) Most of the figures formed by the cracks have four sides; they are examples of "quadrilaterals," the subject of the next unit of the course.

(Add the overlay to Transparency 8-1.) Certain types of quadrilaterals are given specific names; some examples are shown here. How many of them can you identify? (1. square, 2. rectangle, 3. parallelogram, 4. trapezoid, 5. kite.) Some of these quadrilaterals have several properties in common. For example, which ones seem to have four right angles? (1 and 2.) Which ones have two pairs of equal sides? (1, 2, 3, and 5.) Which ones seem to have line symmetry? (1, 2, 4, and 5.) We will study many of these properties in detail in later lessons.

(Remove the overlay.) There is one property that every quadrilateral in this figure has in common: each one is convex. (Show Transparency 8-2 and by placing the edge of a ruler in line with each side—hold the ruler on edge—show that, if a line contains any side of a convex quadrilateral, the rest of the quadrilateral lies in one of the half-planes that has the line for its edge. Show that this is not true of concave quadrilaterals.)

(Show Transparency 8-1 with its overlay again.) If all four angles of the quadrilaterals numbered 1 and 2 are right angles, it is obvious that the sum of the measures of the angles in each of them is $360°$. What about the other quadrilaterals? Although their angles are not right angles, it isn't difficult to prove that the sum of the measures of the angles in each of them is also $360°$. Can you figure out how? (Show Transparency 8-3. This is a convenient time to introduce the term "diagonal." Let your students explain the proof.)

Lesson 2
Parallelograms

Why an octopus can't do geometry

One of the books in the Life Nature Library, Animal Behavior, describes a number of experiments that biologists have devised to study vision in animals. In one of these experiments, crabs were attached to metal plates of various shapes and put in front of an octopus. (Show Transparency 8-4.) Some of the plates were electrified so that, when the octopus touched them, it got a mild shock. After some time, the octopus learned to associate certain shapes with the shocks and hence to avoid them. Certain shapes, however, looked alike to the octopus, so it never learned to distinguish between them. Can you guess which two of the three shapes shown here look the same to an octopus? (Although it would seem to be A and B, the two shapes that the octopus cannot tell apart are A and C. The octopus apparently looks at an object by scanning it vertically and horizontally, observing its dimensions in each direction. Scanning each figure from top to bottom, their horizontal cross sections are the same. Scanning them from left to right, the vertical cross sections of A and C first increase, then remain constant, and then decrease. The vertical cross sections of B, on the other hand, are constant all the way across.)

After observing that figures A and B are examples of parallelograms, ask your students what properties they have in common before defining the term "parallelogram" and proving Theorem 34. (This is a good proof for your students to develop by working together as a class. Transparency 8-5 is for use in doing this.)

Exercise 4 of Lesson 1, Set I, is worth careful consideration; your students may find it more difficult than you might think. Transparency 8-6 is for use in discussing the Set III exercise.

Lesson 3
Quadrilaterals That Are Parallelograms

A trick with parallels

Most of you are probably familiar with number tricks in which someone asks you to choose a number and do certain things with it. Then, somehow, he is able to tell you what number you ended up with. Here is a simple trick, not with numbers of arithmetic but with points and lines of geometry.*

Show Transparency 8-7 and ask a student to mark a point on the triangle that is not a vertex or a midpoint of one of the sides. Label it P. The transparency should have a clear overlay attached to it. Turn off the projector, place the overlay on the transparency and mark, with a bold dot, the point on the same side of the triangle on which the student has chosen P so that your point is the same distance from the vertex closest to

*This trick is based upon one described by Nathan Altshiller Court in his book Mathematics in Fun and in Earnest (Dial Press, 1958).

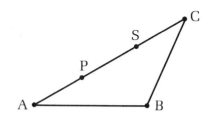

it as P is from its closest vertex. For example, in the figure shown here, if the student has chosen point P on side $\overline{AC}$, you should mark point S such that CS = AP. Do not actually label the point S. Now remove the overlay, turn the projector back on, and explain that you have marked the point where you predict the student will end up at the end of the trick.

Ask the student to draw, as accurately as he can, a line through P that is parallel to one of the sides of the triangle. The class may observe that he has two choices in doing this. Label the other point in which this line intersects the triangle point Q. Now ask him to draw a second line, through Q, that is parallel to one of the sides of the triangle. Label the other point in which this line intersects the triangle point R. Finally, ask him to draw a third line, through R, also parallel to one of the sides of the triangle. Label the other point in which this line intersects the triangle point S.

When he has done this, replace the overlay on the figure to show that you have predicted its position correctly. The figures below show the results that could follow from the example figure above.

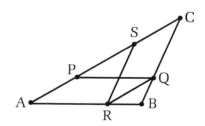

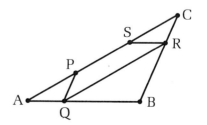

Explain that you did not try to picture any parallel lines in advance and ask if anyone can guess how you located the point in advance. If no one can, explain that you knew that point S would be on $\overrightarrow{CA}$ such that CS = AP. Now help the class, working together, to prove that the trick will always work. The following proof is for the first case shown above.

Given: $\overline{PQ} \parallel \overline{AB}$, $\overline{QR} \parallel \overline{AC}$, and $\overline{RS} \parallel \overline{BC}$.
Prove: CS = AP.
1. $\overline{PQ} \parallel \overline{AB}$, $\overline{QR} \parallel \overline{AC}$, and $\overline{RS} \parallel \overline{BC}$. (Given.)
2. APQR and CQRS are parallelograms. (If both pairs of opposite sides of a quadrilateral are parallel, it is a parallelogram.)
3. AP = RQ and RQ = SC. (The opposite sides of a parallelogram are equal.)
4. AP = SC. (Transitive.)

The proof for the second case is slightly longer in that we first get AS = PC. Since AS = AP + PS and PC = PS + SC, AP + PS = PS + SC, and AP = SC by subtraction.

Transparency 8-8 and its overlay are for use in discussing the Set III exercise of Lesson 2.

To introduce Lesson 3, you might show Transparency 8-9. The three photographs show someone who seems to grow in size as he walks across an Ames room. More information on this subject may be found in an article titled "Visual Perception and Personality" by Warren J. Wittreich in Scientific American, April 1959, pp. 56-60. After showing Transparency 8-9, I suggest that you ask your students to read Lesson 3 in order to learn the explanation.

Lesson 4
Kites and Rhombuses

Why a proof-writing computer had trouble with a problem like those in your homework

Computers have been programmed to do all sorts of things, including drawing pictures, composing music, and playing games. Several years ago an experiment was conducted in the IBM Research Laboratory to see if a computer could be programmed to write geometric proofs. A number of basic postulates and theorems, along with the methods of deductive reasoning, were stored in the memory of an IBM 704 computer and then it was

given some exercises to prove. One of them is similar to a theorem in yesterday's lesson. (Show Transparency 8-10.) The problem was to show that, if two sides of a quadrilateral are both parallel and equal, then the other two sides are equal. If the computer had known the theorem that such a quadrilateral is a parallelogram, the proof would have been simple since both pairs of opposite sides of a parallelogram are equal. Apparently it didn't know this because this is what it did. (Add the overlay to the transparency, and reveal only the top part, including the line SEGMENT AB EQUALS SEGMENT CD. Your students should recognize the "premises" and "goals" as the "given" and "prove." The "syntactic symmetries" are a list of point relationships that had to be included in the program since the computer could not see the figure. Reveal the next line.)

After the computer had "thought" about the problem for 88 seconds, it reported that it was stuck (some of our students exhibit about the same amount of persistence, I am afraid). Can anyone guess why? (In order to develop a proof, an extra line is required. How to add parts to the figure had not been written into the computer's program. Reveal the next three lines and add $\overline{BD}$ to the figure.) After a few more minutes, the computer printed out the following proof. (Reveal it a step at a time, noting that we would take some of the statements for granted.)

Before discussing the exercises in Lesson 3, you might remind your students that we now have five ways to prove that a quadrilateral is a parallelogram and ask them if they can recall all five. (The definition of a parallelogram and Theorems 37-40.) Transparency 8-11 is for use in discussing the Set III exercise.

To introduce Lesson 4, you might show Transparency 8-12, a photograph of a crystal of garnet and a drawing of its structure. Directions for building a model of this solid, called a rhombic dodecahedron, are given in Mathematical Models, by H. Martyn Cundy and A. P. Rollett (Oxford University Press, 1961), p. 120. Point out that every edge of this crystal has the same length; hence its faces are equilateral.

Transparency 8-13 can be used to illustrate the terms "rhombus" and "kite" and to show that a rhombus is both a parallelogram and a kite.

Lesson 5
Rectangles and Squares

An experiment with some linkages

Give each student a ruler, a pair of scissors, and a letter-size envelope containing four thumbtacks and a 1.5" x 6" piece of cardboard. The piece of cardboard is to be ruled and cut into strips as shown in the diagram at the top of Transparency 8-14. The strips are each 1/4" wide: the four labeled "a" are 3" long and the two labeled "b" are 4" long. The shaded section may be thrown away.

Poke two holes in each of the lettered strips, each one about 1/8" from an end. (It is easier to do this with the metal point of a compass than with one of the thumbtacks.) Now attach two "a" strips and the two "b" strips at their ends with the thumbtacks so that they form a parallelogram. (This is illustrated on the lower part of Transparency 8-14.) By changing the size of one of the angles, the figure can be made to assume different shapes. (Have your students do this.) How do you know that in every case the figure is a parallelogram? (If both pairs of opposite sides of a quadrilateral are equal, the quadrilateral is a parallelogram.) What other properties does it always possess? (Its opposite sides are parallel; its opposite angles are equal; its consecutive angles are supplementary; its diagonals bisect each other.) Can you manipulate the shape of the figure so that all four of its angles are equal? (Yes. Show this with a linkage on the projector. The students should recognize the resulting figure as a rectangle and observe that its angles are right angles.) No matter what the shape of the figure, its diagonals always bisect each other. Check this by placing the 6" strips along them. Can you manipulate the figure so that they are perpendicular? (No.) Can you manipulate the figure so that they are equal? (Yes; they seem to be equal when the figure is a rectangle.)

Now take the four strips apart and reconnect them to form a kite. (Give your students time to manipulate it into different shapes. They should discover that the linkage may represent an isosceles triangle and a concave quadrilateral as well as a kite.) Some appropriate questions: Can you manipulate the figure so that

1. both pairs of opposite sides are parallel? (No.)

2. all four angles are equal? (No.)
3. one pair of opposite angles are equal? (Yes; this is true of all kites.)
4. the diagonals are perpendicular? (Yes; this is true of all kites.)
5. the diagonals are equal? (Yes.)
6. the diagonals bisect each other? (No.)

Finally, take the strips apart and connect the four "a" strips so that they form a rhombus. By this point the students should be able to generate their own questions and conclusions.

Before you assign the reading of Lesson 5, you might hold up your copy of the textbook open to page 310 so that the class can see the Lincoln picture from a distance. Two more pictures of this type are in the November 1973 issue of Scientific American. There is a portrait of George Washington on the cover and a picture of the Mona Lisa on page 70, both in color.

Lesson 6
Trapezoids

A test of your ingenuity

(A figure illustrating the following problem is on Transparency 8-15.) Suppose you are playing a game of Ping-Pong with a friend in your backyard. One of you misses the ball; it bounces across the lawn and falls into a small but deep hole. The hole goes down too far for you to be able to reach the ball and it bends to one side so that you can't get the ball by poking a stick into the hole. Can you figure out an easy, practical way to get the ball?*

(Fill the hole with water from a hose and the Ping-Pong ball will float to the top.)

Here is another test of your ingenuity. (Give each student an unlined 3" x 5" file card.) Can you figure out a simple way, using just an ordinary sheet of ruled paper, to divide one of the edges of this card into seven equal parts? (Place a 3" x 5" piece of thick plastic, to represent the card, on Transparency 8-16 and point out that, if the card is placed horizontally on the lines, there are too many spaces along the edge.)

---

*This problem is from Perplexing Puzzles and Tantalizing Teasers, by Martin Gardner, illustrated by Laszlo Kubinyi (Simon and Schuster, 1969), pp. 74-75. Copyright © 1967 by Martin Gardner. Reprinted by permission of Simon and Schuster, Children's Book Division.

One could estimate the number, divide it by seven, and then try to use the result to mark the points on the card. Can you think of a simpler way? (Place the card at a slant so that two consecutive corners fall on lines that are seven spaces apart. Mark the points on the card at which the lines in between these two lines intersect the edge of the card.)

This method is based upon a theorem that your students do not know: if parallel lines intercept equal segments on one transversal, they intercept equal segments on every transversal. Show Transparency 8-17 to illustrate it (note that we have not assumed that t_1 is perpendicular to the lines a, b, c, ..., h). There is probably no advantage in explicitly stating the theorem itself for your students.

Add the overlay and develop a proof such as the following that the method works.

Proof. Through points I, J, etc., draw $\overline{IQ}$, $\overline{JR}$, etc., parallel to t_1. Since the quadrilaterals formed are parallelograms, IQ = AB, JR = BC, etc. But AB = BC = CD, etc., so IQ = JR = KS, etc. Since a ∥ b ∥ c, etc., $\angle$ IJQ = $\angle$ JKR = $\angle$ KLS, etc. Also $\overline{IQ}$ ∥ $\overline{JR}$ ∥ $\overline{KS}$, etc. (in a plane, two lines parallel to a third line are parallel to each other), so $\angle$ QIJ = $\angle$ RJK = $\angle$ SKL, etc. Hence △IJQ ≅ △JKR ≅ △KLS, etc. (A.A.S.) so IJ = JK = KL, etc.

At the end of the proof, you might remove the overlay and point out that the quadrilaterals in the original figure are trapezoids, the subject of the next lesson.

Transparency 8-18 is for use in discussing the Set III exercise of Lesson 5. Show it first with the overlay in place and then remove the overlay before discussing the proof.

Lesson 7
The Midsegment Theorem

Something about a mirror that will give you cause for reflection

(If possible, place a large mirror on one of the walls of your room before class. Be sure that the mirror is vertical.)

You have all looked at reflections of yourselves in large wall mirrors. Do you know how your distance from the mirror affects the amount of yourself that you can see? (Since the farther you are from the mirror, the farther your reflection seems to be behind it, many people assume that you can see more of yourself as you move away from the mirror. Some people, realizing that as you back away from a mirror you see less and less of the surrounding room reflected in it, think that you see less of yourself as well. Actually, your distance from the mirror makes no difference. The amount of yourself that you can see is controlled solely by the length of the mirror and not by how far away from it you happen to be standing. If a student walks toward the mirror in the room while looking at his reflection, he can confirm this.)

To see why this is so, look at this diagram (Transparency 8-19). The vertical segment in the center represents a side view of a wall and $\overline{AB}$ represents a mirror on it. The mirror is just long enough so that the person standing on the left can see his entire image on the right. (Add Overlay A.) If the person moves away from the mirror, so does his image. Notice, however, that his lines of sight to the reflections of the top of his head and bottom of his feet still pass through points A and B. (Replace Overlay A with Overlay B.) This figure shows what happens if the person moves toward the mirror instead. Again his lines of sight pass through points A and B. (Remove Overlay B.) How long do you think the mirror would need to be for the person to see his entire image if he is six feet tall? In other words, if CD = 6, how long do you think $\overline{AB}$ is? It is not difficult to prove that A and B are the midpoints of sides $\overline{EC}$ and $\overline{ED}$ in △ECD. We will call a segment that joins the midpoints of two sides of a triangle a midsegment of the triangle and will prove that such a segment is always parallel to the third side of the triangle and exactly half as long.

Use Transparency 8-20 and its overlay to develop the proof of the Midsegment Theorem with your class.

Review of Chapter 8

The Russian fur dresser's problem

The following problem is from a popular book of puzzles published in Russia.* (Show Transparency 8-21.)

*Reprinted by permission of Charles Scribner's Sons from The Moscow Puzzles by Boris A. Kordemsky, edited by Martin Gardner. Copyright © 1972 Charles Scribner's Sons.

A fur dresser had to put a patch shaped like a scalene triangle on a piece of fur. Suddenly he realized he had made a terrible mistake. The path fitted the hole but the fur faced the wrong way.

The fur dresser, after some thought, cut the triangular patch into three parts, each of which would be unchanged when turned over. How?

This is a rather challenging puzzle. (Show Transparency 8-22 on which you have placed two triangular pieces identical in size and shape to △ABC and △DEF. The pieces should be cut from a thick sheet of colored plastic.) If the triangle were isosceles, the solution would be simple. The patch could be turned over about its line of symmetry and fitted into place. (Demonstrate this and then show that, since the scalene triangle does not have a line of symmetry, it cannot be turned over and fitted into place in this way.)

Given a patch in the shape of a scalene triangle, according to the puzzle it is possible to cut it into three parts so that each part is unchanged when it is turned over. Evidently, all three parts must have line symmetry. We have just observed that isosceles triangles have this property. (Add the overlay to Transparency 8-22.) The two cuts shown here won't quite work because △DGH and △HIF are not isosceles and quadrilateral EGHI does not have line symmetry. Can you figure out a way to move the cuts a bit so that the two triangles become isosceles and the quadrilateral does have line symmetry? (The solution is shown here: G and I are the midpoints of sides $\overline{ED}$ and $\overline{EF}$ and H is the foot of the perpendicular from E to $\overleftrightarrow{DF}$.)

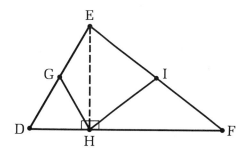

To prove that this will work, we must verify that the triangles are isosceles and show that EGHI has line symmetry. What kind of quadrilateral does it seem to be? (A kite.)

Your class should be able to help you in developing parts of the following proof, which will provide a good review of some of the definitions and theorems in the chapter.

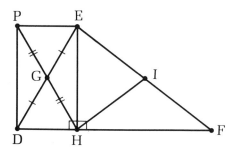

Extend $\overleftrightarrow{GH}$ and choose P so that GP = GH; draw $\overline{PD}$ and $\overline{PE}$. What can you conclude about quadrilateral PEHD? (It is a parallelogram because its diagonals bisect each other. Furthermore, it is easy to show that it is a rectangle. Since $\overline{EH} \perp \overline{DF}$, ∠EHD is a right angle. Since consecutive angles of a parallelogram are supplementary and opposite angles are equal, it follows that all four angles of PEHD are right angles so that it is equiangular.) What can you conclude about PH and ED? (PH = ED because the diagonals of a rectangle are equal.) Since $\overline{PH}$ and $\overline{ED}$ also bisect each other, it follows that GH = GD = GP = GE, so △DGH is isosceles. By extending $\overline{HI}$ in the same fashion, it can be proved in the same way that HI = IE = IF so that △HIF is also isosceles. Why is EGHI a kite? (It has two pairs of equal consecutive sides with no side common to both pairs.) With respect to what line is EGHI symmetric? ($\overleftrightarrow{GI}$, which is the perpendicular bisector of $\overline{EH}$.)

Transparency 8-23 is for use in discussing Exercises 1 and 2 of Lesson 7, Set II. By adding the diagonals of parallelogram HOIE in each figure, it can also be used to show why Ollie's conclusion in the Set III exercise is correct.

Chapter 9

AREA

Lesson 1
Polygonal Regions and Area

If the world lived in Kansas

(Show Transparency 9-1.) The earth's present (1974) population is about 3,800,000,000
people. Suppose everyone moved to the
state of Kansas: how crowded would it be?
(Add the overlay to Transparency 9-1.) At
the center of the United States, Kansas has
an area of about 82,000 square miles. If
all 3,800,000,000 people lived in Kansas,
what would be the average number of people
per square mile? (Approximately 46,000.)

Let's see how this figure compares with
the "population density" of our school.
(Give your class the approximate area of
your campus as a fraction of a square mile
and the number of people on it so that they
can find out. For example, the campus of
the school at which I teach has an area of
about 1/20 square mile and about 3500 people
on it during the school day; hence its "population density" is about 70,000 people per
square mile.) According to the Guinness
Book of World Records, the most densely
populated region in the world is in a section
of Hong Kong, with more than 200,000 people
per square mile.

In each of our calculations, we used a
number called the area of a region. The
idea of "area" is a very fundamental one in
geometry; it will be our subject of study in
the next unit of the course.

Transparencies 9-2 and 9-3 and their
overlays can be used to develop the rest of
Lesson 1. The block letters on the bottom
of 9-2 should be covered while you are explaining the distinction between "triangle"
and "triangular region." They are examples
of a region that is polygonal and one that is
not.

Lesson 2
Squares and Rectangles

Squaring the square

(Hold up a chessboard.) Anyone who has
ever played chess knows that there are 64
squares on the board. Do you suppose it
would be possible to divide the board into
65 squares instead? (If we assume that all
the squares are the same size, the answer
is no.) What if the squares may be different
sizes? The answer to this question is not so
obvious. Let me ask a simpler one. Do you
think it would be possible to divide the board

into just 3 squares? (No; 4 is the minimum number.)

(Hand out dittoed copies of Transparency 9-4.) Divide the first square in the top row into 4 smaller squares. Now, can you figure out a way to add some segments to the figure so that there are 7 squares instead? The squares do not all have to be the same size. (We will not count overlapping squares. The first figure shown here illustrates a solution.) Can you figure out a way to divide a square into 6 smaller squares? (The second figure illustrates a solution.)

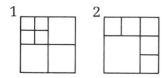

Give your students time to discover some other numbers of squares into which a square can be divided. They can use the squares in the first two rows in the figure below for this purpose. After they have done this, you can ask them to reconsider the problem in the following way:

Instead of making drawings in a haphazard way, we will consider the possibilities in order. We have already observed that 4 is the minimum number. By subdividing one of the 4 squares, we "lose" it but gain 4 new ones, making a net gain of 3. We can repeat this process as many times as we please, each time getting 3 more squares. (See the first row in the figure shown here.

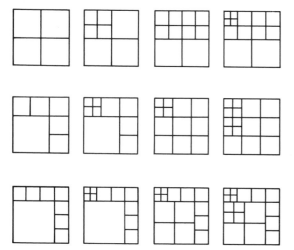

Use the bottom two rows of Transparency 9-4 to demonstrate this and the following.) Hence, it is possible to divide a square into each of the following numbers of smaller squares:

$$4, 7, 10, 13, 16, \ldots$$

There is no way to divide a square into 5 smaller squares, but 6 is possible. Using the subdividing process we have just considered, it follows that we can divide a square into each of the following numbers of smaller squares:

$$6, 9, 12, 15, 18, \ldots$$

(See the second row in the figure.)

Can a square be divided into 8 smaller squares? Yes. It follows from using the same subdividing process as before that a square can be divided into the following numbers of smaller squares:

$$8, 11, 14, 17, 20, \ldots$$

(See the third row in the figure.)

Putting the three sequences together, we see that it is possible to divide a square into any number of smaller squares from 4 up with just one exception: the number 5! We can now answer the question I asked you earlier about the chessboard without even bothering to make a drawing. It is possible to divide the board into 65 squares if they don't all have to be the same size.

Here is a vastly more difficult problem. Is it possible to divide a square into smaller squares so that no two have the same area? For a long time it was thought that the answer to this question was no, but in 1939 somebody discovered a way to do it! Since then, many other solutions have been found: the simplest one known to date is shown on Transparency 9-5. Students who are interested in this problem can learn more about it in the following books:

The Second Scientific American Book of Mathematical Puzzles and Diversions, by Martin Gardner (Simon and Schuster, 1961), pp. 186-209.

Ingenuity in Mathematics, by Ross Honsberger, in the New Mathematical Library (Random House, 1970), pp. 46-60.

Transparency 9-6 and its overlay are for use in presenting Lesson 2. Note that the grid does not nearly fill up the second rectangle with unit squares: this helps make clear the need for postulating the formula for the area of a rectangle.

Lesson 3
Parallelograms and Triangles

A land bonanza in the Klondike*

Several years ago the makers of a popular breakfast cereal included a deed to some land in the Klondike in each package of cereal sold. Although this might seem like a very generous offer, each deed, in fact, was for a lot only one square inch in area.

Suppose the company had sold the land instead at a nominal charge of 25¢ per lot. Can you figure out, at this rate, what the net income per acre would have been? One acre is equal to 43,560 square feet. (The net income would have been $1,568,160 per acre.)

Transparencies 9-8 and 9-9 are for use in discussing Exercises 4 and 5 of Set II and the Set III exercise of Lesson 2.

Transparency 9-10 and its overlay are for use in introducing Lesson 3.

Lesson 4
Trapezoids

An area paradox**

You can either demonstrate the following puzzle with your students as observers or else provide them with materials so that they can try it out themselves. For the demonstration, you need Transparency 9-11 and a set of the six pieces that make up the triangular figure cut from a thick sheet of colored plastic. If you would like to let your students do it, print an equal number of copies of Worksheet 4 on white and colored paper. Gestetner cover stock paper is ideal for this purpose. Cut the sheets into quarters and give each student a pair of scissors and two copies of the pattern: one on white and the other on the colored paper.

The figure drawn on the grid is an isosceles triangle. What do you think its area is if the small squares each have an area of one

---

*This is adapted from a problem in The Lore of Large Numbers, by Philip J. Davis, in the New Mathematical Library (Random House, 1961).

**From The Scientific American Book of Mathematical Puzzles and Diversions, by Martin Gardner (Simon and Schuster, 1959). Copyright © 1959 by Martin Gardner.

square unit? (60 square units.) Cut the figure out of one of the patterns and then cut it along the heavy black lines into six pieces. Place the pieces on the other pattern so that the two larger right triangles are at the top and the smaller ones are at the corners of the bottom. Put the two L-shaped pieces in the remaining space. What do you notice? (There is now a hole of 2 square units.) What seems to be the area of the figure when its pieces are arranged in this way? (58 square units.) This result seems to contradict the Area Addition Postulate. Since the area of each piece surely does not change when it is moved from one place to another, how is it possible that the total area of the six pieces can shrink like this? (I suggest saving the explanation until the following day; perhaps one of your better students, given time, will be able to figure the paradox out. When the pieces are rearranged, their total area is still 60 square units. The two units that seem to have disappeared are now evenly distributed in two narrow bands along the legs of the triangle: the overlay for Transparency 9-11 shows this in a slightly exaggerated way so that it is easier to see. The two bands result from the fact that the lower left and right vertices of the two right triangles at the top in the original figure are not actually intersection points of the grid but lie slightly to the left and right of them, respectively.) The Set III exercise of Lesson 4 is somewhat similar to this; you might save this explanation until some of the students have considered and are ready to discuss it.

Transparency 9-12 is for use in discussing the Set III exercise of Lesson 3.

Lesson 5
The Pythagorean Theorem

What is your area?

Most of you probably know your height and weight quite accurately. Do you know what your area is? (Show Transparency 9-13.) By this, I mean the total surface area of your skin. The lower figure represents the skin of the person in the upper figure stretched out flat like a pelt.

We have developed formulas for finding the areas of a variety of geometric figures but they are of no use in finding the area of a figure as complex as this. The area of a person of average weight and body build depends upon his height. Make an estimate of your own area and then I will give you a formula by means of which you can determine it more accurately. (It might be fun to have each student write his estimate on a scrap of paper, collect the estimates and read some of the more extreme ones to the class before going any further.)

You can find your approximate area by means of the following formula:

$$\alpha_{human} = \frac{3}{5}h^2$$

where h is your height in feet. (After everyone has had time to compute his or her area by this formula, show Transparency 9-14 so that they can check their answers. Each area is rounded to the nearest square foot.)

Transparencies 9-15 and 9-16 are for use in discussing Exercises 4-6 of Set II and the Set III exercise of Lesson 4. The four pieces for the checkerboard puzzle should be cut from a thick sheet of colored plastic. The grid on Transparency 9-16 permits a comparison of the areas of the two arrangements.

Transparencies 9-17 and 9-18 are for use in introducing Lesson 5. The figures illustrating the Pythagorean Theorem have been omitted from the Martian's sleeve and the earth so that you can draw them in in a contrasting color.

Here is a nice way to convey the idea behind the proof of the Pythagorean Theorem presented on page 351 of the text. Cut, in advance, from thick sheets of colored plastic the three squares and four copies of the triangle shown in the top figure on Transparency 9-18. The triangles should be one color and the squares another. Place the three squares and one of the triangles on the transparency figure and point out that we want to show that the sum of the areas of the two smaller squares is equal to the area of the largest one. Then arrange the triangle and large square in the frame at the bottom of the transparency as shown in the third figure on page 351 of the text. Fill in the remaining spaces with the other three triangles. Explain that we can remove the large square and rearrange the four triangles so that there is exactly enough room for the two smaller squares. In demon-

strating this, you might leave the triangle at the lower left in place and slide the other three to the appropriate positions so that the two smaller squares can be fitted into place. (There is no need to bother turning over the two at the upper right as has been done in the fourth figure on page 351.) A formal proof of this is presented in Lesson 5, which can now be assigned for individual study.

Lesson 6
Heron's Theorem

The rope-stretchers

Every year the Nile River in Egypt overflows its banks in late summer and floods the surrounding land. Herodotus, a Greek historian of the fifth century B.C., wrote: "When the Nile inundates the land all of Egypt becomes a sea, and only the towns remain above water, looking rather like the islands of the Aegean. At such times shipping no longer follows the stream, but goes straight across the country." Because the flooding wiped out many boundary lines, the ancient Egyptians developed some of the basic principles of surveying to reestablish them. (Show the top part of Transparency 9-19.) This is a picture of part of a mural more than 3000 years old. It shows surveyors holding a rope with knots equally spaced along it. By stretching the rope out to form a triangle, the surveyors made use of something we considered in yesterday's lesson.

The following makes a nice demonstration. Take a rope about 25 feet long and put 13 knots in it at 2-foot intervals. Give a knot at one end to a student to hold and form, in the middle of your class, a 3-4-5 triangle by having other students hold the appropriate knots. Do not tell the class what lengths the sides of the triangle are but let them observe them for themselves. The sides should be stretched out tight and the students outside it should stand up and look at the result. Let someone tell what he observes and explain. Note that we know that a 3-4-5 triangle is a right triangle not because of the Pythagorean Theorem but because of its converse. There is an impressive photograph of an Egyptian field divided into squares on pages 48-49 of Ancient Egypt, by Lionel Casson, in the Great Ages of Man series (Time-Life Books, 1965).

Transparencies 9-20, 9-21, and 9-22 are for use in discussing the Set II and Set III exercises of Lesson 5. I suggest cutting from a thick sheet of colored plastic the two quadrilateral pieces for the da Vinci proof; also the five pieces for the Set III puzzle.

Even to an accelerated class, I do not recommend presenting the proof of Heron's Theorem. Most students who have taken just one year of elementary algebra have great difficulty in trying to follow it. Instead, the emphasis should be placed upon why the formula is useful and how it is used. You may wish to treat the corollary for determining the area of an equilateral triangle in the same way.

A good way to introduce the theorem is to pose the following problems. (Transparency 9-23.)

Can you figure out the area of this triangle? (Since $5^2 + 12^2 = 13^2$, it is a right triangle. Hence if we choose one leg as its base, the other leg is the corresponding altitude: $\frac{1}{2} 5 \cdot 12 = 30$ square units.)

(Add the overlay to Transparency 9-23.) If we change the length of one side of the triangle as shown here, this method will not work. Instead, we have to draw the altitude to one of the sides and figure out its length.

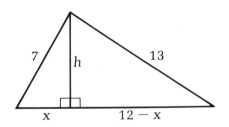

(Draw the altitude and label the lengths as shown here. With your guidance, your students should be able to follow an argument like the one below.)

Applying the Pythagorean Theorem to both right triangles, we get

$$x^2 + h^2 = 7^2 \text{ and } (12 - x)^2 + h^2 = 13^2.$$

Hence $x^2 + h^2 = 49$ and $144 - 24x + x^2 + h^2 = 169$. Since $x^2 + h^2 = 49$, we can simplify the second equation by substitution:

$$144 - 24x + 49 = 169$$
$$-24x = -24$$
$$x = 1.$$

We can use the fact that $x = 1$ to solve the first equation for h.

$$1^2 + h^2 = 49$$
$$h^2 = 48$$
$$h = 4\sqrt{3} \text{ (discarding}$$

the negative root). Now that we know h, we can find the area of the triangle:

$$\frac{1}{2} 12 (4\sqrt{3}) = 24\sqrt{3} \text{ square units.}$$

After working all of this out, your students will be relieved to learn that there is a simpler way to find the area of the second triangle and will be ready to learn how to use Heron's Theorem. After explaining what the formula means, you should point out that its derivation, although much more complex, is based upon the same ideas that we used to find the area of the second triangle. Demonstrate how the formula is used by finding the areas of both triangles with it.

Dr. Polya's commentary on verifying Heron's Theorem is, like all of his work, very much worth reading. See Mathematical Discovery, Volume 2, by George Polya (Wiley, 1965), pp. 146-149.

Review of Chapter 9

First Day

Which one of the following triangles has the largest area: one with sides of lengths 5, 5, 6 or 5, 5, 8 or 5, 5, 10?

This problem provides a nice review of Heron's Theorem and is fun because its answer is so surprising. The 5, 5, 6 and 5, 5, 8 triangles have the same area: 12 square units. The area of the 5, 5, 10 "triangle" is 0 because it is not a triangle at all. After your class has discovered these results, you might show Transparency 9-24, which reveals why they turn out as they do.

Transparency 9-25 is for use in discussing Exercises 2 and 3 of Lesson 6, Set II.

Second Day

The puzzle described in the Set III exercise of the review lesson makes a good class project. Print copies of Worksheet 5 on heavyweight paper, cut them in half, and give one to each student along with a pair of scissors. After the students have cut out the twenty triangular pieces, explain that the object of the puzzle is to arrange them to form a square.

Give them time to try to solve it before offering any suggestions. An explanation is given in the answer section of this guide.

If the pieces are put in letter-size envelopes, they can be kept for use by future classes.

Transparency 9-26 is for use in discussing Exercises 4-6 of the Review Lesson, Set II.

Transparency 9-27 contains a problem that your students will find interesting. It is from a booklet published by the College Entrance Examination Board that describes the S.A.T. and gives example problems comparable to those contained in it.*

The problem is much easier than it would first seem because we do not have to figure out how the pieces would be rearranged. Since the rectangle measures 9 by 16, its area is 144. So the area of the square is 144, its sides are 12, and its perimeter is 48.

A Supplementary Lesson

A dotty way to find area

(This lesson on Pick's Theorem might be included in the area unit any time after Lesson 4.)

The Random House Dictionary of the English Language provides two alternative definitions for the word "dotty." The first is "crazy or eccentric" and the second is "marked with dots or dotted." Today we are going to consider a novel way to find the area of a figure that fits both of these definitions.

(Hand out dittoed copies of Worksheet 6. Show Transparency 9-28 and draw Figure 1 as shown on the accompanying figure sheet, instructing your students to copy it on their worksheet.) If a very naive student were asked to find the area of this rectangle, he might count the dots inside it and say 4. Most people, however, would say that it was

---

*A Description of the College Board S.A.T., 1970-71 booklet, College Entrance Examination Board, Princeton, New Jersey.

10. If we let A be the area and i be the number of dots inside, we have A = 10 and i = 4. (Draw Figure 2.) What are A and i for this rectangle? (A = 9 and i = 4.) Notice that each rectangle has the same number of dots inside it, yet the areas of the two figures are different. It seems reasonable that as the number of dots inside a figure increases, its area will also increase. Yet the area evidently depends upon something more than just the number of dots inside. How about the dots on the border? The first rectangle has 14 border dots and the second one has 12. Letting b be the number of dots on the border and writing our results in a table, we have:

Figure	A	i	b
1	10	4	14
2	9	4	12

Let's increase the area and see what happens. (Draw Figure 3 and add the results to the table.)

Figure	A	i	b
3	12	6	14

Suppose we draw another rectangle with the same area but a different shape. (Draw Figure 4.)

Figure	A	i	b
4	12	5	16

It is obvious from Figures 1 and 3 that the number of border dots by itself does not determine the area of the rectangle either. Yet, if you study this table carefully, you may discover that the two numbers of dots, taken together, do seem to determine the area of the rectangle. Can you figure out exactly how? (Given some time, a few of your students will probably discover that for each figure $A = i + \frac{1}{2}b - 1$.

Ask those who think they have found a pattern to draw another rectangle of their own choosing to check it. One with no dots inside it makes a good test case.)

We seem to have a formula that gives the correct area of a rectangle, and hence square, in terms of the numbers of dots inside it and on its border. Would this formula work on a more general type of figure, such as a parallelogram? (Draw Figure 5.)

Figure	A	i	b	
5	15	8	16	Yes.

We drew the figure so that the slanted sides

passed through dots of the grid. What would happen if they missed them? (Draw Figure 6.)

Figure	A	i	b	
6	8	6	6	Yes.

The formula still works! Draw another parallelogram, choosing the shape yourself, and see what happens. (Anyone who seems to have found a parallelogram for which the formula doesn't work should draw it on the projector grid for the rest of the class to see.)

Since the formulas for the areas of rectangles and parallelograms are the same, A = bh, it seems plausible that the dot formulas would be the same as well. How do you think the formula would have to be changed to give the correct area of a triangle? (A reasonable guess is that everything should be divided in half. Draw Figure 7 to check this.)

Figure	A	i	b
7	6	3	8

It looks as though the original formula still works!

(Draw the remaining figures shown on the figure sheet to test other triangles, trapezoids, another convex figure, concave figures, and a figure with a hole in it. Finding the areas of Figures 9 and 14 is rather challenging.)

Here is a table of the results.

Figure	A	i	b	
8	5	2	8	Yes
9	9	7	6	Yes
10	12	7	12	Yes
11	10	8	6	Yes
12	16	14	6	Yes
13	11	0	24	Yes
14	10	5	12	Yes
15	15	5	20	No

After discovering that everything seems to work except those in the last category, your students should agree that the following theorem seems reasonable:

The area of a polygonal region that has as its vertices the points of a grid and that doesn't have any holes is given by the formula

$$A = i + \frac{1}{2}b - 1$$

where i is the number of points inside and b is the number of border points.

Point out that our faith in this theorem is based on the specific figures that we have considered: that we have been reasoning inductively. The formula it contains was first discovered by a Czechoslovakian mathematician named Pick in 1899. If you think your students can follow it, you might conclude by developing the following proof verifying Pick's Theorem for rectangles (Transparency 9-29).

Suppose a rectangle has base of length B and altitude of length h. Inside it there are (h - 1) rows of dots with (B - 1) dots in each row, so the rectangle has (h - 1)(B - 1) interior dots. On its border there are 4 dots at the vertices, 2(B - 1) dots between them on the horizontal sides, and 2(h - 1) dots between them on the vertical sides, so the rectangle has 4 + 2(B - 1) + 2(h - 1) = 2B + 2h border dots.

Substituting these results into the formula

$$A = i + \frac{1}{2}b - 1,$$

we get

$$A = (h - 1)(B - 1) + \frac{1}{2}(2B + 2h) - 1$$
$$= hB - B - h + 1 + B + h - 1$$
$$= hB,$$

which is correct since the area of a rectangle is the product of the lengths of its base and altitude.

General proofs of Pick's Theorem (requiring more advanced mathematics) are in the following books:

Introduction to Geometry, 2nd ed., by H. S. M. Coxeter (Wiley, 1969), p. 209.
Ingenuity in Mathematics, by Ross Honsberger (Random House, 1970), pp. 27-31.

Chapter 10

SIMILARITY

Lesson 1
Ratio and Proportion

(Show Transparency 10-1.) One of these airplanes is an exact replica of the first plane to be flown on a solo flight around the world. Its pilot was Wiley Post and the year was 1933. Although the other plane looks exactly like it, it could never be flown around the world because it is too small: it is a scale model of the real plane and weighs only 15 pounds. Can you guess which plane is which? (The one pictured at the bottom is the model.)

To look convincing, the model must have the same shape as the actual plane. The plane is 27 ft long and has a wingspan of 42 ft. The model is 4.5 ft long. Can you find out what its wingspan is? (Give your students time to think about this and then let some of those who have the correct answer, 7 ft, explain their methods.)

Use the proportion

$$\frac{27}{4.5} = \frac{42}{7}$$

to review the meaning of "ratio" and "proportion," explain the order and names of the terms of a proportion, and illustrate the properties that are stated as theorems on page 370 of the text. (The proofs of these theorems are included in the Set II exercises of the lesson.)

Lesson 2
More on Proportion

A proportion in Plato's Republic

The Greek philosopher Plato was very much interested in mathematics, especially geometry, and believed that it was basic to any system of thought. In the Republic, Plato uses a proportion to express some of his ideas. (Show Transparency 10-2.) He says:

Suppose you take a line segment cut into two unequal parts [AE cut at C] to represent in proportion the worlds of things seen and things thought, and then cut each part in the same ratio [AC at B and CE at D]. In the world of things seen, one part [AB] represents images such as shadows and reflections and the other part [BC] represents the objects which the images resemble, such as animals and plants.

Now consider how the section for "things thought" should be divided. In the first part [CD] are the thought images of the objects in the world of things seen, such as the concept of an animal or plant. In the second part [DE] are abstract ideas such as "beauty" and "justice."*

*I have freely paraphrased a passage near the close of Book VI, based upon the translation of W. H. D. Rouse (Great Dialogues of Plato, New American Library, 1956, pp. 309-310).

According to what Plato has written, the line segment $\overline{AE}$ has been divided by points B, C, and D so that

$$\frac{AC}{CE} = \frac{AB}{BC} = \frac{CD}{DE}.$$

It is possible to prove that, if this is true, then $\overline{BC}$ and $\overline{CD}$ must have equal lengths.

(Here is one way in which this can be proved. Unless you have a very strong class, I recommend guiding your class in developing it.)

Since $\dfrac{AB}{BC} = \dfrac{CD}{DE}$, $\dfrac{AB + BC}{BC} = \dfrac{CD + DE}{DE}$.

But AB + BC = AC and CD + DE = CE, so

$$\frac{AC}{BC} = \frac{CE}{DE}.$$

Interchanging the means, we get

$$\frac{AC}{CE} = \frac{BC}{DE}.$$

Since it follows from our hypothesis that

$$\frac{AC}{CE} = \frac{CD}{DE},$$

we have

$$\frac{BC}{DE} = \frac{CD}{DE}.$$

Multiplying by DE, BC = CD.

(After finishing this proof, you can use the result to introduce the idea of "mean proportional," since BC, and hence CD, is the mean proportional between AB and DE.)

Transparency 10-3 is for use in discussing the Set III exercise of Lesson 1.

Lesson 3
The Side-Splitter Theorem

The earliest dam in recorded history was built in Egypt in about 2700 B.C. Although its dimensions were quite impressive—370 feet long, 37 feet high, and 270 feet thick—the dam was eventually destroyed when a heavy rain backed up more water behind it than it could hold.

Before a modern dam is built, a lot of mathematics must be worked out to insure that it will not collapse. For example, one of the largest dams in the world is the Grand Coulee dam on the Columbia River in Washington. It is more than 4100 feet long and 550 feet high and has to be able to resist a force of more than 10,000,000 tons.

(Show and hand out dittoed copies of Transparency 10-4.) Present the problem of finding the length of $\overline{EC}$ indirectly from the lengths of $\overline{AD}$, $\overline{DB}$, and $\overline{AE}$ as is done on page 379 of the text. The figure on the transparency is drawn on a somewhat dif-

ferent scale from that of the one shown there. Tell your students that 1 cm on the figure represents a distance of 100 ft and have them measure $\overline{AD}$, $\overline{DB}$, and $\overline{AE}$ (they correspond to 100 ft, 400 ft, and 150 ft, respectively). Ask if they can guess the length of $\overline{EC}$ before they measure it and have someone who guesses correctly explain how he did it.

Transparency 10-5 and its three overlays can be used to develop the proof of the Side-Splitter Theorem. Each overlay should be removed before the next is put into place. The students might take notes on the dittoed sheets that you provided.

Transparency 10-6 is for use in discussing the Set III exercise of Lesson 2.

Lesson 4
Similar Triangles

A paper chase

The following exercise is based upon a mapping game described in an article titled "Analytical Methods in Transformation Geometry" by G. Giles in Mathematical Reflections, edited by members of the Association of Teachers of Mathematics (Cambridge University Press, 1970), pp. 139-166.

(Show Transparency 10-7.) Here is a simple but interesting game whose rules I will explain as someone plays it with me. (Choose a student who is neither especially clever nor slow.) We will each draw a path that consists of a series of connected line segments on this grid. (Add the overlay to Transparency 10-7.) We will take turns, drawing one segment per turn that may be horizontal, vertical, or diagonal and either one or more "units" long. Here is an example of a path of one player: it started at point A and took six turns to draw. I will explain the object of the game after we have each taken several turns. (Remove the overlay and ask the student who is to play the game with you to choose a point somewhere on the grid that is not very far from its center and draw the first segment of his path. Without explaining what you are doing, choose a different point and draw a segment twice as long in the same direction. Each time the student has made a move, make your move so that it is twice as far in the same direction. After you have both made several moves and it is obvious to the student and the rest of the class that you are copying each of his moves but going twice as far each time, explain that the object of the game is for the student to move so that you are forced to move to the same point to which he has gone. After awhile, your class will probably not be able to resist offering advice to your opponent about how they think he should play to catch you.

A Paper Chase

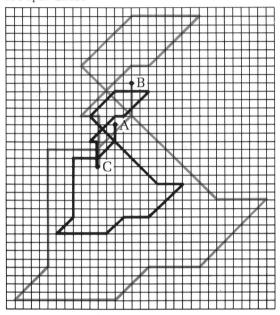

An example of the outcome of a game that one of my students actually played with me in front of a class is shown here. The student started at A and her path is shown in black. I started at B and my path is shown in gray. She finally caught me at point C. It is interesting to note that the "catching point" is not determined by the individual moves but rather by the two starting points: it is the reflection of my starting point through the student's starting point. Don't tell your students this if you think any of them would enjoy playing the game themselves because it takes the fun out of the game by making its strategy obvious.

After the game is finished, point out that the two paths have the same shape and that two geometric figures with this property are said to be "similar." Also call attention to the fact that the corresponding segments are proportional and that the corresponding angles are equal.)

Transparency 10-8 and its overlay can be used to illustrate similar triangles and how their vertices may be paired to establish a similarity correspondence from which the equal angles and proportional sides may be read.

Transparency 10-9 is for use in discussing the Set III exercise of Lesson 3.

Lesson 5
The A.A. Similarity Theorem

First Day

How to build a house quickly

The following exercise is based upon a problem in a fascinating book titled Children Solve Problems, by Edward de Bono (Harper and Row, 1974). Children of various ages were asked to solve such problems as how to stop a cat and dog from fighting, how to weigh an elephant, and how to build a house quickly. Your students would enjoy some of the solutions they came up with.

One boy, when given the problem of how to build a house quickly, drew this diagram. (Show Transparency 10-10.) He figured that, since toy houses are sometimes made by cutting and folding cardboard, the same method might be applied to constructing a house from sheet metal. One problem with his solution is the design he proposes. (Add the overlay to Transparency 10-10.) The roof of the house slants down to one side so that someone walking in the front door would soon bump his head on the ceiling.

Suppose that the right-hand wall of the house as shown here is 10 feet high and that the house is 30 feet wide. How far do you think a 6-foot man could walk before his head would touch the ceiling?

(On the assumption that the two triangles in the figure are similar, we can write a proportion between their sides, such as

$$\frac{6}{10} = \frac{30 - x}{30} \quad \text{or} \quad \frac{4}{10} = \frac{x}{30},$$

to find that the man could walk 12 feet.)

This raises the question of why we can assume that that the triangles in the figure are similar. Remind your students that we never bother to show that all six pairs of parts of two triangles are equal to prove that they are congruent. Certain sets of three pairs of parts are sufficient. (Ask someone to name them.) Then tell them that it is even easier to prove that two triangles are similar. All we have to show is that two pairs of angles are equal. Observe that this is quite easy to do with the diagram of the house we have just been using. The triangles have equal right angles and common angles.

Use Transparency 10-11 and its overlay to prove the A. A. Similarity Theorem. (The overlay is for use in showing how the smaller triangle can be copied in either of two corners of the larger triangle.)

If you plan to do the height-measuring experiment on the next day, you might assign just the Set I exercises of Lesson 5.

Transparency 10-12 is for use in discussing the Set III exercise of Lesson 4.

Second Day

How to measure up by looking down

If possible, take your class outside and let them try to measure the height of your school flagpole or a tree by means of the mirror method described on pages 389-390 of the text. Small 4" x 4" mirrors such as those used in Chapter 5 are perfectly satisfactory. I suggest assigning the students to groups of three each: one student in each group can act as the observer, one as the measurer, and one as the recorder. Transparency 10-13 can be used to review the strategy before you go outside. Note that the method assumes that the feet of the observer, the mirror, and the base of the pole are in a horizontal plane; also, that the mirror is level. You might ask your students why these things are important. (They are necessary if the angles in the two triangles are to be equal; this, of course, is the basis for our treatment of them as similar when we write a proportion between their pairs of corresponding sides.)

Several 50-ft tape measures would be helpful. However, if necessary, you can manage with just one and a supply of string.

Although the students work in small groups, I suggest that each one be held responsible for making and turning in his own calculations.

The Set II (with Set III optional) exercises of Lesson 5 can be assigned for homework.

Lesson 6
Proportional Line Segments

(Show Transparency 10-14.) At first, this picture may seem to many of you to be no more than a lot of meaningless spots. If you study it carefully, however, you may notice something more. (It is a photograph of a spotted dog against a mottled background, perhaps a sidewalk and lawn.) Although the dog is easy to see once you have recognized it, some people find it very difficult to separate from the surroundings in which it has been hidden.

(Show Transparency 10-15.) Not being able to see something in a figure is a difficulty that many geometry students have. Look closely at this figure: what do you see? (A perceptive student may describe it as consisting of an obtuse triangle, $\triangle ABC$, and two of its altitudes. The new lesson includes a theorem about altitudes of triangles, so this is a good chance to review the meaning of the term. To check everyone's understanding, ask where the third altitude of the triangle would be if it were shown also.)

Now the "hidden dog" part of the problem. Can you find a pair of triangles in the figure that can be proved similar? ($\triangle ADC \sim \triangle AEB$ because they each contain a right angle as well as sharing an angle.)

To introduce Lesson 6, you might show two photographs taken by Ansel Adams with a "pinhole camera" (actually an ordinary camera in which the lens was replaced with a thin disk pierced by a pin). They both show a barn and fence: one was taken through a pinhole 1/8 inch in diameter and the other through a pinhole 1/50 inch in diameter. The photographs are reproduced on pages 104 and 105 of The Camera, a book in the Life Library of Photography (Time-Life Books, 1970).

I suggest assigning the lesson (including Theorem 57 and its proof) for individual study.

Lesson 7
The Angle Bisector Theorem

The shadow of a leaf

Dr. Henry S. Horn, a member of the biology department of Princeton University, has written a book titled The Adaptive Geometry of Trees (Princeton University Press, 1971).

In it he uses mathematics to develop a theory to explain the growth patterns of trees in forests. One chapter, titled "Theoretical Strategies of Leaf Distribution," begins with an analysis of the length of the shadows cast by leaves. (Show the top part of Transparency 10-16.) This figure represents a side view of three layers of leaves: each line segment represents one leaf. The rate of photosynthesis of each leaf depends upon the amount of sunlight that hits it and this, in turn, is affected by the shadows of the leaves between it and the sun. (Add the overlay to Transparency 10-16.) The shaded regions represent the shadows of the leaves when the sun is directly overhead. Whether or not the shadows of the leaves in each row hit the leaves in the next row depends upon the distance between each row and the lengths of the shadows.

(Show the bottom part of Transparency 10-16.) This figure, necessarily distorted, shows the sun, one of the leaves, and its shadow. Why is $\triangle DEC \sim \triangle ABC$? (Since $\overline{AB}$ and $\overline{DE}$ are perpendicular to the same line, they are parallel to each other; hence $\angle A = \angle EDC$ and $\angle B = \angle DEC$.) The diameter of the sun is about 860,000 miles; although $\overline{AB}$ is actually slightly shorter than the diameter, we can assume that AB = 860,000 miles with very little error. The sun is about 93,000,000 miles from the earth and we will assume that this is the distance from C to $\overline{AB}$ in the figure. The letters w and s stand for the width of the leaf and the length of its shadow, respectively. Can you figure out a formula for the length of the shadow of a leaf in terms of the width of the leaf? (Since the corresponding altitudes of similar triangles have the same ratio as their corresponding sides, we can write the proportion

$$\frac{s}{93,000,000} = \frac{w}{860,000}$$

Solving for s, we get $s \approx 108w$.) It follows from our assumptions that the shadow of the leaf is about 108 times its width. According to this, how many feet long would the shadow of a leaf having a width of 2 inches be? (18 ft.)

In reality, we have somewhat oversimplified the situation; taking other factors into account, it can be shown that leaf shadows are actually shorter than what we have calculated.

Your students will be impressed by Transparency 10-17, which reproduces one of the pages of Dr. Horn's book and reveals how complex the mathematics used by a biologist can become.

Transparency 10-18 is for use in discussing the Set III exercise of Lesson 6.

To introduce Lesson 7, you might show your class a copy of The Great International Paper Airplane Book (see the footnote on page 398 of the text). Hand out dittoed copies of Transparency 10-19 and explain that the figure represents a very simple, but lopsided, paper airplane. Point out that the sides of the triangle are 4, 5, and 6 units long. Ask your students to fold side $\overline{AB}$ of the triangle onto side $\overline{AC}$ and tell what they observe.

(The fold bisects $\angle A$ of the triangle and passes through one of the points marked on side $\overline{BC}$. It evidently divides $\overline{BC}$ into two segments that are 2 and 3 units long.) If you give your students time to compare the lengths of these two segments and the lengths of the other two sides of the triangle, some of them will be able to discover the Angle Bisector Theorem for themselves. The proof of this theorem is sufficiently complex that it ought to be developed as a class exercise. Transparency 10-20 can be used for this purpose.

Whenever a proof requires the addition of some unexpected lines to the figure, it is tempting to simply present the proof without taking time to see how someone might have ever happened to think of the lines in the first place. A discussion comparable to that on pp. 399-400 of the text (following the statement of the theorem) should always precede the proof itself.

Lesson 8
Perimeters and Areas of Similar Triangles

Your students will enjoy the following demonstration, which is simple to do and which produces a surprising effect. Before class, place two identical candles in front of and behind a vertical pane of glass as shown in this photograph. The candle in back should be carefully positioned so that, when viewed from the front, it coincides with the reflection of the candle in front. During the demonstration it is important that everyone who observes it sees glass behind the candle in front and glass in front of the candle behind.

The room should be darkened for the best effect.

Introduce the demonstration by telling your students that you are going to do several simple things with the two candles that you want them to observe carefully. First light the candle in back. Then light the candle in front, at the same time snuffing out the candle in back with your fingers. (The students will see the reflection of the front candle flame over the candle in back and assume that both candles are still lit. The candle in back was not lit when the photograph above was taken.) Wait a little while and then, facing the candle in front, quickly blow it out. (Since the reflection disappears at the same instant, it will seem to your students that you have blown through the glass!) Without explaining what has happened, repeat the first part of the demonstration, relighting the candle in back and then snuffing it out as you relight the candle in front. This time, after waiting for a few moments, slide the candle in back several inches to one side. Your students will be startled to observe that you have somehow separated the candle in back from its flame!

Let someone explain everything and then present the following problem. (Show Transparency 10-21.) This figure represents an overhead view of the room. The top edge of the pane of glass lies on line ℓ and points C and C' represent the positions of the two candles. Points E and F represent the positions of two observers whose distances from line ℓ are the same. (Add the overlay to Transparency 10-21.) These line segments show why the observers at E and F think they see a candle flame at point C' when it is really the reflection of the flame at point C.

Can you figure out why the ratio of the first and second parts of each path is the same for both observers? In other words, why is $\frac{CA}{AE} = \frac{CB}{BF}$? You may assume the following: C' is the reflection of C through line ℓ, and $\overline{EG}$ and $\overline{FH}$ are both perpendicular to ℓ, and EG = FH.

(It is not necessary to assume that the angles of incidence are equal to the angles of reflection.) Here are two possible explanations:

1. $\triangle C'AD \cong \triangle CAD$ and $\triangle C'BD \cong \triangle CBD$ since a triangle and its reflection through a line are congruent; it follows that the triangles in each of these pairs must also be similar. Since $\triangle EAG \sim \triangle C'AD$ and $\triangle FBH \sim \triangle C'BD$ (by right angles and vertical angles), $\triangle EAG \sim \triangle CAD$ and $\triangle FBH \sim \triangle CBD$ (two triangles similar to a third triangle are similar to each other). Hence $\frac{CA}{AE} = \frac{CD}{EG}$ and $\frac{CB}{BF} = \frac{CD}{FH}$ (corresponding sides of similar triangles are proportional). But EG = FH, so $\frac{CB}{BF} = \frac{CD}{EG}$ and hence $\frac{CA}{AE} = \frac{CB}{BF}$.

2. Draw $\overline{EF}$. Since $\overline{EG}$ and $\overline{FH}$ are both perpendicular to ℓ, they are parallel. But they are also equal, so EFHG is a parallelogram. Hence ℓ ∥ $\overline{EF}$ and so $\frac{C'A}{AE} = \frac{C'B}{BF}$ (the Side-Splitter Theorem). But C'A = CA and C'B = CB (reflection of a set of points through a line preserves distance), so $\frac{CA}{AE} = \frac{CB}{BF}$.

Transparency 10-22 is for use in discussing the Set III exercise of Lesson 7.

To introduce Lesson 8, you might show Transparency 10-23, which illustrates the pictures of the man discussed in Lesson 2 who "blew himself up to poster size." Suppose the store charges according to the area of the photograph. If the small photo costs 10¢, what should the medium-sized one cost? (90¢.) What should the largest one cost? ($8.10.) Suppose a frame for the smallest one also costs 10¢. If the store charges for frames according to their perimeters, what should a frame for the medium-sized picture cost? (30¢.) What should a frame for the largest one cost? (90¢.) The proofs for similar triangles of the area and perimeter relationships illustrated are included in the exercises of Lesson 8.

Review of Chapter 10

A new way to solve a problem that most algebra students hate

Many algebra students have trouble with word problems; one type of word problem that they especially dislike is the so-called work problem. Here is an example. (Show Transparency 10-24.)

"If one man can do a job in 6 hours and another man can do it in 4 hours, how long would it take them if they worked together?"

There is an easy way to solve this problem without doing any algebra at all. (Add Overlay A to Transparency 10-24 and give each student a sheet of graph paper.)

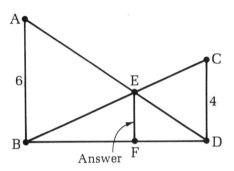

Draw two vertical segments ($\overline{AB}$ and $\overline{CD}$ in this figure) that are 6 cm and 4 cm long: these segments represent the time it takes each man to do the job alone. $\overline{BD}$ can be any length. Draw $\overline{AD}$ and $\overline{BC}$ and from E, the point in which they intersect, draw $\overline{EF} \perp \overline{BD}$. The segment $\overline{EF}$ represents the time it would take the men to do the job if they worked together. If the figure has been drawn carefully, its length should be 2.4 cm. It would take the men 2.4 hours if they worked together.

Before we consider why this method gives the correct answer, let's consider how the problem is solved algebraically. (Remove Overlay A and add Overlay B.) Since the fractions of the job that each man can do in

one hour are 1/6 and 1/4, and together they can do 1/x of it, we have:
$$\frac{1}{6} + \frac{1}{4} = \frac{1}{x}.$$
Solving for x, we get 2.4. Notice the pattern of the equation that gave us this answer.

Now we are ready to show why the geometric method gives the same result. (Remove Overlay B and add Overlay C.) We have labeled the lengths of the original vertical segments as a and b rather than 6 and 4 since the method is independent of any specific numbers. The answer is labeled x. To show that the method is correct, we must show that
$$\frac{1}{a} + \frac{1}{b} = \frac{1}{x}.$$
(Most of your students will need help in developing the following proof.)

First, we will label the lengths of the two segments on the bottom c and d, respectively. Since $\triangle EFD \sim \triangle ABD$ (as shown in the figure above),
$$\frac{x}{a} = \frac{d}{c + d}.$$
Also, since $\triangle EFB \sim \triangle CDB$,
$$\frac{x}{b} = \frac{c}{c + d}.$$
Adding the two equations, we get
$$\frac{x}{a} + \frac{x}{b} = \frac{d}{c + d} + \frac{c}{c + d} = \frac{d + c}{c + d} = 1.$$
Finally, dividing by x,
$$\frac{1}{a} + \frac{1}{b} = \frac{1}{x}.$$

Note that c and d do not appear in the final equation: this is why the horizontal distance between the original two segments does not matter.

The pattern on Worksheet 7 for the Sphinx Puzzle pieces can be used to cut the nine pieces from either a thick sheet of colored plastic or cardboard. A student can use them to show the solutions to the two puzzles in the Set III exercise of Lesson 8.

The figures on Transparency 10-25 can be used to discuss the Set I exercises in the review lesson.

Chapter 11

THE RIGHT TRIANGLE

Lesson 1

Proportions in a Right Triangle

A chambered nautilus shell cut in half so that the compartments can be seen is an attractive visual aid to have for the mathematics classroom and is worth looking for. The photograph on page 414 is of a shell I bought for only $1.50 at an oceanside store.

The chambered nautilus is most abundant in the southwest Pacific where it swims on the ocean floor in search of food. The nautilus lives in the outermost chamber of its shell and can let air into or out of the other chambers to help in moving upward or downward through the water.

Show Transparency 11-1 (mark and label the center point of the shell point P). Have a student draw a line through point P in any direction and a second line through P that is perpendicular to the first. Then label some of the consecutive points in which the curve of the shell intersects these lines and develop the rest of Lesson 1 as presented on pages 415-416 of the text. Transparency 11-2 is for use in discussing Theorem 61 and its corollaries.

Lesson 2

The Pythagorean Theorem Revisited

Evans G. Valens has written a delightful book titled The Number of Things: Pythagoras, Geometry and Humming Strings (Dutton,

1964). In it he describes a "Pythagorean guitar." A Pythagorean guitar is not very difficult to build and your musically inclined students will find it especially interesting. The photograph shown here is of one that I made.

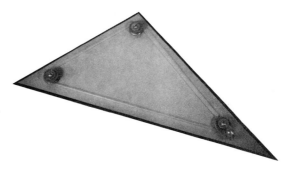

If a guitar string is stretched around three nails at the vertices of a 3-4-5 right triangle, the three sides of the string triangle, when plucked, will sound a musical chord. (Show Transparency 11-3.) If the hypotenuse is tuned to G, the longer and shorter legs will sound B and E, respectively. Valens notes that these are the top three strings of a guitar and that the chord sounded is a minor triad. If a randomly shaped "triangle guitar" is played, it ordinarily will not produce a musical chord. Why does the 3-4-5 right triangle do so? Because Pythagoras, as well as being a great mathematician, was also the founder of the science of music. His belief in the importance of whole numbers led him to define the intervals in the musical scale in terms of them. Chapters 14-16 of Valens' book go into great detail on the scales of Pythagoras.

Transparency 11-4 is for use in discussing the Set III exercise of Lesson 1.

To introduce Lesson 2, you might show your students a copy of the book The Pythagorean Proposition, by Elisha Scott Loomis (privately printed in 1927 and 1940 and available from N.C.T.M.). This book contains a history of the Pythagorean Theorem and 370 different proofs. One of the more elegant proofs, based upon the fact that each leg of a right triangle is the mean proportional between the hypotenuse and its projection on the hypotenuse, is presented on page 422 of the textbook. Transparency 11-5 is for use in considering this proof with your class.

Lesson 3
Isosceles and 30°-60° Right Triangles

Six people at a dinner table

"People like to keep certain distances between themselves and other people or things. This invisible bubble of space that constitutes each man's 'territory' is one of the key dimensions of modern society." These words are from the back of a book by an American anthropologist, Edward T. Hall, titled The Hidden Dimension (Anchor Books, 1969). In the book, Dr. Hall discusses personal and social space and man's perception of it.

(Show Transparency 11-6.) One situation that Dr. Hall describes concerns the conversations between six people seated at a dinner table. A psychologist observed fifty different groups of people seated at a table as shown in this figure and recorded, at regular intervals, which pairs of people were talking with each other. He found that conversations between two people seated across a corner, such as A and B, were more frequent than any other seat relationship. Can you guess for which arrangements conversations were second and third most frequent? (Two people seated side by side, such as B and C, talked with each other second most frequently and two people seated across from each other, such as B and F, talked third most frequently. No

conversations were observed for the other seat relationships.)

Is it correct to conclude from this that the closer two people are seated at a table, the more frequently they talk with each other? To find out, we can use the Pythagorean Theorem. For simplicity, we will determine the distances between the points marked on the sides of the table: we will assume that A and D are the midpoints of the shorter sides and that the other points are a quarter of the way in from their neighboring corners. There are six different seat relationships (add the overlay to Transparency 11-6). Given that the dimensions of the table were 36 inches by 72 inches, can you figure out the distance for each? (AF = $18\sqrt{2}$, BF = 36, CF = $36\sqrt{2}$, DF = $18\sqrt{10}$, EF = 36, and AD = 72.)

After the class has made these calculations, point out that the method for finding AF and CF is the same: in each case, we are determining the length of the hypotenuse of an isosceles right triangle from the length of its legs. Observe that in each case, the hypotenuse is $\sqrt{2}$ times the length of either leg. This leads naturally into a discussion of the theorem about the sides of an isosceles right triangle. Transparencies 11-7, 11-8, and 11-9 are for use in presenting it and the theorem about the sides of a 30°-60° right triangle, and their corollaries.

Transparency 11-10 is for use in discussing the Set III exercise of Lesson 2.

Lesson 4
The Tangent Ratio

Some inventions you won't believe

Some extraordinary inventions have been patented in the United States Patent Office. A book titled Absolutely Mad Inventions by A. E. Brown and H. A. Jeffcott, Jr. (Dover, 1970) reproduces the original drawings and descriptions filed for some of these patents.

Two of them are shown on Transparency 11-11. The first is a pair of goggles for a chicken, to protect its eyes in case other chickens peck it in the head. The second, a device for catching fish, is rather quaintly described by its inventor in these words: "the fish B, when approaching the bait s, will see the reflection B', of himself in the mirror, also coming for the reflection of the bait s', and will be made bolder by the supposed companionship, and more eager to take the bait before his competitor seizes it. He will lose his caution, and take the bait with a recklessness that greatly increases the chances of his being caught on the hook."

Another remarkable invention is the one for preventing train collisions. It is described on page 431 of the text and can be used to introduce and develop the lesson on the tangent ratio. Transparencies 11-12 and 11-13 are for this purpose.

Transparencies 11-14 and 11-15 are for use in discussing Exercises 2-4 of Lesson 3, Set II.

Lesson 5
The Sine and Cosine Ratios

Yesterday you learned about a strange idea intended to prevent train collisions. Each train has rails running up and over it so that one train can travel along the track on the other. Today we will consider a problem about the track of an ordinary railway.

According to the Encyclopedia Britannica, many of the rails in a track are welded into lengths of up to a half-mile. Suppose a track is made of rails each 2000 feet long and that, on a hot summer day, each rail expands slightly so that its length becomes 2000 feet 6 inches. If the rails were set flush against each other, they would buckle slightly because of this increase in length. How far would the midpoint of each rail rise above the roadway? (Show Transparency 11-16.) For simplicity, we will assume that, when one of the rails buckles, it forms an isosceles triangle with the roadway below it, as shown in this figure. The amount of buckling is obviously greatly exaggerated in the figure if $AC = 2000$ feet and $AB + BC$ is only 6 inches longer. How long would you guess $\overline{BD}$ to be? One inch? A foot? To find out, we can apply the Pythagorean Theorem to right $\triangle ABD$. Since
$$BD^2 + 1000^2 = 1000.25^2,$$
$BD = \sqrt{1000.25^2 - 1000^2}$. Factoring the difference of the two squares, we get
$$BD = \sqrt{(1000.25 - 1000)(1000.25 + 1000)}$$
$$= \sqrt{.25(2000.25)}$$
Since $2000.25 \approx 2000$,
$$BD \approx \sqrt{500} = 10\sqrt{5}; \sqrt{5} \approx 2.2 \text{ so}$$
$$BD \approx 22 \text{ feet!}$$

If a rail 2000 feet long expanded only 6 inches, it would buckle about 22 feet at its midpoint! (To prevent this from happening, the rails are securely anchored to the ties and some space is left between each pair of rails.)

If the rail does buckle at its midpoint as we have calculated, can you find the angle that the track makes with the roadway at each of its ends? (tan $A = \dfrac{22}{1000} = .022$; the smallest angle in the table on page 433, 5°, has a tangent of .087 so the angle is less than 5°.) Referring to the table on page 439 (reproduced on Transparency 11-17), we see that $\angle A \approx 1^\circ$.

You may wish to introduce the sine and cosine ratios at this point or else leave them for your class to study on their own when they read Lesson 5.

Review of Chapter 11

The surfer's puzzle reconsidered

At the beginning of this course, we considered a story about two men shipwrecked on a tropical island. (Show Transparency 0-4.) One of them liked the place and decided to go surfing on the beaches. The other wanted to escape and spent his time looking for a ship that might rescue him.

The island, overgrown with vegetation, was in the shape of an equilateral triangle 12 kilometers on each side. The surfer wanted to build a house so that, when he cleared paths to the three beaches, he would have to do as little work as possible. His problem was to find the point in the triangle for which the sum of the lengths of the perpendicular segments from that point to the sides is a minimum. When we tried to solve this problem before, we chose several points in different places and measured the three perpendicular segments for each. You may or may not remember what happened.

(Hand out dittoed copies of Transparency 11-18.) Mark a point inside the triangle at random and construct the three perpendicular line segments from it to the sides. Measure each segment to the nearest 0.1 cm and find their sum. (After everyone has done this, ask some of the students for their results. Those who have done it accurately will get a sum of about 10.4 cm.) It seems that the point the surfer might have chosen doesn't matter. We can now prove that this is so.

(Add the overlay to Transparency 11-18.) Label the point you chose point P and the other endpoints of the three perpendicular line segments D, E, and F as shown. Also draw $\overline{PA}$, $\overline{PB}$, and $\overline{PC}$. These three segments divide △ABC into three triangles: △APB, △BPC, and △CPA. What relationship do the segments $\overline{PD}$, $\overline{PE}$, and $\overline{PF}$ have to these triangles? (They are altitudes of the triangles.) We want to show that, no matter where P is inside the triangle, PA + PB + PC is always the same number. We will do this by means of area.

(Label the length of $\overline{AB}$, $\overline{BC}$, and $\overline{CA}$ s and the lengths of the segments $\overline{PD}$, $\overline{PE}$, and $\overline{PF}$ d, e, and f, respectively. Then help your students as necessary in developing the following proof.)

$$\alpha \triangle ABC = \alpha \triangle APB + \alpha \triangle BPC + \alpha \triangle CPA,$$

so $\quad \dfrac{s^2}{4}\sqrt{3} = \dfrac{1}{2}sd + \dfrac{1}{2}se + \dfrac{1}{2}sf$

and $\dfrac{s^2}{4}\sqrt{3} = \dfrac{1}{2}s(d + e + f)$. Simplifying,

we get

$$d + e + f = \dfrac{s}{2}\sqrt{3}.$$

What does $\dfrac{s}{2}\sqrt{3}$ mean to you in terms of △ABC? (It is the length of one of its altitudes.)

We have shown that the sum of the lengths of the three paths from point P is equal to the length of an altitude of the triangle. Since this depends only upon the length of a side of the triangle, we have proved that the sum is the same for every position of point P within the triangle.

We can use the result to find this sum without any measuring. Since s = 12 cm and $\sqrt{3} \approx 1.73$,

$$d + e + f = \dfrac{12}{2}\sqrt{3} \approx 10.4 \text{ cm}.$$

Transparency 11-19 is for use in discussing the Set III exercise of Lesson 5.

Chapter 12

CIRCLES

Lesson 1
Circles, Radii, and Chords

(Show the photograph at the top of Transparency 12-1 and ask if anyone can identify where it was taken.) This photograph was taken in downtown Anchorage, Alaska, after an earthquake in 1964. It is apparent that this street was not very far from the earthquake's epicenter, or point of origin.

Scientists are now able to locate the epicenter of an earthquake quite accurately, even though it may be hundreds of miles from any populated area. (If one of your students can explain how they do it, you might let him do so.) When an earthquake occurs, its vibrations are recorded by seismographs. (Show the figure at the bottom of Transparency 12-1.) This graph, made on a rotating drum in a seismograph, shows the shock waves of an earthquake. The vertical segments mark off minutes. A little after 2 minutes from the beginning, the primary, or P, wave appears; about 5 minutes

later, it is followed by a secondary, or S, wave. By measuring the time interval between these two waves, seismologists can determine the distance they traveled and, hence, how far away the epicenter is.

(Show Transparency 12-2.) Suppose the waves of an earthquake are picked up by a seismograph at Cal Tech in Pasadena and that they show that the epicenter is 230 miles away. Where could the epicenter be? (Somewhere on a circle with a radius of 230 miles and Pasadena as its center. Add Overlay A to Transparency 12-2 to show this.) Suppose a seismograph at the University of California at Berkeley shows that it is 210 miles away from the epicenter of the same earthquake. Is this enough to determine where the epicenter is? (No. Add Overlay B to show that the two circles intersect in two points.) A third seismograph reading is sufficient to determine the location of the epicenter exactly. If the University of Nevada at Reno reports that the earthquake is 180 miles away (add Overlay

C), we can conclude that its epicenter must have been the point in which the <u>three circles</u> intersect, near Bishop, California.

The circle is of great importance in geometry both because of its many interesting properties and because of its wide variety of practical applications. It is the subject of the next unit of the course. (Rather than going through a list of the terms and theorems in the first lesson with your students, I think it best to assign the lesson for individual study.)

Lesson 2
Tangents

(Show Transparency 12-3.) This cartoon was drawn in 1883 and shows a young lady studying what seems to be a lesson in geometry. On an oval screen, a professor is shown standing in front of a blackboard on which there is a geometric diagram. The artist has imagined the existence of something like television, long before the radio was even invented.

Television waves travel in straight paths. Because of this and the earth's curvature, they cannot travel beyond a certain distance. (Show Transparency 12-4.) This diagram represents a television transmitting tower sending out waves from point A. Of course its height is greatly exaggerated in comparison with the radius of the earth shown below it. The waves can reach as far as points B and C but no further on the earth's surface. Rays $\overrightarrow{AB}$ and $\overrightarrow{AC}$ are said to be <u>tangent</u> to circle O because they each intersect it in exactly one point.

Suppose the tower reaches 1000 feet above the surrounding land. How far can the waves transmitted by it travel? It looks as if the distances from A to B and C are the same. How long is each? (Add the overlay to Transparency 12-4.) To find the length of $\overline{AB}$, we can use the triangle determined by A, B, and O, the center of the earth. Triangle ABO looks like a right triangle. If it is, we can use the Pythagorean Theorem to find AB. The radius of the earth is approximately 4000 miles; we said the height of the tower is 1000 feet; for simplicity, let's call it 0.2 mile. Hence BO = 4000 miles and AO = 4000.2 miles. If $\triangle ABO$ is a <u>right triangle</u>,

$$AB^2 + BO^2 = AO^2 \text{ and } AB = \sqrt{AO^2 - BO^2}.$$

To avoid having to actually square any num-bers, we can factor the difference of the two squares.

$$AB = \sqrt{(AO - BO)(AO + BO)}.$$

Substituting,

$$AB = \sqrt{(0.2)(8000.2)} \approx \sqrt{1600}$$
$$\approx 40 \text{ miles}.$$

The waves can travel about 40 miles.

As the height of the transmitter is increased, this distance also increases. It is for this reason that television transmitters are located as far above their surroundings as possible.

Our calculation of the transmission distance is based upon the assumption that $\triangle ABO$ is a right triangle. To show that this is true, we will prove that, if a line is tangent to a circle, such as $\overleftrightarrow{AB}$ in the diagram, then it must be perpendicular to the radius drawn to the point of contact. (Use Transparency 12-5 to develop the proof of this theorem, as is done on page 454 of the text.)

Transparency 12-6 is for use in discussing the Set III exercise of Lesson 1.

Lesson 3
Central Angles and Arcs

How to find yourself by stargazing

As you will recall, the ancient Greeks knew that the earth is spherical. In fact, the Greek astronomer Hipparchus, who lived in the second century B.C., invented the system by which places even today are located on the earth's surface. (Show Transparency 12-7.) In this system, each place is located by two coordinates, called its <u>latitude</u> and <u>longitude</u>.

The first figure shows some of the circles of latitude: the equator corresponds to 0° and the poles to 90°N and 90°S. The circles of longitude pass through the poles and some of them are shown in the second figure. The third figure shows both sets of circles: the arrow points to the place whose latitude is 60°N and whose longitude is 30°E.

The latitudes of various places on the earth were found accurately long before their longitudes. The reason for this is that the latitude of a place can be easily found by means of the star that seems to be directly over the North Pole, Polaris. (Show Transparency 12-8.) This figure represents the earth rotating on its axis within the so-called celestial sphere, an imaginary sphere in which the stars of the night sky seem to be embedded. It is easy to locate Polaris: because it is above the North Pole, which does not move as the earth rotates, Polaris is the only star in the sky that seems to always be in the same place. Notice that, if you are at the North Pole, a latitude of $90°$, Polaris is directly overhead. If you are on the equator, a latitude of $0°$, Polaris would appear on the horizon.

(Show Transparency 12-9.) The method for finding the latitude of a place between the equator and the North Pole is very simple: measure the number of degrees that Polaris appears above the horizon. This angle is equal to the latitude of the place. (Add the overlay to Transparency 12-9.) For example, if you are at point P on the earth and the angle of elevation of Polaris, $\angle 1$, has a measure of $40°$, then the latitude of point P, $\angle 2$, is $40°$. It isn't difficult to prove why this must be so. First we will assume the following things: that the line of the horizon at P is tangent to the circle representing the earth, that the pole line is perpendicular to the equator line, and that Polaris is so far away that the two rays in the figure pointing toward it are parallel. What angle can you immediately conclude must be equal to $\angle 2$? ($\angle$ PCO = $\angle 2$, since parallel lines form equal alternate interior angles with a transversal.) What relationship does $\angle$ PCO have to $\angle$ COP? (They are complementary. Since PC is tangent to the circle at P, PC $\perp$ OP, and so $\triangle$COP is a right triangle; the acute angles of a right triangle are complementary.) What relationship does $\angle$ COP have to $\angle 1$? (They are also complementary.) How does it follow from these facts that $\angle 1 = \angle 2$? (Complements of equal angles are equal.)

The figure for this exercise can be used to introduce some of the ideas of Lesson 3. It is probably best not to try to include all of them; your students can become acquainted with the rest when they read the lesson.

Lesson 4

Inscribed Angles

What not to do at the House of Pies

(Show the top row of pies on Transparency 12-10.) Obtuse Ollie recently got a job at the House of Pies. His job was to cut each pie into eight equal pieces like this. At first Ollie really liked the job because it was easy and he didn't have to think. (Reveal the rest of the rows of pies, one at a time, while telling the next part.) After a few days, however, the monotony of doing this over and over again really got to him. While cutting some banana cream pies, he finally "went bananas" and began cutting each pie in a different way. He still made four cuts across each pie, but some of the pieces were much larger than others. Needless to say, some of the customers weren't very happy about this.

Notice that, when the cuts are made at random, the number of pieces produced varies. Although four cuts have been made across each of the last three pies, they were cut into 10, 9, and 6 pieces. Can you figure out the minimum and maximum numbers of pieces into which a pie can be divided with four cuts of a knife? We will assume that each cut is straight and that it goes all the way across the pie. (Give your students time to make some drawings. The minimum is 5 and the maximum is 11.)

Can you guess, without making any drawings, the minimum and maximum numbers of pieces into which a pie can be divided with five cuts of a knife? (It isn't difficult to guess that the minimum is 6; that the maximum should be 16 is not at all obvious, however.) Have your students make drawings and develop the following table:

Number of cuts	Minimum no. of pieces	Maximum no. of pieces
0	1	1
1	2	2
2	3	4
3	4	7
4	5	11

After they have done this, they should be able to guess the maximum number for 5 cuts. In general, if n straight cuts are made across a pie, the minimum number of pieces into which it may be divided is $n + 1$ and the maximum number is $\frac{1}{2}n(n + 1) + 1$.

A proof that the second formula is correct is given on page 242 of Martin Gardner's New Mathematical Diversions from Scientific American (Simon and Schuster, 1966).

Transparencies 12-11 and 12-12 are for use in presenting Lesson 4.

Lesson 5
Secant Angles

The Trojan asteroids

(Show Transparency 12-13.) Some of you may possibly recall that one of the people who tried without success to prove the Parallel Postulate was the eighteenth-century mathematician Joseph Louis Lagrange.* Something that Lagrange did successfully prove is that two objects can orbit the sun so that they, together with the sun, are always at the corners of an equilateral triangle. Until about 70 years ago, no actual examples of this in the solar system were known. In 1906, an asteroid was discovered traveling in the same orbit as Jupiter but 60° ahead of it. (Show Transparency 12-14.) The asteroid was named Achilles and, since its discovery, nine more asteroids have been found in the same general vicinity. (Add the overlay to Transparency 12-14.) Moreover, five other asteroids have been found in Jupiter's orbit following 60° behind it. Named for characters in Homer's Iliad, they are called the "Trojan asteroids." As Jupiter travels about the sun, these asteroids move about with it, remaining locked at the corners of two immense equilateral triangles. (Isaac Asimov has written an interesting essay on these asteroids. It is titled "The Trojan Hearse" and is included in his book View From a Height, Doubleday, 1963.)

We will use this figure of Jupiter and the Trojan asteroids to review briefly some angle and arc relationships that we have learned. What type of angle is $\angle$ ASB with respect to the circle? (A central angle.) What relationship does its measure have to that of the minor arc $\overset{\frown}{AB}$? (They are equal, both having a measure of 120°.) What type of angle is $\angle$ AJB with respect to the circle? (An inscribed angle.) What relationship does its measure have to that of its intercepted arc? ($\angle$ AJB $= \frac{1}{2}$ major $\overset{\frown}{AB}$.) Suppose point J moved along the circle so that it was closer to point A than to point B. If points A and B remained fixed, what would happen to the measure of $\angle$ AJB? (It would stay the same because it would still be an inscribed angle intercepting the same arc.) Suppose point S

───────────

*This is mentioned on page 268 of the text.

moved toward point J. If points A and B remained fixed, what would happen to the measure of $\angle$ ASB? (It would evidently increase.) In today's lesson, we will consider how such an angle, which is neither a central angle nor an inscribed angle, can be measured by means of the circle.

Transparency 12-15 is for use in discussing the Set III exercise of Lesson 4.

Transparency 12-16 and its overlays are for use in presenting Lesson 5. After discussing the design of the Escher woodcut, add Overlay A and explain that the circle has been divided into 10° arcs. Then place Overlay B so that the devil coincides with the corresponding arc in the woodcut. Compare the measure of the central angle to that of its intercepted arc. Then slide the devil down the vertical line so that the positions shown at the top of page 470 (and the bottom of page 469) are illustrated. After the class has discovered the measure relationship between secant angles whose vertices are inside and outside a circle and their intercepted arcs, point out that, in every position of the devil considered, it was placed symmetrically with respect to the vertical line through the center of the circle. Then show, by tilting the devil and placing it in other positions, that these measure relationships still seem to hold. The proofs for both cases are included in the exercises for Lesson 5.

Lesson 6
Tangent Segments

How Galileo measured the height of a mountain on the moon

Before Galileo first looked at the night sky through his telescope in the fall of 1609, it was generally believed that the surface of the moon, unlike that of the earth, was perfectly smooth. (Show Transparency 12-17.) Galileo noticed that the boundary between the dark and light sides of the moon was very ragged and concluded from this that the moon must have mountains and valleys. He made the drawing shown here from observations made through his telescope.

Notice that there are several light spots on the dark side, not far from the boundary of the lighted side. Galileo figured that these spots must be mountain peaks high enough to catch some light from the rising or setting sun. Reasoning on this basis, he used some simple geometry to measure the height of a mountain on the moon.

(Show Transparency 12-18.) The first figure represents the moon and one of the light spots, at B, as seen through Galileo's telescope. The second figure represents a "side view" of the same thing: a ray of light from the sun is tangent to the moon at A and hits the top of the mountain peak at B. (Add the overlay to Transparency 12-18.) Galileo estimated the distance from A to B by comparing it with the diameter of the moon. Suppose that he figured AB was about 1/24 as long as the diameter. If we represent AB by the letter x, how should we represent the moon's radius? (It would be 12x.) Notice that we have labeled the lengths of two sides of $\triangle AOB$. How can we find the length of the third side? (Since $\overleftrightarrow{AB}$ is tangent to the circle at A, $\overleftrightarrow{AB} \perp \overline{OA}$, so $\triangle AOB$ is a right triangle. The Pythagorean Theorem can be used to express OB in terms of x.)

$$OB^2 = OA^2 + AB^2$$
$$= (12x)^2 + x^2$$
$$= 145x^2$$
$$OB = \sqrt{145}\,x \approx 12.04\,x.$$

Given that the radius of the moon is 1080 miles, use this result to find the height of the mountain at B.

$$x = \frac{1}{12}OA = \frac{1}{12}(1080) = 90 \text{ miles.}$$

$OB \approx 12.04x = 12.04(90) = 1083.6$ miles. Hence, the mountain at B is about 3.6 miles high.

Transparency 12-19 is for use in discussing the Set III exercise of Lesson 5.

I suggest assigning Lesson 6 for individual study.

Lesson 7
Chord and Secant Segments

Several years ago an article in Time magazine described an idea for a rapid transit system that would run by gravity.* Actually

---
*Time magazine, February 11, 1966.

the idea was not new because Lewis Carroll had thought of it in the 1890s and described it in the following conversation in his novel Sylvie and Bruno. (Show Transparency 12-20.)

"They run their railway-trains without any engines—nothing is needed but machinery to stop them with."

"But where does the force come from?" I ventured to ask.

"They use the force of gravity," he said.

"But that would need a railway going down-hill,...you can't have all your railways going down-hill?"

"They all do."

"Not from both ends?"

"From both ends. Each railway is in a long tunnel, perfectly straight: so of course the middle of it is nearer the center of the globe than the two ends: so every train runs half-way down-hill, and that gives it force enough to run the other half up-hill."

According to the article in Time, a train in such a tunnel would be accelerated by the force of gravity during the first half of its journey, gaining just enough speed to coast up to the other end. (Add the overlay to Transparency 12-20.) If a tunnel were built from Los Angeles to New York, it would be 2412 miles long, dropping at its midpoint to a depth of 188 miles below the earth's surface. Needless to say, such a tunnel would be both extremely difficult and expensive to build.

Since the train would be powered merely by gravity, it is possible to calculate exactly how long the trip would take. It is surprisingly short: only 42.2 minutes. In fact, a trip through a tunnel between any two points on the earth's surface would take 42.2 minutes. Two people leaving Los Angeles at the same time for San Francisco and London would arrive at their destinations simultaneously: 42.2 minutes later.

Although this takes some knowledge of physics to prove, there is another remarkable fact about these gravity tunnels that is relatively easy to prove. (Show Transparency 12-21.) Suppose two tunnels are built that cross each other. In this figure, for example, the tunnel from A to B intersects the tunnel from C to D at point P. Then, no matter where point P is, the distances from it to the four points on the earth's surface always satisfy the following equation:

$$PA \cdot PB = PC \cdot PD.$$

(Add the overlay to Transparency 12-21 and develop the proof of the Intersecting Chords Theorem. Then help your students apply it to solving the following problem on Transparency 12-22.)

How long would a tunnel through the earth be if the depth of the tunnel at its midpoint is 800 miles? (Assume that the diameter of the earth is 8000 miles.)

On the assumption that $\overline{AB}$ is not a diameter, since P is its midpoint, $\overrightarrow{CD} \perp \overline{AB}$ (if a line through the center of a circle bisects a chord that is not a diameter, it is also perpendicular to it).

Let $AP = PB = x$. $CP = 800$ and $PD = 7200$. Since

$$AP \cdot PB = CP \cdot PD,$$
$$x^2 = 800 \cdot 7200$$
$$x = \sqrt{800 \cdot 9 \cdot 800} = 3 \cdot 800$$
$$= 2400.$$

Since $AB = 2x$, the tunnel would be 4800 miles long.

Although this exercise covers most of Lesson 7, it should still be assigned for individual study. The bicycle wheel illustration should reinforce the idea of the Intersecting Chords Theorem, after which the comparable Secant Segments Theorem is introduced.

Transparency 12-23 is for use in discussing the Set III exercise of Lesson 6.

Lesson 8
The Inverse of a Point

A problem by Longfellow

The most popular American poet of the nineteenth century was Henry Wadsworth Longfellow. Longfellow was also an amateur mathematician and among the problems that he created was one about a water-lily in a lake. * (Show Transparency 12-24 with Overlay A in place.)

---

*This problem was originally in Sam Loyd's Cyclopedia of Puzzles, privately published in 1914. It is included in Mathematical Puzzles of Sam Loyd, Volume 1, selected and edited by Martin Gardner (Dover, 1959).

A water-lily growing in a lake is 10 inches above the surface of the water. If it were pulled over to one side, it would disappear under the surface at a point 21 inches from where it originally stood. What is the depth of the water?

To solve this problem, we need a diagram. (Remove Overlay A and add Overlay B.) This figure represents a vertical cross section of the lake: the horizontal lines represent the bottom of the lake and the surface of the water. As the water-lily is pulled over to one side, what kind of path does it follow? (An arc of a circle with the base of the lily as center.) Draw the entire circle of which this arc is a part. (Add Overlay C. You may wish to point out that we are considering a two-dimensional cross section of a three-dimensional situation. All points equidistant from the base of the lily actually lie on a sphere.)

What are the lengths of AP and the radius of the circle? (Since a line through the center of a circle that is perpendicular to a chord also bisects it, $AP = x$. The radius of the circle is $x + 10$.)

Without adding anything more to the figure, write an appropriate equation and solve for x.

(By the Intersecting Chords Theorem,
$$AP \cdot PB = CP \cdot PD.$$
Hence
$$21^2 = 10(2x + 10).$$
Solving for x, $x = 17.05$.)

Since the lengths given in the problem are each given as a whole number of inches, it is appropriate to round this answer and to say simply that the lake is about 17 inches deep.

Transparency 12-25 is for use in discussing the Set III exercise of Lesson 7.

Before introducing Lesson 8, it is probably best to review briefly the reflections of a point through a line and through a point. Transparency 12-26 can be used for this purpose. Then show Transparency 12-27 and point out that, since we have not defined what we mean by the "reflection" of a point through a circle, the best we can do is guess. Since we got our idea for the definition of the reflection of a point through a line from observing what happens when a physical point is reflected through a flat mirror, a good way to get an idea of how to answer this question would be to observe what happens when a physical point is reflected through a circular mirror. (I recommend obtaining some chrome-plated tubing from a hardware store, cutting it up into short lengths, and giving a piece to each student to experiment with. I have found that 1.5" diameter tubing cut into 2.5" lengths works very well. This mirror model is not entirely satisfactory because the images appear to be on the surface of the cylinder rather than inside it and their apparent locations depend upon the perspective with which the reflected points and the mirror are viewed. Nevertheless, it does provide some insight into the basis for the mathematical definition of point reflection through a circle.)

After some experimenting, your students should observe that the reflection of a point on the circle seems to be the same point and that the reflection of a point outside the circle seems to be a point inside the circle. As a point moves outward from the circle, its reflection seems to move inward. In introducing the definition of the "inverse of a point" be careful to emphasize that it is not like a theorem that can be derived from other ideas but is merely an arbitrary statement that yields some convenient results. Some of your better students may recognize that, since for a given circle r

and hence r^2 are constant, OP and OP' vary inversely. As OP increases, OP' decreases, so, as P moves away from the circle, P' moves toward its center. Furthermore, if OP = r, then so does OP', so each point on the circle is its own inverse.

Transparency 12-28 is for use in demonstrating how the inverse of a point outside a circle can be found geometrically. Permit your students to guess the positions of the tangent and perpendicular lines. Otherwise, they will become confused by extraneous details.

Lesson 9
Inverses of Lines and Circles

If you have a set of the small chrome-plated cylinders described in the preceding lesson, your students will find the following exercise amusing. Print copies of Worksheet 8, cut them up into quarters, and give one to each student, along with a mirror cylinder. If the cylinder is placed behind the figure in

the appropriate position, it will produce an image like the one shown here. *

The problem is to draw a frame around the figure so that its reflection in the cylinder looks like a rectangle. This has been done in the figure shown in the photograph.

Although reflections in a cylindrical mirror are not a perfect model of inversions in a circle, this exercise clearly illustrates that this transformation does not preserve collinearity, betweenness, or distance.

Transparencies 12-29 and 12-30 can be used to develop Lesson 9. Use a template to draw a circle on Transparency 12-29 as shown in the figure on page 490. Before showing the transparency, cover the interior of this circle with a disk cut from a card. Explain that the artist inverted the checkerboard through this circle before removing the disk to reveal what the inverted checkerboard looks like.

Review of Chapter 12

The Peaucellier linkage was invented in 1864 by a French engineer for whom it is named. If a model like the one shown on page 494 of

---

*Peter and the anteater are used with the permission of John Hart and Field Enterprises Inc.

the text is constructed from a thick sheet of plastic, it can be used on your overhead projector to demonstrate the linkage in action. (Drinking straws and pins can be used for the rods and hinges.) The point marked A will not actually travel all the way around the circle with center at Y because the linkage jams after a certain point. The Peau-cellier linkage was used in machinery for a brief time to change rotary motion into linear motion. Improvements in the cam and piston, however, have made this practical application of it obsolete.

Transparency 12-31 is for use in discussing Exercise 1 of Lesson 9, Set II.

Chapter 13

THE CONCURRENCE THEOREMS

Lesson 1
Concyclic Points

(The following problem provides a nice introduction to the ideas of Lesson 1. I will describe it exactly as I present it to my own class; if it is not possible to recast the problem in terms of your own neighboring schools, you might state it in terms of other local landmarks.)

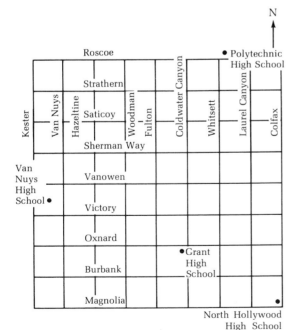

N

North Hollywood
High School

Before Grant opened in 1959, the three high schools nearest this area were North Hollywood High, Van Nuys High, and Polytechnic High. (Hand out a dittoed map comparable to the one shown here to each student.) This map shows the locations of these schools and of Grant. For simplicity, each has been represented by a single point. As you can see, Grant is closer to North Hollywood High than to the other two schools. It might have been better to have located Grant so that its distances to the three schools were the same. For convenience, we will refer to the points representing the schools by the first letters of their names. Guess, without doing any measuring, where you think the point that is equidistant from V, P, and N is located and mark it with a small x.

If the point you have guessed is really equidistant from V, P, and N, it should be possible to draw a circle with it as center that passes through all three points. See if you can do this.

Can you think of a way to use your straightedge and compass to find the point equidistant from V, P, and N that does not involve any guessing? (If necessary, ask where the points that are equidistant from just two of these points are located. After someone has suggested constructing the perpendicular bisectors of the segments joining the points, have your students draw △VPN and construct the perpendicular bisectors of two of its sides.)

How close is the point in which the two lines intersect to the point you marked x?

Try to draw a circle with it as center that passes through all three vertices of the triangle.

(Explain that points V, P, and N are said to be "concyclic" and that △VPN is called "cyclic." Then use Transparency 13-1 and its overlay to prove Theorem 78 and its corollaries.)

Lesson 2
Cyclic Quadrilaterals

The mystery of Oak Island

Ever since 1795, men have been searching for buried treasure on a small island off the coast of Nova Scotia. It has been speculated that as much as 30 million dollars worth of treasure may be buried on the island, perhaps by Blackbeard the Pirate or Captain Kidd.

(Show Transparency 13-2.) There is an elaborate maze of tunnels below the island's surface, which engineers say must have taken several years to construct. Unfortunately for those looking for the treasure, these tunnels seem to have been designed to flood any holes that may be dug on the island. Even though little evidence of buried treasure has been discovered, the tunnel system may very well have been built to protect it. For the past five years, a group of Canadian and American businessmen have spent $500,000 drilling holes and sinking shafts on the island.*

It would certainly help if there were a map that contained some clues on where to dig. Here is a fictitious map of Oak Island that could be used for this purpose. (Hand out dittoed copies of Transparency 13-3.) Suppose whoever dug the tunnel system buried the treasure in a spot that can be located in the following way.

Some of the oak trees on the island had symbols carved into their trunks so that they could be distinguished from the rest. The locations of these trees on the island are identified by the lettered points: there are 12 of them in all. Find, among these trees, those which are not in line with two others.

---

*Los Angeles Times, April 20, 1974.

Then find the point that is equidistant from them. It is at this point that the treasure is buried.

(Trees A, I, and J are collinear, so they can be eliminated; also trees I, C, and D, and so forth. After this has been done, four trees remain: B, H, F, and E. The perpendicular bisectors of the segments joining two pairs of these points intersect in a point equidistant from all four of them, so it is at this spot, which we will call T, that the treasure is buried. To verify this, ask your students to draw a circle with T as center that contains all four points; add the overlay to Transparency 13-3 to show it.)

Are all four trees needed to find T? (No. Three noncollinear points determine a circle.) Do you think that any four randomly chosen points would lie on a circle? (An example such as the four points C, B, H, and G makes it evident that the answer to this question is no.) So the fact that B, H, F, and E are concyclic seems to verify that T is the spot we are looking for.

We have proved that every triangle is cyclic. From what we have just observed, it is evident that every quadrilateral is not. (Show Transparency 13-4.) Can you guess which of these quadrilaterals are cyclic? (After the students have done this, point out that there doesn't seem to be any obvious relationship between the relative lengths of the sides of a quadrilateral and whether it is cyclic. For example, although both pairs of opposite sides of quadrilaterals 1 and 2 are equal, one quadrilateral is cyclic whereas the other is not. Then add the overlay to Transparency 13-4.)

Circles are shown circumscribed about the four quadrilaterals that are cyclic and the measures of their angles are given. Can you discover a relationship between the measures of a quadrilateral's angles and whether it is cyclic?

Transparency 13-5 and its overlays can be used to develop the proofs of Theorem 79. (Note that part of the second proof is left to the student as an exercise.)

Transparency 13-6 and its overlays are for use in discussing the Set III exercise of Lesson 1. Overlay A is to show the relationship between the midpoint of the hypotenuse of a right triangle and its circumcenter. It should be removed before adding Overlays B and C.

Lesson 3
Incircles

A penguin kidnaping

Several years ago several zoologists conducted some interesting experiments with penguins in Antarctica.* (Show the top of Transparency 13-7.) In one of these experiments, five adult penguins were taken from their home, flown 1200 miles across the Antarctic continent, and released. Ten months later, three of the penguins had come back home. Since they cannot fly, the birds covered the entire distance through unfamiliar territory by walking, swimming, and tobogganing. How were the penguins able to figure out their way home?

To try to find out, another experiment was performed in which penguins taken a shorter distance from their home were tracked to see where they went. (Show the bottom of Transparency 13-7.) The two figures show the positions of two penguins at five-minute intervals following their release. Penguin A seemed to know exactly where it was going. The track of Penguin B, on the other hand, seems to indicate that it was unsure at first of what direction in which to head. After a time, however, it also travelled in a definite direction. Why the difference? Because Penguin A was released when it was sunny and Penguin B began under a cloudy sky that later cleared. Evidently, penguins somehow use the sun as a compass in telling directions.

(Show Transparency 13-8.) To track the penguins, three transits were set up at the vertices of an equilateral triangle measuring 200 meters on each side. A penguin was released from a pit located at the point equidistant from the three vertices of the triangle. Readings were then taken at five-minute intervals of the bird's positions until it disappeared from sight.

What is the point from which the penguins were released called with respect to the triangle? (Its circumcenter.) Why? (Because it is the center of the circumcircle of the triangle. Add Overlay A to Transparency 13-8 to illustrate this and then remove it.)

*John T. Emlen and Richard L. Penney, "The Navigation of Penguins," Scientific American, October 1966, pp. 104-113.

Notice that this point is also equidistant from the sides of the triangle. Because of this, it is also possible to draw a circle with this point as center that is tangent to each side of the triangle. (Add Overlay B to Transparency 13-8 to illustrate this and explain the meanings of the words "incenter" and "incircle.")

The centers of the triangle's circumcircle and incircle are the same point because the triangle is equilateral. Where would they be if it were scalene instead? (Show Transparency 13-9.) This figure shows the penguin at the point equidistant from the vertices of a scalene triangle: the circumcenter of the triangle. Is this point also equidistant from the sides of the triangle? (No.) Do you think that there is a point that is? How do you think you could find it? (Check out any guesses the students make to see if they seem reasonable. Add the overlay to Transparency 13-9 after the point has been located from the intersection of two of the triangle's angle bisectors. It can be used for developing the proof of Theorem 80 and its corollary.)

Lesson 4
Ceva's Theorem

Something old and something new

(Hand out dittoed copies of Transparency 13-10.) If the calendar were suddenly turned back 2000 years and you were still a high school (or college) student, you wouldn't be taking some of the courses that you take now because they wouldn't exist. Other courses that you are taking would probably be radically different from what they are now. Much of geometry, however, would be very much the same.

For example, the proof that we considered yesterday that every triangle has an incircle is Theorem 4 in Book IV of Euclid's Elements. This theorem is a consequence of the fact that the angle bisectors of every triangle are concurrent. Use your straightedge and compass to construct, as accurately as you can, the angle bisectors of the triangle at the top of the sheet you have been given. (After the students have done this, show Transparency 13-10 with its overlay. Label the figure "The angle bisectors of a triangle are concurrent—proved by Euclid c. 300 B. C. ")

What would happen if, instead of bisecting the angles of a triangle, we trisected them? You may recall that it is impossible to trisect most angles with just a straightedge and compass. Since this is the case, we will use a protractor instead. (Give your students time to draw the trisectors of each angle as accurately as they can. To make this easier, the triangle has been drawn so that the measures of its angles are 30°, 51°, and 99°. No overlay has been prepared to illustrate the result, since it is probably best to do this with the class. If the three points of intersection of the adjacent trisectors of the angles are joined with line segments, an equilateral triangle is formed!)

This is a relatively new theorem in elementary geometry because it was discovered at the end of the nineteenth century. (Label the figure "The angle trisectors of a triangle determine the vertices of an equilateral triangle—discovered by Frank Morley in 1899. " Frank Morley was a professor of mathematics at Johns Hopkins University and the father of the author Christopher Morley. It was not until ten years after Morley made this discovery that someone figured out how to prove it. A proof of Morley's Theorem is included in Geometry Revisited, by H. S. M. Coxeter and S. L. Greitzer, a book in the New Mathematical Library, Random House, 1967, but it is by no means easy.)

Although it is probably best to present Lesson 4 in class, no transparencies have been made in advance for this purpose. I suggest developing the part of the lesson given on pp. 516-517 of the text by having your students draw some of the figures and work out the proof with you. You may prefer to use small letters to refer to the lengths of the various segments that are included in the proof.

Transparency 13-11 is for use in discussing the Set III exercise of Lesson 3.

Lesson 5
The Centroid of a Triangle

A problem of gravity

(Give each student a 4"x 6" file card and a pair of scissors.) Mark the point on the upper edge 2" from the left corner as shown

on Transparency 13-12 and draw lines from this point to the lower left and right corners of the card. Cut along these lines and put the two smaller pieces aside.

It is easy to balance the largest triangular piece on three fingers so that it is horizontal. (Illustrate this and have everyone do it.) It is not as easy to balance it on just two fingers. Can you do it? Can you balance the "triangle" on just one finger? (After a few attempts, most students should be able to do this.) Now a very challenging question. Can you balance the "triangle" on the metal point of your compass? You may poke a small hole in the card at whatever point you think will work. (It is unlikely that anyone will be able to guess the precise point on which the triangle may be balanced.)

Let's see if we can find the balancing point by construction. Make a careful tracing of the triangular piece on a sheet of paper. What lines do you think we should draw in order to find the balancing point? (Have everyone try out any suggestions made. Someone will probably guess that the triangle will balance on its circumcenter and someone else its incenter. When each of these points has been located, it should be labeled on the card as shown here. After

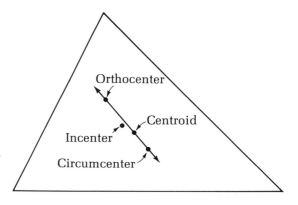

discovering that neither point will work, someone may think of the triangle's altitudes. If so, construct them, and, after the class has observed that they seem to be concurrent, label the point as the orthocenter. Since the idea of a median in a triangle has not been considered previously in the course, no one may think of drawing the medians. If this is the case, you might ask the following.)

It seems that, if the triangle is to balance on one point, half of it should be on one "side" of the point and half on the other. In other words, each of the lines determining this point should divide the triangle in half. Where do you suppose a line from one vertex of the triangle should be drawn in order to divide the triangle in half? (The midpoint of the opposite side. After everyone has drawn the medians, observe that they also seem to be concurrent and then let everyone see if the triangle will balance on this point.)

By using Ceva's Theorem, it is very easy to prove that the medians of every triangle are concurrent. (After everyone has had time to think about this, let someone explain how. Two different proofs that the altitudes of every triangle are concurrent are included in the exercises of Lesson 5.)

You may wish to finish this lesson by observing that three of the four points that we have located in the triangle seem to be collinear and asking which they are. (The orthocenter, centroid, and circumcenter.) It can be proved that these points are collinear in every triangle that is not equilateral. What do you suppose happens in that case? (They are all the same point.) The three points determine the so-called Euler line, named after the great eighteenth-century Swiss mathematician Leonhard Euler. It can be proved that, in every nonequilateral triangle, the centroid is a point of trisection of the segment joining the orthocenter and the circumcenter.

Lesson 6
Some Triangle Constructions

The spotter's puzzle reconsidered

Today we return to the other problem that we considered at the beginning of this course. (Show Transparency 0-4 and briefly review the story of the surfer and the spotter.)

You may recall that we have proved that it doesn't matter where the surfer builds his house on the island: the sum of the lengths of the perpendicular segments to the sides from every point on the island is the same.

For the spotter, who wanted to build his house so that the sum of the lengths of the paths from it to the three corners of the island is a minimum, the situation is quite different. The sum depends upon the position of the point. Do you recall where that point seemed to be? (The "center" of the

triangle, which, since the triangle is equilateral, is all four special points "rolled into one.")

(Show Transparency 13-13.) To prove this, we will first choose a random point, P, inside the triangle. The sum of the lengths of the line segments joining point P to the vertices is PA + PB + PC. Next, we will imagine rotating △BPC about point B 60° clockwise. (Add the overlay to Transparency 13-13.) Triangle BP'C' is the rotation image of △BPC, so the two triangles are congruent. Hence BP = BP', BC = BC', and PC = P'C'.

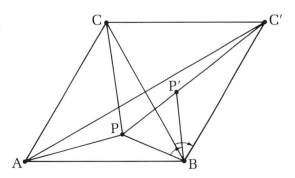

(Draw $\overline{PP'}$ and $\overline{CC'}$.) Since ∠PBP' = 60° and ∠CBC' = 60°, it follows that △PBP' and △CBC' are equilateral.

The sum of the lengths of the line segments joining point P to the vertices, PA + PB + PC, is thus equal to AP + PP' + P'C', the length of a path from A to C'. The length of this path is shortest when it is straight. (Draw $\overline{AC'}$.) Therefore, in order for it to be a minimum, P must lie on $\overline{AC'}$. (Label the point in which $\overline{AC'}$ intersects $\overline{BC}$ point D.) What do you notice about $\overline{AD}$? (Since ABC'C is a rhombus, $\overline{AD}$ is the perpendicular bisector of $\overline{BC}$, the bisector of ∠CAB, an altitude of △ABC, and also one of its medians.) By using the same reasoning, it can be shown that, for the sum of the three paths to the vertices to be a minimum, P must lie on the perpendicular bisectors of the other two sides of △ABC, on the bisectors of its other two angles, on its other altitudes, and on its other medians. So the spotter should build his house at the point on the island that is its circumcenter, incenter, orthocenter, and centroid.

This puzzle is a special case of Fermat's problem, which is discussed on pages 21-22 of Introduction to Geometry, 2nd ed., by H. S. M. Coxeter (Wiley, 1969).

To begin Lesson 6, you might show Transparency 13-14, which contains a quotation from Finnegan's Wake, by James Joyce. This book, Joyce's last, is written in a strange "stream of consciousness" style and its meanings have not yet been completely deciphered. The sentence seems to say: "Problem the first, construct an equilateral triangle problem!" Joyce is probably referring to Euclid, since the construction of an equilateral triangle is the first problem posed in the Elements.

Transparency 13-15 is for use in presenting the example constructions in Lesson 6 if you wish to do so.

Transparency 13-16 and its overlay are for use in discussing the Set III exercise of Lesson 5.

Review of Chapter 13

A nine-point surprise

Today we are going to do a rather elaborate construction that will provide a good review of what we have been learning. If done carefully, it has a rather interesting result. (Show Transparency 13-17.) First, construct a large scalene triangle like △XYZ so that XY = 5 in, XZ = 4 in, and YZ = 4.5 in.

Construct the three altitudes of the triangle and name them $\overline{XE}$, $\overline{YG}$, and $\overline{ZA}$. Label the orthocenter of the triangle point O.

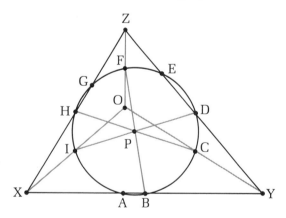

Next, bisect the three line segments joining the orthocenter to the vertices of the triangle. Label their midpoints as follows: $\overline{OX}$, midpoint I; $\overline{OY}$, midpoint C; $\overline{OZ}$, midpoint F.

Next, find the midpoints of the sides of the triangle and label them as follows: $\overline{XY}$,

midpoint B; $\overline{YZ}$, midpoint D; $\overline{XZ}$, midpoint H.

What do you notice? (The points labeled A through I appear to be concyclic.) Suppose you were blindfolded and marked three points at random on a sheet of paper. When you took the blindfold off, would it be surprising to discover that they were concyclic? (No, if they are not collinear. We have proved that three noncollinear points are always concyclic.) What if you had marked four points at random on your paper while you were blindfolded. Would it be surprising to discover that they were concyclic? (Yes. They would be concyclic only if they happened to be the vertices of a quadrilateral whose opposite angles were supplementary.) That the nine points we have labeled A through I should be concyclic is quite remarkable. It is not difficult to find the center of the circle on which they lie because six of them happen to be the endpoints of three of the circle's diameters. Can you guess which points these are? (The three diameters are $\overline{FB}$, $\overline{HC}$, and $\overline{ID}$.) Draw the three diameters, label the point in which they are concurrent point P, and draw the "nine point" circle.

Two interesting properties of the "nine point" circle are that its center is the midpoint of the line segment joining the orthocenter and the circumcenter of the triangle and that its radius is half the radius of the circumcircle of the triangle.

Some of your better students might be interested in seeing a proof of why the nine points are concyclic. An especially straightforward one is on pages 119-120 of Excursions in Geometry, by C. Stanley Ogilvy (Oxford University Press, 1969). Historians are not sure of who first noticed the "nine point" circle. The first proof of its existence seems to have been published in 1821.

Transparencies 13-18, 13-19, 13-20, and 13-21 are for possible use in discussing some of the exercises of Lesson 6.

Overlay A for Transparency 13-21 illustrates the result of the Set III exercise: if equilateral triangles are constructed on the sides of any triangle so that each faces outward from it, their centers determine an equilateral triangle. Overlay B shows that if equilateral triangles are constructed on the sides of a triangle so that each faces inward, their centers also determine an equilateral triangle. These triangles are called the outer and inner Napoleon triangles.

Chapter 14

REGULAR POLYGONS
AND THE CIRCLE

Lesson 1
Polygons

So far, our study of geometry has essentially been limited to three basic geometric figures: the triangle, the quadrilateral, and the circle. Triangles and quadrilaterals, because they consist of line segments, are called "polygons." In this unit we will expand our study of polygons to include those having more than four sides. We will eventually apply some of the theorems that we develop about polygons to furthering our knowledge of the circle.

(After this introduction, Transparency 14-1 and its overlay can be used to prepare your students for the formal definition of "polygon." You may want to tell them that, since the definition will not be used as a reason in proofs, there is no need to memorize it. It is, of course, important however that they understand the definition's meaning.)

Transparency 14-2 is for use in showing that, if the definition did not specify that n > 2, then a line segment would qualify as a polygon. (Number the points in each figure as you consider it.) Three noncollinear points determine the simplest polygon, the triangle. Four points determine more than four line segments: as a result, whether they are the corners of a quadrilateral depends upon how the points are joined. As the number of points increases, the order in which they are joined to form a specific polygon becomes very important. The set of five points at the lower right, for instance, determine four different concave pentagons.

The remainder of the lesson might be assigned for individual study.

Lesson 2
Regular Polygons

(Show Transparency 14-3.) This photograph was taken through an electron microscope by an entomologist. (If a student is familiar with the word, he might explain its meaning: a person who studies insects.) It shows the surface of one of the eggs of a water bug. The extreme magnification (820x) reveals that the surface is covered with an elaborate network: this network seems to consist of polygons of various shapes. In what way are all of the polygons alike? (They are all convex.)

(Add the overlay to Transparency 14-3 and ask your students to identify the three polygons shown by name.) The hexagon seems to be more symmetric than the other two. Why? (Because its sides and angles are close to being equal.) A convex polygon that is both equilateral and equiangular is called <u>regular</u>.

You might provide each student with a pair of hinged mirrors so that he can carry out the following exercise based upon the symmetry of the regular polygons before proving that they are cyclic.

Draw a horizontal line segment several inches long on a sheet of paper and place the mirrors so that they are standing on the segment as shown in the diagram on Transparency 14-4. If the mirrors are adjusted correctly, you will see an equilateral triangle. (Add the overlay to Transparency 14-4.)

Now slowly turn the mirrors toward each other until you see a square. As the angle of the mirrors is made smaller and smaller, regular polygons having more and more sides will appear.

After observing that every regular polygon seems to be cyclic, Transparency 14-5 and its overlay can be used to develop the proof.

Transparency 14-6 is for use in discussing the Set III exercise of Lesson 1.

You might reproduce the dissection puzzle on Worksheet 9 (preferably on cover stock) and provide those students who are interested in doing the Set III exercise of Lesson 2 with a copy.

Lesson 3
The Perimeter of a Regular Polygon

Euclid began the <u>Elements</u> with an explanation of how to construct the simplest of the regular polygons—the equilateral triangle. Later he showed how to construct several other regular polygons by inscribing them in circles. (Show Transparency 14-7.) These include the square, regular pentagon, and regular hexagon. By bisecting their central angles, other regular polygons having twice as many sides can be constructed. (Call attention to how this has been done to form the dodecagon, octagon, and decagon. Then make a list like the one below on the lower left section of the transparency.)

$$3 \quad 6 \quad 12 \quad 24 \ldots$$
$$4 \quad 8 \quad 16 \quad 32 \ldots$$
$$5 \quad 10 \quad 20 \quad 40 \ldots$$

Notice that, among others, the regular heptagon and regular nonagon are missing from this list. Is it possible to construct them with a straightedge and compass?

The first person to be able to give a definite answer to this question was Karl Friedrich Gauss, a German mathematician born in 1777 who is generally considered to be one of the greatest mathematicians who has ever lived. (Show Transparency 14-8.) Although this portrait shows Gauss in his old age, he solved the problem of the regular polygons when he was just seventeen years old. Using some rather advanced mathematics, Gauss proved that a regular polygon having an odd number of sides can be constructed only if the odd prime factors of n are different numbers of the form

$$2^{\left(2^k\right)} + 1.$$

To see what this means, we will find some values of this expression for different values of k. (Explain how the expression is evaluated for k = 0 and k = 1 and record the results in the table at the bottom of the transparency.)

k	n
0	3
1	5

Notice that the only odd prime factors of the numbers of sides of the polygons in our previous list (made on the bottom of Transparency 14-7) are 3 and 5. What happens if k = 2? (If k = 2, n = 17.) Since 17 is a prime number, it is possible to construct a regular polygon having 17 sides! (Show Transparency 14-9 and explain that, as the result of a very elaborate procedure, the vertical segments at the left and right cut off an arc of the circle that is exactly two-seventeenths of its length. This arc can then be bisected to determine an arc that is one-seventeenth of the circle. The method used is described on page 27 of Coxeter's <u>Introduction to Geometry</u>.)

Gauss's formula doesn't stop working at the number 17. (Show Transparency 14-8 again.) If we let k = 3, n = 257. This is also a prime number and in 1832 a very patient man named Richelot constructed a regular polygon having 257 sides. With so many sides, it would have been very difficult to distinguish from the circle in which it was inscribed.

If k = 4, n = 65,537. This number is also prime and a man with vastly more patience than wisdom spent ten years of his life figuring out how to construct a regular polygon having 65,537 sides! His manuscript is in the library of the University of Göttingen in Germany.

If k = 5, n = 4,294,967,297. This number is <u>not</u> prime and, although modern computers <u>have</u> been used on the problem, no larger values of k for which n is prime have been discovered.

Returning to our original question, Gauss's formula shows that it is impossible to construct either a regular heptagon or a regular nonagon because 7 does not appear in the list and the odd prime factors of 9, 3 and 3, are not different but the same.

Two excellent references for students who might be interested in reading more about the constructibility of regular polygons are:

The Borders of Mathematics, by Willy Ley (Pyramid Publications, 1967): Chapter 2, "The Seven-spoked Wheel" and Chapter 3, "Enter Carl Friedrich Gauss."

Famous Problems of Mathematics, by Heinrich Tietze (Graylock Press, 1965): Chapter 9, "The Regular Polygon of 17 Sides."

Transparency 14-10 and its overlay can be used to introduce Lesson 3 with the story of General Turtle and to develop the formula for the perimeter of a regular polygon in terms of its radius. (I do not hold my students responsible for memorizing either this formula or the one in Lesson 4 for the area of a regular polygon.)

General Turtle was founded by Dr. Seymour Papert, a professor of applied mathematics and director of the Artificial Intelligence Laboratory of M.I.T. Articles on his work have been published in Saturday Review of Education (May 1973, p. 50) and Newsweek (August 13, 1973, p. 70).

Lesson 4
The Area of a Regular Polygon

When a child makes mistakes in arithmetic classes, he...might conclude, "I'm dumb" or "I'm not mathematically minded" or "I never could understand that" or (at best) "to hell with it." The child rarely engages in constructive thinking about how and why the mistake happened and what can be done about it. But when the turtle [does something unexpected], the reaction is more constructive.... Children almost unanimously see the turtle (rather than themselves) as doing the "wrong thing." And, of course, we strongly encourage this, for the child is then much more ready to be objective about what happened. *

---

*Seymour Papert in New Educational Technology.

(Show the top half of Transparency 14-11.) Here is a set of directions similar to those given to the turtle to make it draw a square. They cause it to go round and round a square 10 inches on each side.

Slightly different directions are needed to get the turtle to draw other regular polygons. (Show the lower half of Transparency 14-11 but keep the hexagon covered.) For example, this set of directions is intended to cause the turtle to draw an equilateral triangle. However, when the turtle is given them, it draws a regular hexagon instead! (Uncover the hexagon.) Can you figure out why? (In order for the turtle to travel once around the figure, it must turn through 360°. At 60° per turn, it draws a figure with 6 sides. The second direction should be: Turn right 120°. In general, the number of degrees named in the second step should be the measure of an exterior angle of the polygon rather than one of its interior angles. This was not apparent in drawing the square because the two angles have the same measure.)

We have developed a formula for the perimeter of a regular polygon in terms of its radius. Today we will derive a formula for its area. (Transparency 14-12 can be used for doing this. I do not expect my students to memorize the result.)

Lesson 5
Limits

A nice way to introduce limits is to show a set of nested boxes. I bought the set shown in this photograph at a novelty store. They happen to be in the shape of hexagonal prisms but the shape is not important. The

set contains seven boxes with heights of approximately 76 mm, 66 mm, 57 mm, 49 mm, 42 mm, 36 mm, and 31 mm. Each successively smaller box is about 86% as tall as the one before it.

Suppose that there were no end to the smaller boxes and that this size ratio continued. To what number do you think the heights of the successive boxes would get closer and closer? (Zero.) Even though we would never come to a box whose height is actually zero, we say that the heights of the boxes approach zero as a limit.

Now suppose that, as we take out each successive box, we stack them one on top of another. Do you think that we could make the stack as tall as we please? Since the answer to this question doesn't seem very obvious, it might be helpful to make a list of heights and see what happens.

(Show Transparency 14-13.) To make the calculations simpler, let's suppose that we start with a box 100 mm high and that each successive box is 50% as tall as the preceding one. (Fill in the first four lines with your students' help.

Box	Height	Total height of stack
1	100	100
2	50	150
3	25	175
4	12.5	187.5

Then add the overlay to Transparency 14-13.)

Here are the heights of the individual boxes and the stack as more and more boxes are added to it. Beginning with the eighth line, the numbers have been rounded to four decimal places. For the last two lines, we have jumped ahead to the twentieth and fiftieth boxes. Can you guess what the entries would be for the hundredth box? (The same as those for the fiftieth, but closer to 0 and 200, respectively.) Even though the height of the stack would never make it to 200, we say that it approaches 200 as a limit.

(To introduce the limit notation, you might write just below the heads of the columns of the table, n, h_n, and H_n, respectively, and at the bottoms of the columns, ∞, 0, and 200.) We write:

$$\lim_{n \to \infty} h_n = 0 \quad \text{and} \quad \lim_{n \to \infty} H_n = 200.$$

(Show Transparency 14-14 and explain that, since a mathematically precise definition of the word "limit" is beyond the scope of this course, we will settle for the description given here. Then illustrate its

meaning with the following pair of examples.)

Suppose the first four terms of a sequence are 2.4, 2.49, 2.499, and 2.4999. (Write these in the indicated column.) What do you think the next three terms would be? (2.49999, 2.499999, and 2.4999999.) What do you think the limit of the sequence might be? (2.5. Write the successive differences between 2.5 and each term in a column: 0.1, 0.01, 0.001, etc., and note how, by letting n get sufficiently large, these differences can be made as small as we please. You might want to follow this up by asking what would have happened if we had thought 2.6 was the limit of the sequence. Although the successive differences would still become smaller, we cannot make them as small as we please.)

Suppose the first four terms of a sequence are 3.1, 3.2, 3.3, and 3.4. What do you think the next three terms would be? (3.5, 3.6, and 3.7.) What do you think the limit of the sequence might be? (Give your students a chance to discover that the sequence has no limit.)

Transparency 14-15 is for use in discussing the Set III exercise of Lesson 4.

Lesson 6
The Circumference and Area of a Circle

Before class, stretch adding machine tape on which you have written the value of π to several hundred decimal places either across the front of the room or around several walls. A table listing 500 decimal places of π is given here. I found a spacing of 2 in. per digit convenient.

Five hundred decimal places of π

3.
14159 26535 89793 23846 26433 83279 50288
41971 69399 37510 58209 74944 59230 78164
06286 20899 86280 34825 34211 70679 82148
08651 32823 06647 09384 46095 50582 23172
53594 08128 48111 74502 84102 70193 85211
05559 64462 29489 54930 38196 44288 10975
66593 34461 28475 64823 37867 83165 27120
19091 45648 56692 34603 48610 45432 66482
13393 60726 02491 41273 72458 70066 06315
58817 48815 20920 96282 92540 91715 36436
78925 90360 01133 05305 48820 46652 13841
46951 94151 16094 33057 27036 57595 91953
09218 61173 81932 61179 31051 18548 07446
23799 62749 56735 18857 52724 89122 79381
83011 94912

The number π has such an interesting story that an entire book has been devoted to it. (A History of π, by Petr Beckmann, The Golem Press, 1971. Every mathematics teacher should have a copy.) It was being used in calculations as long ago as 2000 B.C. The Greek mathematician Archimedes used geometry to find the value of π accurately to two decimal places: 3.14. By the late Renaissance its value had been computed to 35 decimal places. In the nineteenth century an English mathematician figured it to more than 700 decimal places but, unfortunately, they were not all correct. With the development of computers, it became possible to determine the value of π to thousands of decimal places. The longest calculation to date, recorded in the Guinness Book of World Records, was made on a computer at the French Atomic Energy Commission in Paris in 1967. It was to 500,000 decimal places.

One of the exercises in Lesson 5 was to find some of the values of ν, the product $n \sin\dfrac{180}{n}$ as n gets larger and larger. If you did this correctly, you may have noticed that they get closer and closer to this number π. (Show Transparency 14-16.) This table shows the value of each term in the sequence carried to eight decimal places. From this table, it seems reasonable that
$$\lim_{n \to \infty} n \sin\frac{180}{n} = \pi$$
and we will assume that this is so.

The exercises of Lesson 5 should be reviewed before going on to Lesson 6. To introduce the new lesson, you might pose the following question, which is from the second of the two delightful books by Julius Sumner Miller titled Millergrams (Doubleday, 1970). Transparency 14-17 is for use in illustrating it.

Consider the Earth as exactly 25,000 miles around. Let us put a tight ribbon around this Earth. The ribbon is, of course, exactly 25,000 miles long. Now you slit the ribbon and insert a length of one foot. The ribbon is now exactly 25,000 miles plus one foot long. Now let us get on a magic carpet and run around the Earth pulling away the ribbon so that it is equally far from the Earth everywhere. That is, we take up the slack everywhere equally. Now, of course, a little gap exists between the Earth and the ribbon. How large is this gap? Ideas: It is just a very, very tiny gap so that only light can creep under? It is big enough for water to run under? It is big enough for a mouse to crawl under? Which best fits the situation?*

This drawing represents the earth as seen from the North Pole. The lengthened ribbon, very much exaggerated, is shown around the equator. It seems reasonable to assume that the equator and the ribbon are concentric circles. We are given the length of each circle and want to find the difference in their radii.

To solve the problem, we need to know a relationship between the length of a circle, called its circumference, and the length of the circle's radius. (Use Transparencies 14-18 and 14-19 to develop the definitions and theorems on the circumference and area of a circle.)

Now we are ready to figure out the answer to the question about the ribbon around the earth. If we let r = the radius of the earth in feet and x = the amount of the gap (mark these on Transparency 14-17), then the circumference of the earth is $2\pi r$ and the length of the ribbon is $2\pi(r + x)$. But the length of the ribbon is 1 foot longer than the circumference of the earth, so
$$2\pi r + 1 = 2\pi(r + x).$$
Solving for x, we get
$$x = \frac{1}{2\pi}.$$
Since $\pi \approx 3$, $x \approx \frac{1}{6}$ foot, or about 2 inches.

Although only one foot was added to 25,000 miles, the gap would be big enough for a mouse to go under easily. Also quite remarkable is the fact that neither the radius nor the circumference of the earth is actually used in the calculations. This means that, if the ribbon had been tied around other spheres and lengthened by the same amount, the gap would be the same! That it would also be 2 inches for the sun, or even a basketball, defies the intuition.

Lesson 7
Sectors and Arcs

The geometry of turning a corner

(Show Transparency 14-20.) When a car turns a corner, its outer wheels have to travel a greater distance than its inner

---
*Copyright © 1970 by Doubleday and Company. Used by permission.

wheels. Do you know what permits them to do this without skidding? (The back wheels, which drive the car, are connected to the drive shaft through a differential gear that permits the two to rotate at different rates. The front wheels are free to rotate independently on their own short axles.)

Suppose a car whose left and right wheels are 5 feet apart turns 90° around a corner. Can you figure out how much further the outer wheels travel than the inner ones? (Let r = the radius of the circle about which the inner wheels turn. Then the radius about which the outer wheels turn is r + 5. Since both travel around a quarter of their respective circles, the difference in the distances traveled is

$$\frac{1}{4}2\pi(r + 5) - \frac{1}{4}2\pi r = \frac{5}{2}\pi \approx 7.9 \text{ feet.})$$

The result of this problem is analogous to the "ribbon around the earth" problem in that the radius of the circle turns out to be irrelevant. Whether the car makes a very sharp or very wide turn does not matter: its outer wheels will always travel approximately 7.9 feet farther than its inner wheels.

Now suppose the car travels around a curve that is a 150° of a circle. (Transparency 14-21.) If the radius of the circle traveled by its inner wheels is 100 feet, can you figure out how far they travel? (Students who solve this problem have figured out Theorem 90 for themselves.)

$$\frac{150}{360}2\pi(100) \approx 262 \text{ feet.}$$

The remainder of Lesson 7, including the definition of "sector" and the theorem for finding its area, can be left for individual study.

Review of Chapter 14

Man is almost the only creature on the earth whose population has been steadily increasing Most animal populations remain fairly constant from year to year.* Biologists think that the reason for this is that animals have ingrained social behaviors that automatically limit their population density in a given region.

An example of this is the territorial system of birds. In many species of birds,

___

*An interesting article on this subject by V.C. Wynne-Edwards, "Population Control in Animals," is in Scientific American, August 1964, pp. 68-74.

each male will take over a certain region during the breeding season and keep all other males out of it. Colonies of seabirds will not permit other birds to settle within their general vicinity. (Show Transparency 14-22.) This map shows some islands on which several colonies of seabirds have established fishing rights within a given distance from their nesting sites. The lettered points represent the colonies and the circles represent the boundaries of their fishing territories.

These territories overlap in certain places. (Add the overlay to Transparency 14-22.) For instance, colonies A and B share the shaded region. If they are 6 miles apart and each colony's territory is bounded by a circle with a radius of 6 miles, can you figure out the area of the region shared by both colonies?

(Since this problem is rather challenging, you may want to have your students work on it together.)

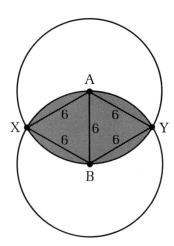

In the figure shown here, the region has been divided into two equilateral triangles and four identical circular segments. The area of one of these segments is

$$\frac{60}{360}\pi 6^2 - \frac{6^2}{4}\sqrt{3}$$

so the area of the entire region is

$$2(\frac{6^2}{4}\sqrt{3}) + 4(\frac{60}{360}\pi 6^2 - \frac{6^2}{4}\sqrt{3}) =$$
$$24\pi - 18\sqrt{3} \approx 44.$$

The area of the region shared by both colonies is approximately 44 square miles.

Transparencies 14-23 and 14-24 are for use in discussing Exercise 4 of Set II and the Set III exercise of Lesson 7.

GEOMETRIC SOLIDS

Lesson 1
Lines and Planes in Space

Four Generations, a company that manufactures attractive games and puzzles, sells a clever toy called Top Secret. It consists of a small top, which, if spun on a special base, will continue to spin for a seemingly endless period. Hidden inside the base are a battery and other components of a simple motor that turns itself on when the spinning top is placed on it and off when it is removed. The top can spin for as long as a week on the power of the battery. Top Secret can be purchased by mail directly from the manufacturer: Four Generations, 6005 Gravenstein Hwy. South, Sebastopol, Calif. 95472.

To introduce the first lesson, you might spin the top and let your students observe its strange behavior.

Physicists studying the behavior of the motions of objects in space make use of a lot of three-dimensional geometry. In this unit we will become acquainted with a variety of three-dimensional figures and their properties. We will begin by studying some basic relationships between lines and planes.

(Show the top figures on Transparency 15-1.) The figure at the left represents a side view of the top spinning so that its axis is perpendicular to the plane of the base; the figure at the right represents the same thing. (Add the overlay to Transparency 15-1 and use the figure to discuss the meanings of "parallel planes" and "a line perpendicular to a plane." You might make the observation that the figure seems to suggest a theorem in three-dimensional geometry comparable to one we have proved in two-dimensional geometry: In space, if a line is perpendicular to one of two parallel planes, it is also perpendicular to the other.)

Then show the bottom figures on Transparency 15-1, which represent the top as it is about to tip over and use them to discuss the meaning of "a line oblique to a plane" and "oblique planes." Ask your students what they think the intersection of planes A and B is.

To reinforce these ideas and to introduce a couple of additional ones, Lesson 1 should be assigned for individual study.

Here is an alternative demonstration, from the book Science Magic by Kenneth M. Swezey.

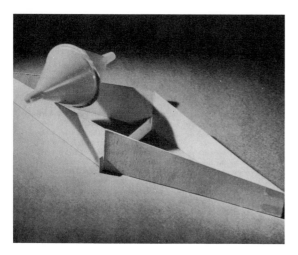

Place a pair of joined funnels at either end of the track shown here. Seeming to defy gravity, they will roll to the middle, the highest point!

Don't believe for a moment, however, that the funnels really disobey the law of Newton. As in most scientific paradoxes, the catch lies in an incorrect interpretation of the facts. Although the funnels seem to be rolling uphill, their center of gravity is really going downhill, because of the widening track.

Any funnels having a smooth surface may be used. Join their mouths with tape. Make the cardboard track higher at the center than at the ends by an amount less than the radius of the funnels; spread the track less than the distance between their necks.*

After this demonstration, show Transparency 15-2, which represents a somewhat simplified view of the funnels rolling toward the center. Add the overlay to Transparency 15-1 and use the figures to discuss the meanings of "a line parallel to a plane," "a line perpendicular to a plane," and "perpendicular planes." Ask your students what they think the intersection of planes A and B is.

Lesson 2
Rectangular Solids

(Before class, stretch a cord or a piece of brightly colored yarn diagonally across the room from one of the corners of the ceiling to the opposite corner of the floor.)

As you probably know, television screens are measured by the lengths of their diago-

---

*Copyright 1952 by McGraw-Hill Book Company.

nals. A 21-inch screen, for example, measures 21 inches from one corner to the opposite corner. If it were customary to measure a room in the same way, we would find the length of one of its diagonals, such as the one represented by the cord. First, guess how many feet long you think this diagonal is.

Given the dimensions of the room, it is possible to figure out the diagonal's precise length. Before we do this, let's consider how the same problem might be solved for a television screen. If a television screen is 15 inches high and 20 inches wide, how could you find the length of one of its diagonals? (By the Pythagorean Theorem. It would be 25 inches long.)

(Hand out dittoed copies of Transparency 15-3 and have your students draw diagonal $\overline{AB}$ in the first figure, as shown here. Also

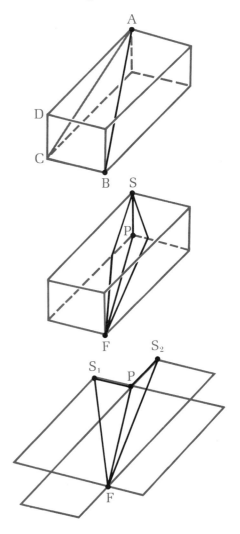

give the dimensions of your room.) Is $\overline{AB}$ the side of a triangle in the figure? What line segment could be added to the figure so that it would be? (Any face diagonal from either A or B, such as $\overline{AC}$.) What kind of triangle is △ABC? Why? (A right triangle. Assuming that $\overline{BC} \perp$ plane ADC, $\overline{BC} \perp \overline{CA}$ since, if a line is perpendicular to a plane, it is perpendicular to every line in the plane that passes through the point of intersection.)

Guide your students in finishing the problem by applying the Pythagorean Theorem to △ABC and △ADC. Since the final calculation with the actual dimensions of your room is to find the square root of a rather large number, I suggest settling for a rough estimate and then giving the students a more precise answer, which you determined in advance.

Your students might enjoy the following exercise as well:

Suppose a spider is at point A and a fly is sound asleep at point B. The spider wants to get to the fly by the shortest possible route but is reluctant to crawl along the cord. It prefers to stay on the walls (including the ceiling and floor) of the room. Can you figure out what path it should take? (Label the corners of the second figure S and F.)

Someone will probably suggest that the spider either crawl along an edge to an adjacent corner and then diagonally across a wall or vice versa. For example, along $\overline{SP}$ and $\overline{PF}$. Explain that the third figure represents the room with the ceiling removed and the walls folded out flat (or with the floor removed if it has been suggested that the spider crawl on the ceiling; in this case the third figure should be drawn accordingly). When the path is drawn on the flattened figure (it could be either $\overline{S_1P}$, $\overline{PF}$ or $\overline{S_2P}$, $\overline{PF}$), it will be obvious that it is not actually the shortest. Since $\overline{S_1F}$ and $\overline{S_2F}$ are not necessarily the same length, some calculations are necessary to determine which is shorter. Both paths might be added to the second figure as shown. An amusing way to conclude is to try to trace the spider's shortest route in your room. (There are actually two but, unless you have a very sharp class, it may be wise not to call attention to this.)

Transparency 15-4 is for use in discussing the Set II exercises of Lesson 1.

Lesson 2 can be assigned for individual study.

Lesson 3
Prisms

(Show Transparency 15-5.) This photograph is of crystals of iron pyrite found in Spain. Do you recognize their basic shape? (They consist of interlocking cubes of various sizes.) Many minerals have crystals in the shape of polyhedra. Transparency 15-6 shows the dust jacket and a page from Introduction to Crystal Geometry, by Martin J. Buerger (McGraw-Hill, 1971).

The intersections of the cubes within the pyrite crystal are quite intricate. Can you imagine what the intersections of a cube with a simple plane would look like? To find out, let's try drawing some of them. (Hand out dittoed copies of Transparency 15-7.)

The intersections of a geometric solid and various planes are called its cross sections. If a cube is cut by a plane parallel to one of its faces, its cross section would have the shape of a square. For example, if the plane passed through the midpoints of four parallel edges of the cube, the cross section would look like this. (Draw the square shown in the first figure here.)

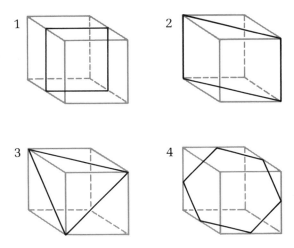

What other simple shapes could a cross section of a cube have? (The other three figures shown here illustrate some interesting ones: a rectangle, an equilateral triangle, and a regular hexagon. Models of these, especially the hexagonal cross section, would be helpful. This photograph shows a set that I made from poster board and tape. The edge length of each cube is 8 cm.)

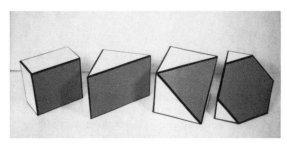

Which of these cross sections do you suppose has the greatest area? If the edge of the cube is 8 cm, find the exact area of each. (Square: 64 sq cm, rectangle: $64\sqrt{2}$ sq sm, equilateral triangle: $32\sqrt{3}$ sq cm, regular hexagon: $48\sqrt{3}$ sq cm. Of these four cross sections, the rectangle has the greatest area.)

Transparency 15-8 is for use in discussing the Set III exercise of Lesson 2. Students who find this interesting may want to read Four-Dimensional Geometry, by Richard F. Marr, a booklet in the Houghton Mifflin Mathematics Enrichment Series, 1970.

To introduce Lesson 3, you might show some models of prisms and ask what they seem to have in common. For example, I use a triangular glass prism, an unsharpened hexagonal pencil (that does not have an eraser), and an octangular jigsaw puzzle box. These are all right prisms with regular polygon bases. Your students should observe that each prism has two faces that are essentially different from the rest; these two are congruent and parallel. The edges joining the corresponding vertices of these faces are, in each case, parallel. Transparency 15-9 and its overlay should make the general definition of "prism" clear.

Lesson 4
The Volume of a Prism

"Put a tiger in your tank"

Several years ago, one of the gasoline companies had the advertising slogan "Put a tiger in your tank." (Show Transparency 15-10 with Overlay A.) Although it was not intended that this slogan be taken literally, let's see what would happen if we did. Here is a picture of the tiger hiding rather reluctantly behind the tank. For his sake, let's suppose that it contains water rather than gasoline.

If the tiger was put in the tank (remove Overlay A and add Overlay B), the level of the water would rise. Although you may never have thought about it, the same thing happens when someone dives into a swimming pool. Suppose the tank is in the shape of a rectangular solid that is 12 ft long and 10 ft wide and that the water is 8 ft deep. If the tiger is completely submerged, can you figure out by how much the level of the water would rise? (Someone should observe that this depends upon how big the tiger is: more specifically, what his volume is. This will provide an opportunity to discuss what we mean by "volume.")

(Remove Overlay B.) How could you find the volume of water in the tank before the tiger was put in it? (After someone has suggested that we multiply the given dimensions, add Overlay C to show why this is correct.) It seems reasonable to assume that the volume of any rectangular solid could be found by multiplying its dimensions. (Remove Overlay C and add Overlay B again.) With this in mind, what is the volume of the water displaced by the tiger? (120x cu ft.) The volume of water that the tiger displaces is equal to the volume of the tiger himself. Suppose the tiger's volume is 15 cu ft. How much would the level of the water rise? (120x = 15, so x = 1/8 ft = 1.5 in. The water would rise only 1.5 in.)

(Show Transparency 15-11.) It is easy to imagine how the volume of a rectangular solid, such as the one shown at the left, might be found by dividing it into cubes. This method won't work very well for the other two prisms shown here because they are oblique and, in the one at the right, the bases are not even rectangular. To discover a method for finding the volume of prisms that are not rectangular solids, we will have to think of something other than counting cubes.

If the first prism were cut into thin slices and the slices pushed toward the right, it would look very much like the second prism. (A nice way to demonstrate this is to place two reams of 8.5"x11" paper in a stack to represent a rectangular solid—then shove the stack so that it tilts to one side.) Although this prism does not have the same shape as the original one, it has the same volume, base, and altitude. This implies that the volume of an oblique prism with a rectangular base can be found by the same formula as that for a rectangular solid: lwh. Slicing the prism in this way suggests a way of finding the volume of the third prism. (Slide Overlay B up Transparency 15-11 to illustrate its cross sections. Note that they are congruent to the base. Then replace Overlay B with Overlay A, consider Cavalieri's Principle, and show how it implies that, if the bases of the three prisms have equal areas and their altitudes are the same, they must have equal volumes. Note that Cavalieri's Principle is an assumption about volume, not something that we will prove.) From Cavalieri's Principle, it seems reasonable that the volume of any prism can be found by multiplying the area of its base by the length of its altitude. If we assume that this general method is valid, then the formula for the volume of a rectangular solid follows as a special case.

Transparency 15-12 can be used to compare some of the basic area and volume formulas.

Transparency 15-13 is for use in discussing the Set III exercise of Lesson 3. Two interesting articles about the use of computers to develop pictures of three-dimensional objects are "Computer Displays" by Ivan E. Sutherland (Scientific American, June 1970) and "Computer Graphics in Architecture" by Donald P. Greenberg (Scientific American, May 1974).

Lesson 5
Pyramids

Pyramid power

(Show Transparency 15-14.) This photograph shows Mr. Patrick Flanagan sitting in front of his Cheops Pyramid Tent. The tent is supposed to be a good place for transcendental meditation and yoga because it surrounds its occupants with energy. Mr. Flanagan believes that the shape of the tent, a square pyramid, "acts as a focus or lens, through which flows energy created by the earth's magnetic field. "*

The tent is named after Cheops (also called Khufu), one of the ancient Egyptian pharoahs, for whom the Great Pyramid was built more than forty centuries ago. Many other pyramids have been built in Egypt as well as in other places including Africa, Italy, Mexico, and India. Although they vary greatly in size, they all have square bases and triangular faces that meet at a point at the top. To become acquainted with some of the properties of one of these pyramids, we will make a small model of one.

(For this exercise, each student will need a pair of scissors and one copy each of patterns A and B, on Worksheets 10 and 11, which should be printed on cover stock. A glue stick would be useful but is not essential.)

Pattern A can be cut and folded to form the base and three lateral faces of a regular square pyramid, along with a vertical cross section through its vertex. The dimensions of the model are approximately 1/3600 those of the Great Pyramid. If its base is glued to a sheet of paper, it can be unfolded and kept in a notebook. Transparency 15-15 shows how it might be labeled.

After noting how the lengths in the pyramid are related by the Pythagorean Theorem, Pattern B can be used to discover the relationship of the volume of a pyramid to that of a prism having the same base and altitude. After the pattern has been cut out, it can be folded into three square pyramids (they are not regular because their lateral edges are not equal), which can, in turn, be folded toward each other to form a cube. Transparency 15-16 illustrates how this can be done. Note that the three pyramids seem to be identical, so they have equal volumes. Since they can be folded together to form a cube, its volume is three times that of each pyramid. Hence the volume of one of the pyramids is one-third that of the cube. Because the cube and pyramids have equal bases and altitudes, the volume of one of the pyramids is evidently one-third the product of the area of its base and the length of its altitude.

Transparency 15-17 and its overlay can be used to present the definition of the general pyramid.

Lesson 6
Cylinders and Cones

Some sand-pile geometry

(Show Transparency 15-18.) If a bag of sand is slowly poured onto the ground, it will form a pile in the shape of a cone. The height of the cone depends upon the type of sand that forms it: smooth sand from a

---

*Time magazine, October 8, 1973.

beach and rough sand from a gravel-pit will produce cones with different shapes. Can you figure out which kind of sand would produce the steeper cone? (The coarser the sand, the steeper the cone it produces. This is because the forces of friction within the cone are stronger, preventing it from being spread out so much by the influence of gravity.)

Now suppose that equal volumes of the two types of sand formed cones such that the diameter of the base of the second is twice that of the first. How do you think their heights would compare? The two cones shown in the figure are not necessarily drawn to scale. (Give your students some time to think about this. They will probably decide that the height of the second cone would be half that of the first.)

To be sure of our conclusion, it would be helpful to have a formula for the volume of a cone. What geometric solid do these cones seem very much like? (After someone has observed that they are like pyramids, add Overlay A to Transparency 15-18.) In this figure, the circular base of the cone has been replaced by a regular polygon inscribed within it. Recall that, as the number of sides of a regular polygon inscribed in a circle is increased, the polygon looks more and more like the circle itself. We used this fact to develop formulas for the circumference and area of a circle. In a similar way, as the number of sides of the base of a regular pyramid is increased, the pyramid looks more and more like a cone. We can use this fact to develop a formula for the volume of a cone.

(After doing this, go back to the problem of the two sand piles and show that, if the two have equal volumes and the diameter of the base of the second is twice that of the first, its height would actually be one-fourth that of the first. Remove Overlay A and add Overlay B.)

$$V_1 = \frac{1}{3}\pi r_1^2 h_1 \text{ and } V_2 = \frac{1}{3}\pi r_2^2 h_2$$

If $V_1 = V_2$ and $r_2 = 2r_1$,

$$\frac{1}{3}\pi r_1^2 h_1 = \frac{1}{3}\pi (2r_1)^2 h_2 ,$$

so

$$r_1^2 h_1 = 4 r_1^2 h_2$$

and

$$h_2 = \frac{1}{4}h_1.$$

Lesson 7
Spheres

First Day

Here is another good puzzle by Julius Sumner Miller.

You know how very light cork is. When you have a cork stopper in hand—just now taken out of a bottle—it weighs practically nothing. If thrown into a bowl of water it floats hardly submerged. The stuff is very, very light. So—quick now—we have a ball of cork—a sphere of cork—5 feet in diameter. Question: What does it weigh? Could you lift it? No calculations! Just give us a quick guess. *

(Show Transparency 15-19 and ask each student to write his guess down before continuing.) In order to figure out what a ball of cork 5 feet in diameter would actually weigh, we need to know two things: the density of cork—that is, how much a given volume of it weighs—and, how to find the volume of a sphere.

One cubic inch of cork weighs about 0.14 ounce. To find out how many cubic inches of cork there would be in a ball 5 feet in diameter, we need a formula for the volume of a sphere.

(Show the top half of Transparency 15-20.) We know that the area of a circle is a little more than three times the square of its radius: more precisely, πr^2. Would you expect the volume of a sphere to also be measured in terms of the square of its radius? (No. Since volume is measured in cubic units, it should be some number times the cube of the radius; that is, $? r^3$.) To find this number, we can use Cavalieri's Principle.

(Show first the lower left figure on Transparency 15-20, then the lower right figure, then Transparency 15-21 and its overlay, and finally Transparency 15-22 while developing the volume formula as is done on page 612 of the text. Before adding the overlay to Transparency 15-21, ask your students to try to imagine what sort of geometric solid might have the second set of cross sections.)

---

*From Millergrams I, by Julius Sumner Miller (Doubleday, 1970). Used by permission.

After finishing the derivation, show Transparency 15-20 again and note that we have found the number we were looking for: it is $\frac{4}{3}\pi$. Then return to Transparency 15-19 and find the volume and weight of the cork ball.

Since the diameter of the ball is 5 feet, its radius is 2.5 feet or 30 inches.

$$V_{ball} = \frac{4}{3}\pi(30)^3 = 36,000\pi$$
$$\approx 113,000 \text{ cubic inches.}$$

Since one cubic inch of cork weighs about 0.14 ounce, the ball would weigh

$$113,000(0.14) = 15,820 \text{ ounces,}$$

or almost half a ton!

The derivation of the formula for the surface area of a sphere may be either assigned for individual study or considered in a second lesson.

Transparencies 15-23 and 15-24 are for use in discussing the Set II and Set III exercises of Lesson 6.

Second Day

In yesterday's lesson we found the weight of a ball of cork, an extremely light substance. Today we will find the weight of a speck of one of the heaviest substances known.

An American astronomer recently discovered, from photographs taken through one of the telescopes on Mount Palomar, a star that is so dense that one cubic inch of it is estimated to weigh more than 1600 tons!*

Suppose we had a speck of dust from this star that was spherical in shape and had a radius of just one-hundredth of an inch. Can you figure out about how many pounds it would weigh? (Show Transparency 15-25.)

The volume of the speck would be

$$\frac{4}{3}\pi\left(\frac{1}{100}\right)^3 \text{ cubic inches}$$

and its weight would be

$$\frac{4}{3}\pi\left(\frac{1}{100}\right)^3(1600)(2000) \approx 13 \text{ pounds.}$$

Transparency 15-26 and its overlays are for use in developing the formula for the surface area of a sphere.

---

*Dinsmore Alter, Clarence H. Cleminshaw, and John G. Phillips, <u>Pictorial Astronomy</u>, 4th ed. (Crowell, 1974), p. 167.

Lesson 8
Similar Solids

A giant can of Campbell's soup

An amusing way to introduce this lesson is with a large wastebasket that has been painted to look like a can of soup or soda. The photograph on Transparency 15-27 shows a large Campbell's Soup can that I bought at a novelty store. An actual can of soup stands beside it.

Although this giant can is a wastebasket, it looks very much like a can of Campbell's soup. It is about five times as tall as an actual can and has about five times its diameter. As a result, the two cans, giant and genuine, have the same shape. (Show Transparency 15-27.) Without knowing the actual dimensions of either can, can you figure out how many times larger the label of one is than the other? (The labels, unrolled flat, have the shape of similar rectangles with areas of πdh and $\pi(5d)(5h) = 25\pi dh$. Hence the label of the larger can has 25 times the area of that of the smaller one.)

Can you figure out how the volumes of the two cans compare? (The cans have the shape of right cylinders. If the volume of the smaller one is $\pi r^2 h$, the volume of the larger is $\pi(5r)^2(5h) = 125\pi r^2 h$. The volume of the larger can is 125 times that of the smaller one.)

The actual can of soup weighs $10\frac{3}{4}$ oz and costs 14¢. If the giant can were filled with soup, how much do you think it would weigh and cost? (Having 125 times the volume of the small can, it is reasonable to think that it would weigh 125 times as much, or about 84 lb. If it also costs 125 times as much, it would cost $17.50.)

Suppose an even larger can, still similar in shape to the small one, was ten times as tall. How many times bigger do you think its label, weight, and cost would be? (After your students have thought about this, develop the following general formulas for two similar cylinders before discussing the answers.)

If two right cylinders are similar and have altitudes h_1 and h_2 and bases of radii r_1 and r_2,

$$\frac{h_1}{h_2} = \frac{r_1}{r_2}.$$

The ratio of their lateral areas is

$$\frac{2\pi r_1 h_1}{2\pi r_2 h_2} = (\frac{r_1}{r_2})(\frac{h_1}{h_2}) = (\frac{h_1}{h_2})^2.$$

The ratio of their volumes is

$$\frac{\pi r_1^2 h_1}{\pi r_2^2 h_2} = (\frac{r_1}{r_2})^2 (\frac{h_1}{h_2}) = (\frac{h_1}{h_2})^3.$$

Hence the larger can, being 10 times as tall as the smaller can, has a label with $10^2 = 100$ times the area and a volume $10^3 = 1000$ times as great. It would weigh about 670 lb and would cost $140.

Show Transparency 15-28 and point out that these theorems hold true, not just for similar cylinders, but for any pair of similar solids. It may be helpful to point out that the area ratio is found by squaring and that the volume ratio is found by cubing; this is easy to remember since area and volume are measured in square units and cubic units, respectively.

Lesson 9
Euler's Theorem

The hidden animals

(Show the top half of Transparency 15-29.) It has been estimated that there may be as many as 30,000 animals living in each square foot of forest land! These animals are called cryptozoa, which means "hidden animals."* You may be able to detect some of them in this drawing, which shows a region extending several inches above and below the surface of the ground. (Show the bottom half of Transparency 15-29.) This drawing shows the creatures in the figure above, apart from their environment. The larger ones are: a) a snail, b) a sow bug, c) a slug, d) an earthworm, e) a millipede, and f) a centipede. The smaller ones include mites, roundworms, and a variety of other insects.

Two characteristics of these creatures are their tiny size—most are less than 5 mm long—and the fact that they always live where it is damp. One of the most serious problems for any very small creature is loss of

water by evaporation. It is easy to show, using geometry, that the smaller the animal is the more acute this problem becomes.

(Show Transparency 15-30.) This figure represents three bugs having lengths of 3, 2, and 1 mm, respectively. If they all have the same shape—in other words, if they are similar—how do their surface areas compare? (9 to 4 to 1.) How do their volumes compare? (27 to 8 to 1.)

The rate at which an animal loses water by evaporation depends upon both its surface area and its volume. The greater the surface area, the faster the evaporation rate. And the greater the volume, the faster the evaporation rate because the larger the animal is, the more water it contains. But, as we have seen, as the size of an animal changes, its surface area and volume do not change at the same rate.

(Add the overlay to Transparency 15-30.) This is easier to see in a set of cubes. Suppose three cubes have edges of lengths 3, 2, and 1 unit, respectively. Find the ratio of the surface area to the volume for each cube. (The ratios are 2, 3, and 6, respectively. In general, if the edge of a cube has length e, its surface area/volume ratio is

$$\frac{6e^2}{e^3} = \frac{6}{e}.$$

As e gets smaller, the ratio $\frac{6}{e}$ gets larger.)

We see that, for a given amount of volume, the smallest cube has three times as much surface area as the largest one. Thinking in terms of bugs rather than cubes, for a given amount of water, the smallest bug has three times as much surface area from which it can evaporate as the largest bug has. It is no wonder that many very tiny insects stay underground; if they were to remain in the direct rays of the sun very long, they would dry out and die.

Transparency 15-31 is for use in introducing Lesson 9. The photograph at the top was taken through an electron microscope and shows particles of a virus enlarged about 58,000 times. Note the double shadows of the particles and the constancy of their shape. A geometric solid that casts shadows exactly like these particles is pictured at the bottom of Transparency 15-31. It is called an icosahedron and, because its shadows match those of the virus, biologists think that the particles of the virus are in

*The pictures and information in the lesson are from "Hidden Lives" by Theodore H. Savory, Scientific American, July 1968, pp. 108-114.

the shape of tiny icosahedra. Models like those shown on page 624 of the text would be helpful in introducing the other regular polyhedra.

Transparency 15-32 is for use in discussing Exercise 3 of Set II, Lesson 8.

Review of Chapter 15

The geometry of smell

A Roman poet and philosopher named Lucretius speculated two thousand years ago that the sense of smell is based upon geometry. He thought that every substance that has an odor gives off tiny particles of a specific shape. When these particles enter a person's nose, they fit into certain pores that match their shape. The pores into which the particles fit enable the person to identify the substance from which they came.

Modern scientists now think that Lucretius' theory is correct. An article in Scientific American several years ago described several experiments that support the idea that the sense of smell can be explained in terms of the geometry of molecules.* (Show Transparency 15-33.) There seem to be seven basic odors, as listed in this table. Each of the first five is associated with molecules of a particular geometric shape. (Show Transparency 15-34.) These figures show perspective, top, and side views of the receptor sites for these five odors. The

camphoraceous site is hemispherical in shape. The site corresponding to the odor of musk is shaped like a right cylinder. Those for floral and pepperminty odors are more complex in shape, whereas the ethereal site is long and rod-shaped. (Add the overlay to Transparency 15-34.) These diagrams represent molecules that fit each of the five sites.

The two basic odors not shown here, pungent and putrid, are determined not by the shape of the molecule but rather by its charge. Pungent odors, such as that of vinegar, are caused by positively charged molecules, whereas putrid odors are caused by molecules that are negatively charged.

(Show Transparency 15-35.) It appears that all odors can be explained in terms of the seven basic ones. For example, the odor of almonds is a combination of camphoraceous, floral, and pepperminty odors. Molecules that possess this odor can fit any one of the three sites (actually two of them in the floral site). A remarkable consequence of this theory is that, by putting their knowledge of three-dimensional geometry to use, chemists have been successful in synthesizing substances having various odors simply by producing molecules of the right shape.

Models of the sequence of polyhedra illustrated in the Set III exercise of Lesson 9 are shown on page 40 of a beautifully illustrated book titled Shapes, Space, and Symmetry, by Alan Holden (Columbia University Press, 1971). A comparable sequence beginning with an icosahedron and ending with a dodecahedron is shown on page 41 of this book. Either or both of these sequences would make a handsome set of models for your classroom.

---

*This lesson and its illustrations are adapted from that article: "The Stereochemical Theory of Odor" by John E. Amoore, James W. Johnston, Jr., and Martin Rubin, Scientific American, February 1964, pp. 42-49.

Chapter 16

NON-EUCLIDEAN GEOMETRIES

Lesson 1
Geometry on a Sphere

Before beginning to teach this unit, it may be helpful to read the following:

Mathematics in Western Culture by Morris Kline (Oxford University Press, 1953), Chapter 26, "New Geometries, New Worlds."

What is Mathematics? by Richard Courant and Herbert Robbins (Oxford University Press, 1941), Chapter 4, Section 9, "Axiomatics and Non-Euclidean Geometry."

(Show Transparency 16-1.) Here is a map on which the cities of San Francisco and Tokyo have been located. If a ship sailed from one city to the other, it seems reasonable that it should travel along a straight line as shown here (add Overlay A to Transparency 16-1). The distance along this path is about 5650 miles.

Gerardus Mercator, the Flemish cartographer who devised the method of mapping the earth used here, wrote:

If you wish to sail from one port to another, here is a chart, and a straight line on it, and if you follow this line carefully you will certainly arrive at your destination. But the length of the line may not be correct. You may get there sooner or may not get there as soon as you expected but you will certainly get there.*

---

*From Mapping by David Greenhood (University of Chicago Press, 1964), p. 128.

Mercator was referring to a problem that many people are not aware of when they look at a map such as his. It would seem that any other path between Tokyo and San Francisco would be longer than the one we have drawn, yet here is a path (add Overlay B to Transparency 16-1) that is significantly shorter! Can you explain how this can be?

Since these paths are on the surface of a sphere, neither one is straight. Both, in fact, are arcs of circles. Strange as it may seem, the shorter arc is part of a larger circle than the longer one. (Show the top figure on Transparency 16-2.) Here are two points, A and B, joined by three arcs numbered 1, 2, and 3. Which arc is shortest? (Arc 1.) How does the circle of which it is a part compare with the other circles? (It is the largest.) If you could not draw a straight line through points A and B, but could only draw a circle, what would you do to make the arc from A to B as short as possible? (Make the circle as large as possible.)

(Show the bottom figure on Transparency 16-2.) Because Tokyo and San Francisco are on the surface of a sphere, we cannot draw a straight line along it from one point to the other. We will have to settle for a circle instead. How should we choose it to make the arc from A to B as short as possible? (Choose the largest possible circle through A and B that lies on the surface of the sphere; namely, the circle whose radius is the same as that of the sphere. Add the overlay to Transparency 16-2 and explain the idea of a great circle.)

Transparency 16-3 can be used to develop the rest of Lesson 1 as is done on pages 637-638 of the text.

Lesson 2
The Saccheri Quadrilateral

What if the world were...?

Mr. Joseph N. Portney has designed a very attractive set of 9" x 12" posters on the theme "What if the world were...?" There are twelve posters in the set, showing photographs of models of an earth that is flat, cubical, dodecahedral, pyramidal, cylindrical, conical, toroidal, hyperboloidal, hyperbolic paraboloidal, oblate spheroidal, "Wegeneroidal," and "cataclysmal." The price of the set is $6.00 and it can be ordered directly from Mr. Portney, 4981 Amigo Ave., Tarzana, Calif., 91356.

You might show the following posters from this set—flat, dodecahedral, conical, toroidal, and cataclysmal—and ask your students the following questions.

You know that the shortest path between two points in a plane is the line segment joining them. What is the shortest path between two points on a sphere? (An arc of a great circle.) What do you think the shortest path between two points on the surfaces of each of these other solids would be? (Transparency 16-4 is for use in illustrating some of the paths. If the flat earth is a one-sided disk, every path joining two points is obviously a line segment. For each of the others, the path depends upon the relative positions of the two points. For example, on the cone it could be a line segment, an arc of a circle, an arc of another curve, or a combination of a segment and an arc. The problem of finding the shortest path between two points on the cataclysmal surface is overwhelmingly complex.)

It is apparent that geometries on surfaces such as these would be quite complex. Although some of the ideas in the lesson dealing with geometry on the surface of a sphere may seem strange to you, they are relatively simple in comparison. (A brief review of lines, polar points, and parallels is probably in order before discussing Lesson 1.)

After you have explained what biperpendicular and Saccheri quadrilaterals are, you might use Transparency 16-5 to introduce the theorems about them.

Lesson 3
The Geometries of Lobachevsky and Riemann

The American geometer Paul Kelly has pointed out a valuable lesson to be learned from studying non-Euclidean geometry.

From early school days we get used to the Euclidean explanation of space, and for ordinary problems this system of ideas works—indeed, it works so satisfactorily that we regard it as the "true" system, and we tend to feel an ingrained disbelief in non-Euclidean geometry. Now each person is a kind of system of beliefs, emotions, attitudes, and so forth, picked up from his parents, teacher, society, and experiences in general, and, for him, in ordinary circumstances, this system "works." As a result he tends to regard his system as "true," and to view with suspicion, perhaps even with contempt or disbelief, any personal philosophy, ... or culture that differs from his own, such as those of foreigners or of people in a different stratum of society. Achieving a genuine understanding of someone radically different from oneself is thus seen to be emotionally parallel to achieving a genuine understanding of the possibility of our world's being closer to some non-Euclidean model than to a Euclidean one. *

Show Transparency 16-6, which illustrates the relationships between Euclidean geometry and the two non-Euclidean geometries that we will briefly explore in this and the following lesson. Riemannian Highway is drawn separately from the other two roads well before the junction because the geometry it represents diverges from Euclidean and Lobachevskian geometries long before the adoption of a postulate about parallels. In our study of geometry, we have traveled along Euclidean Boulevard a long distance past the junction. Now we are, in effect, returning to the junction so that we can travel a short way along each of the other highways in order to see what the scenery along them looks like. Before the

---

*A thesis proposed by Professor Paul Kelly in Mathematical Circles Revisited by Howard W. Eves (Prindle, Weber and Schmidt, 1971), p. 83.

nineteenth century, it was assumed that Euclidean Boulevard was the "only way to go"—that no other roads existed. Since Lobachevskian Highway is merged with Euclidean Boulevard until they separate at the junction, we will do most of our exploring along it.

(Show Transparency 16-7 and its overlays; explain that, in each case, either statement can be proved to follow from the other.) We will not attempt to do this because it would be beyond the scope of an elementary course. Since the fact that the summit angles of a Saccheri quadrilateral are acute in Lobachevskian geometry leads much more easily and quickly to interesting results than the Lobachevskian parallel postulate does, we will begin with it instead.

Transparency 16-8 is for use in discussing the Set III exercise of Lesson 2.

Lesson 4
The Triangle Angle Sum Theorem Revisited

Mercury's strange behavior

Sir Isaac Newton, one of the greatest scientists of all time, was strongly influenced by Euclid. Of his book, the Principia, which is modeled after Euclid's Elements, the Encyclopedia Britannica says: "It explained for the first time the way in which a single mathematical law could account for phenomena of the heavens, the tides, and the motions of objects on the earth. The whole development of modern science begins with this great book."

The Principia was published in 1687. One hundred fifty years later a French astronomer made a surprising discovery about the planet Mercury. (Show the top figure on Transparency 16-9.) This figure, greatly exaggerated to make it easier to see, represents the orbit of Mercury about the sun. In the course of each revolution, the orbit shifts very slightly. This is strange because, according to Newton's laws of gravity, Mercury's orbit shouldn't do this. (Show the lower-left figure on Transparency 16-9.) It should be a simple ellipse that remains fixed in space. Instead, Mercury's orbit rotates very slowly, by about 43 seconds of arc each century.

In 1915, Albert Einstein figured out why. (Read the following passages, which are from Chapter 8 of Einstein: The Life and Times, by Ronald W. Clark:

... Thus the universe which Newton had seen, and for which he had constructed his apparently impeccable mechanical laws, was not the real universe but only what he had seen through the misleading spectacles produced by gravity. The law which appeared to have worked out so well had been drawn up for a universe that did not exist, as though a tailor had made a suit for a man he had seen only in a distorting mirror....

Einstein's paper gave not only a corrected picture of the universe but also a fresh set of mathematical laws by which its details could be described.... These laws utilized Riemannian geometry, the need for which had been the direct result of the assumption that light would be deflected by a gravitational field and that the shortest distance between two points in such a field would not, when viewed from outside it, be coincident with a straight line....

Einstein had seen that his assumption of a curvature of light in a gravitational field meant that Euclidean geometry, satisfactory enough when coping with the small distances of everyday life, had to be replaced by something more sophisticated when dealing with the universe....

Einstein used Riemannian geometry to create equations by which the movements of the stars in their courses and the structure of the universe itself could be described....*

(Show the lower-right figure on Transparency 16-9.) Whereas Newton's theory of the universe, based upon Euclidean geometry, predicts an orbit for Mercury that does not match its actual path, Einstein's theory, based upon Riemannian geometry, predicts it perfectly. According to Einstein, the orbit should rotate 43 seconds of arc each century—the very amount that it does!

Because of this and other evidence, Einstein's theory of relativity is generally accepted as correctly explaining the nature of the universe. It seems incredible that it could be based upon a geometry that is non-Euclidean.

_____

*From Einstein: The Life and Times by Ronald W. Clark. Copyright © 1971 by Ronald W. Clark, with the permission of Thomas Y. Crowell Company, Inc., publisher, and The Harold Matson Company, Inc.

Students who are interested in this will enjoy reading Relativity and Cosmology by William J. Kaufmann III (Harper and Row, 1973).

Transparencies 16-10 and 16-11 are for use if you wish to review Lobachevskian Theorems 1 and 2.

Review of Chapter 16

Hamburger stands and stars*

There are more than 2500 McDonald's drive-ins and restaurants in the United States and the number is said to be growing by one each day!** Suppose the president of the McDonald's chain wanted to find out whether his restaurants are distributed uniformly throughout the country. (Show Transparency 16-12.) He might choose a point in the center of the United States—say Kansas City—and decide to count the number of restaurants within 100 miles from this point, 200 miles from it, 300 miles from it, and so on.

Suppose there are 25 McDonald's restaurants within 100 miles of Kansas City. If the restaurants are distributed uniformly throughout the country, how many would you expect to find within 200 miles of Kansas City? (Since the area of a circle varies as the square of its radius, it seems as if there should be four times as many restaurants in the circle whose radius is twice as large. Complete the expected-number column at the bottom of Transparency 16-12. The numbers are: 25, 100, 225, 400, 625, and 900.)

Now suppose that the actual numbers of restaurants turn out to be as shown here. (Add the overlay to Transparency 16-12.) We see that, as we get further and further from Kansas City, the actual numbers of restaurants fall further and further behind what we had expected. Does this mean that the restaurants are not uniformly distributed but are concentrated around Kansas City?

The answer is no! Our calculations were based upon the assumption that the earth's surface is flat, but it is not. It is curved. (Show Transparency 16-13.) These figures represent the sets of points within 1, 2, 3, 4, and 5 units from a given point in a plane and on a sphere. The relationships of the

areas of the circles on the plane are what we assumed in predicting the numbers of McDonald's restaurants at various distances from Kansas City. The areas of a comparable set of circles on the sphere have a different relationship. As their radii increase, their areas do not grow quite as fast. This explains how the restaurants could be uniformly distributed and yet fall short of the numbers we predicted. (The decline in numbers of McDonald's restaurants was actually highly exaggerated in order to make the point more obvious.)

The point to be learned from this story is that, if we assume that something is uniformly distributed over a surface, we can determine whether the surface is flat (Euclidean) or curved (non-Euclidean) by measuring numbers of the thing at varying distances from a given point in the surface. This is one of the methods astronomers have used to try to determine whether physical space is Euclidean or non-Euclidean. Although the problem is now three-dimensional rather than two-dimensional, the principle is the same.

Ratio astronomers at Ohio State University recently finished a five-year survey of radio sources in space.* They have discovered that the farther out in space one looks, the more the number of observed radio sources falls short of what one would expect if space were Euclidean. If we assume that radio sources are uniformly distributed throughout space, one implication that can be drawn is that space is non-Euclidean—specifically, Riemannian—in nature. This, as you may remember, is in agreement with Einstein's theory of relativity.

It would be interesting to know, if there are other intelligent civilizations in the universe, whether they also began with Euclidean geometry as we did. Of course they would call it by a different name. Since, on a small scale, Euclidean geometry seems so obvious, it seems very probable.

It would also be interesting to know how long it took them to realize that there are other geometries, one of which we now think actually fits physical space. It took mankind two thousand years to do so!

Transparencies 16-14 and 16-15 are for use if you wish to review Lobachevskian Theorems 3 and 4.

---

*This story is adapted from one by George Gamow in his book Mr. Tompkins in Paperback (Cambridge University Press, 1965).
**Time magazine, September 17, 1973.

---

*William J. Kaufmann III, Relativity and Cosmology (Harper and Row, 1973), pp. 112-113.

ANSWERS TO EXERCISES

Chapter 1, Lesson 1

The exercises in this lesson are intended to create some controversy. Since some of the answers depend upon how literally the passages are interpreted, the ones listed below are merely my opinion and your students should certainly not be graded according to their extent of agreement with them. In fact, the many disagreements that will arise as your class discusses this lesson will help in motivating the study of deductive reasoning that comprises the rest of the chapter.

Set I

1. True.

2. Not certain. (Mother may have sent boxes of candy to other people as well.)

3. Not certain.

4. True.

5. True (if the sentence "Nobody could understand why we didn't get rid of the dog" is taken literally).

6. Not certain.

7. Not certain. (Perhaps he just wanted to scare him.)

8. Not certain. (Perhaps Muggs was wounded.)

9. True.

10. False.

11. Not certain.

12. Not certain.

13. True. (He said he got nothing out of the class so he did answer the question, even though his answer may not have been honest.)

14. True.

15. Not certain. (In some schools he might be considered a very good speller.)

16. Not certain.

17. Not certain.

18. Not certain (although the statement does seem quite probable).

19. True.

20. Not certain.

Set II

1. Not certain. (Perhaps the sacks were very large.)

2. True.

3. Not certain (although those students who have read The Hobbit know that Gandalf and the wizard are the same person).

4. False. (We do not know this.)

5. Not certain.

6. Not certain. (Perhaps he was thrown into it or jumped into it in fright.)

7. Not certain.

8. Not certain.

9. False.

10. Not certain (but very probable).

11. True (because it says "maybe").

12. Not certain.

13. Not certain.

14. Not certain.

15. False.

16. True.

Set III

This photograph shows an ocean liner, the Morro Castle, washed up on the beach at Asbury Park, New Jersey, in 1934. The ship was still smouldering from a fire in which 134 people died.

Chapter 1, Lesson 2

Set III

1. If God had wanted you to ride on a wheel, he would have given you a bug screen.

2. If God did not give you a bug screen, he does not want you to ride on a wheel.

Chapter 1, Lesson 3

Set III

1. No.

2. Converse: If you're out of beer, you're out of Schlitz. Inverse: If you're not out of Schlitz, you're not out of beer. Contrapositive: If you're not out of beer, you're not out of Schlitz.

3. The converse and inverse are true, whereas the contrapositive is false.

Chapter 1, Lesson 4

Set III

The logic of the ad is not valid. In effect, it says:

> If the world looked like this, you probably wouldn't buy a Volkswagen Station Wagon.
> The world doesn't look like this.
> You will decide to buy a Volkswagen Station Wagon.

To assume that the conclusion necessarily follows is to make the inverse error. To criticize the ad on this account, however, is perhaps unfair. Its intent, obviously, is to be humorous rather than to present a logical argument.

Chapter 1, Lesson 5

Set III

The form of the argument seems to be: a → b, b → c; therefore, a → c. However, the word "nothing" has different meanings in the first and second statements. This is apparent if we replace it with the phrase "having no food to eat." Since the actual form of the first two statements is a → b, c → d, no conclusion follows.

Chapter 1, Lesson 6

Set II

2. Euclid probably meant that a point has no dimensions.

4. Depending upon their geometric sophistication, your students may provide a

wide variety of answers to this. It is appropriate to point out that in mathematics the term "line" is used in a much more restricted sense than it is in everyday speech.

5. This exercise is a challenging one. Among the definitions given for these words in the Random House Dictionary of the English Language are: flat— level, even, or without inequalities of surface; surface— any figure having only two dimensions.

Set III

Humpty Dumpty's assertion that words do not have inherent meanings is certainly true. Alice is bothered by the fact that, if one person decides to assign his own meanings to words, other people will not be able to understand him.

Chapter 1, Lesson 7

Set III

Yes, the rumor may be true. Saying that someone may become a member only if he is a descendant is equivalent to saying that, if someone may become a member, he is a descendant. Franklin had the converse in mind—if someone is a descendant, he may become a member—which is not implied at all.

Chapter 1, Lesson 8

Set II

4.

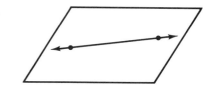

6.

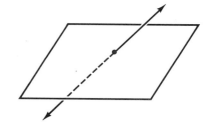

1. Five points: ten lines.

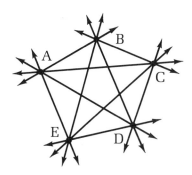

2. Six points: fifteen lines.

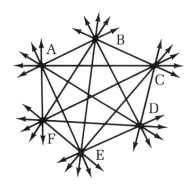

3. Ten points: 45 lines. Most students who answer this correctly will probably do it by observing the pattern of increasing differences.

No. of points	3	4	5	6	7	8	9	10
No. of lines	3	6	10	15				45

$$\underset{3\quad 4\quad 5\quad 6\quad 7\quad 8\quad 9}{}$$

Each additional point results in one more line than the point before it. You might challenge your students to try to discover a formula for the number of lines, ℓ, in terms of the number of points, p. It is:

$$\ell = \frac{p(p-1)}{2}.$$

Chapter 1, Lesson 9

Set III

This proof is not arranged in logical order.
If a proof is not arranged in a logical order, I can't understand it.
If I can't understand a proof, I get dizzy while I study it. (This is the contrapositive of the third statement.)
If I get dizzy while studying it, a proof is giving me trouble.
If I have trouble with a proof, it is not easy.

Theorem. This proof is not easy.

Chapter 1, Lesson 10

Set II

1. To prove that the last answer is false by the indirect method, we must begin by assuming that it is true.

   Suppose the last answer is true. Then the first answer is true since the first and last answers are always the same. It follows that the second answer is false because if the first answer is true, the next one is false. But this contradicts Dilcue's observation that the second answer is true. So the original assumption is false. Hence the last answer is false.

2. We cannot conclude that the stone in Lorelei's ring is a diamond from the first two statements. To use the argument

   If a stone is a diamond, its index of refraction is more than 2.
   The stone in Lorelei's ring has an index of refraction that is more than 2.
   Therefore, the stone in Lorelei's ring is a diamond,

   is to make the converse error. We can use the last three statements, however, to prove indirectly that it is a diamond.

   Proof.

   Suppose the stone is not a diamond. If the stone is not a diamond, its hardness is less than 10. If its hardness is less than 10, it can be scratched by corundum. But this contradicts the fact that it cannot be scratched by corundum.

So, the assumption that the stone is not a diamond is false. It must be a diamond.

Set III

Let n = the number of friends Tarkus actually has.
  1. Emerson says, $n \geq 100$.
  2. Lake says, $n < 100$.
  3. Palmer says, $n \geq 1$.
Suppose Emerson is telling the truth. Then
  1. $n \geq 100$. 2. $n \geq 100$. 3. $n < 1$,
a contradiction. If Lake is telling the truth,
  1. $n < 100$. 2. $n < 100$. 3. $n < 1$,
the statements are consistent. Since $n = 0$, Tarkus doesn't have any friends. Palmer cannot be telling the truth because
  1. $n < 100$. 2. $n \geq 100$. 3. $n \geq 1$
also contains a contradiction.

Chapter 1, Lesson 11

Set III

1. Indirectly.

2. Suppose the two dogs share more than one flea. This contradicts Postulate 1, which says: "For any two fleas, there is exactly one dog that has them." So the supposition is false and the dogs do not share more than one flea.

3. Replace the words "dog" and "flea" with "line" and "point," and we have the theorem stated in Exercise 2 of Set I.

Chapter 1, Review

Set III

1. If a rabbit is over six feet tall, his name is Harvey.
   If a rabbit's name is Harvey, he is invisible.
   If a rabbit is invisible, then only his best friends can see him.
   If only a rabbit's best friends can see him, everyone else will think he is imaginary.
   If he is thought to be imaginary, a rabbit will not be taken seriously.

2. If a rabbit is over six feet tall, he will not be taken seriously.

Chapter 2, Lesson 1

Set III

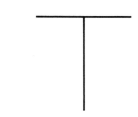

Although the two line segments in the figure are the same length, the vertical one appears to be longer.

Chapter 2, Lesson 2

Set III

The following figure, in which the crows on the fence are represented by points on a line, satisfies all four conditions.

To solve the problem, it is probably easiest to start with the second clue.

Chapter 2, Lesson 3

Set II

*4. In each of these figures, $\overleftrightarrow{HO}$ contains W and $\overline{WL}$ contains O. Statements a and c are the only ones that apply to all four.

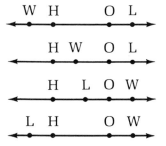

---

*Complete or partial answers are included in the textbook for those exercises marked with an asterisk.

1. No. An angle is a pair of rays that <u>do not lie on the same line.</u>

2. Yes. After the line has bent itself into an angle, it could turn the two sides until they coincide to form just one ray.

3. No. The sides of an angle are <u>rays</u>, not line segments.

Chapter 2, Lesson 4

Set III

The center of the protractor is at A rather than C.

Chapter 2, Lesson 5

Set III

Since the second hand of a clock makes one revolution during 60 seconds of time, it moves

$$\frac{1}{60} \cdot 360^{O} = 6^{O}$$

during one second of time.

Since a degree is equal to 3,600 seconds, it moves

$$6 \cdot 3,600" = 21,600",$$

or 21,600 angular seconds during one second of time.

Chapter 2, Lesson 6

Set II

6. Possible answers:

a)

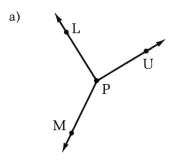

b)

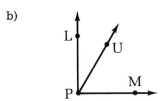

Set III

1.

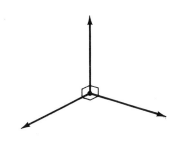

2. No.

Chapter 2, Lesson 7

Set III

If points were atoms and line segments were "strings" of atoms, every line segment would not have exactly one midpoint. Line segments containing an <u>even</u> number of points would have <u>no midpoint</u> because there is no point on them that divides them into two equal segments.

Chapter 3, Lesson 1

Set III

1. "Is older than" is not an equivalence relation because, although it is transitive, it is neither reflexive nor symmetric.

2. "Is the same color as" is an equivalence relation because it possesses all three properties.

3. "Is a friend of" is not an equivalence relation because it is not transitive.

Chapter 3, Lesson 2

Set III

This, of course, is a Moebius strip. Cutting the strip along its center all the way around does not result in two identical loops, but rather just one that is half as wide and twice as long.

Chapter 3, Lesson 3

Set III

This is a proof of the vertical angle theorem. Although I do not know any Chinese, I assume that the following is a fairly accurate translation.

Theorem 3. Vertical angles are equal.

Hypothesis: Lines $\overleftrightarrow{AB}$ and $\overleftrightarrow{CD}$ intersect at point O. $\angle$ AOD and $\angle$ BOC are vertical angles, $\angle$ AOC and $\angle$ BOD are vertical angles.

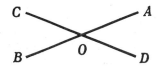

Conclusion: $\angle$ AOD = $\angle$ BOC, $\angle$ AOC = $\angle$ BOD.

Proof: $\angle$ AOD + $\angle$ AOC = 180° (2 right angles)

$\angle$ BOC + $\angle$ AOC = 180°
(They form linear pairs, and angles in a linear pair are supplementary. The sum of the measures of two supplementary angles is 180°.)

∴ $\angle$ AOD + $\angle$ AOC = $\angle$ BOC + $\angle$ AOC (Substitution)

∴ $\angle$ AOD = $\angle$ BOC (Subtraction)

In the same way, $\angle$ AOC = $\angle$ BOD.

You may want to ask your students how this proof differs from the one on page 124. (It, in effect, includes the proof that supplements of the same angle are equal.)

Chapter 3, Lesson 4

Set III

Perhaps two of the slats have breaks in them, as shown in this figure.

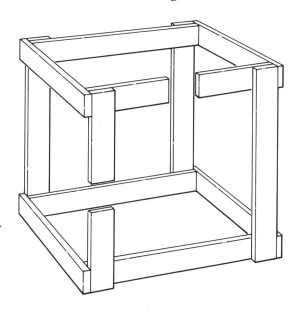

Chapter 3, Lesson 5

Set II

Proof for Exercise 1.

1. $\angle$ 2 and $\angle$ 3 are a linear pair. (Given.)
2. $\angle$ 2 and $\angle$ 3 are supplementary. (If two angles are a linear pair, they are supplementary.)
3. $\angle$ 1 and $\angle$ 3 are supplementary. (Given.)
4. $\angle$ 1 = $\angle$ 2. (Supplements of the same angle are equal.)

Proof for Exercise 2.

1. $\angle$ 1 and $\angle$ 3 are vertical angles. (Given.)
2. $\angle$ 1 = $\angle$ 3. (Vertical angles are equal.)
3. $\angle$ 2 = $\angle$ 3. (Given.)
4. $\angle$ 1 = $\angle$ 2. (Substitution.)
5. $\overrightarrow{NA}$ bisects $\angle$ SNT. (If a ray divides an angle into two equal angles, it bisects it.)

Proof for Exercise 3.

1. $\overrightarrow{HE}$ and $\overrightarrow{HR}$ are opposite rays. (Given.)
2. $\angle$ 1 and $\angle$ 2 are a linear pair. (If two angles have a common side and their other

sides are opposite rays, they are a linear pair.)
3. $\angle 1 = \angle 2$. (Given.)
4. $\angle 1$ and $\angle 2$ are right angles. (If the two angles in a linear pair are equal, then each is a right angle.)
5. $\overleftrightarrow{AT} \perp \overleftrightarrow{ER}$. (If two lines form a right angle, they are perpendicular.)

Proof for Exercise 4.

1. $\overline{OT} \perp \overline{CE}$. (Given.)
2. $\angle OTE$ is a right angle. (If two lines are perpendicular, they form right angles.)
3. $\angle OTE = 90^{\circ}$. (A right angle has a measure of 90°.)
4. $\angle OTE = \angle M$. (Given.)
5. $\angle M = 90^{\circ}$. (Substitution.)
6. $\angle M$ is a right angle. (An angle having a measure of 90° is a right angle.)

Set III

Translation: $\angle AOC$ is a right angle; demonstrate that $\angle 1$ and $\angle 3$ are complementary.

Proof. Since $\angle AOC$ is a right angle, its measure is 90°. Since $\angle AOC = \angle 1 + \angle 2$ (betweenness of rays), $\angle 1 + \angle 2 = 90^{\circ}$. But $\angle 2 = \angle 3$ (vertical angles are equal) so $\angle 1 + \angle 3 = 90^{\circ}$ (substitution). Hence $\angle 1$ and $\angle 3$ are complementary.

Set III

1. The fact that two angles are not vertical angles does not imply that they are a linear pair.

2. It has not been established that $\angle 1 + \angle 2 = 180^{\circ}$.

3. Measure relationships may not be assumed from the figure.

4. It has not been established that $\angle 1$ and $\angle 2$ are right angles.

5. A number has not been added to both members of the previous equation.

6. See step 4.

7. It has not been established that two lines in the figure are perpendicular.

8. See step 4.

9. This is the theorem that is being proved. It cannot be used to prove itself.

Chapter 3, Review

Set II

4.

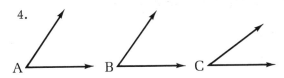

Hypothesis: $\angle A$ and $\angle C$ are complementary, $\angle B$ and $\angle C$ are complementary.
Conclusion: $\angle A = \angle B$.

Proof.

1. $\angle A$ and $\angle C$ are complementary, $\angle B$ and $\angle C$ complementary. (Hypothesis.)
2. $\angle A + \angle C = 90^{\circ}$, $\angle B + \angle C = 90^{\circ}$. (If the sum of the measures of two angles is 90°, they are complementary.)
3. $\angle A + \angle C = \angle B + \angle C$. (Substitution.)
4. $\angle A = \angle B$. (Subtraction.)

Chapter 4, Lesson 1

Set II

1. a) It has rounded corners and two of its sides do not intersect.
   b) It has rounded corners and suggests that a triangle consists of points other than those on its sides.

2. The triangles that are impossible are f and i.

Set III

A good strategy is to first determine which of the twelve polyiamonds will fit in the six corners of the star. Only six will do so, so all of them must be used. One quite efficient method for solving the puzzle is described below.

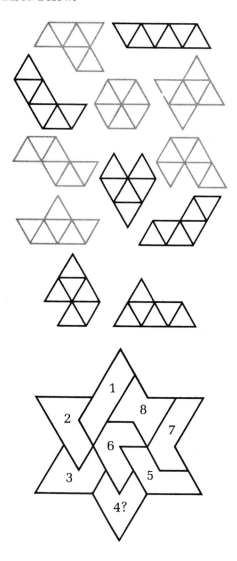

Starting with the polyiamond numbered 1 in this figure and going around the star counterclockwise, the polyiamonds numbered 2 and 3 are the only ones that can occupy their positions. Some trial and error will then reveal that only if polyiamond 4 is placed at the bottom can the rest of the figure be completed. Once this is recognized, the polyiamonds numbered 5, 6, 7, and 8 logically fall into place in that order.

Chapter 4, Lesson 2

Set II

Proof for Exercise 4.
(The purpose of this proof is to reveal how inconvenient it is to prove triangles congruent by means of the definition of congruence.)

1. C is the midpoint of both $\overline{AE}$ and $\overline{NP}$. (Given.)
2. AC = CE and NC = CP. (The midpoint of a line segment divides it into two equal segments.)
3. PE = AN. (Given.)
4. $\overline{PN} \perp \overline{PE}$ and $\overline{PN} \perp \overline{NA}$. (Given.)
5. ∠P and ∠N are right angles. (Perpendicular lines form right angles.)
6. ∠P = ∠N. (Right angles are equal.)
7. ∠PCE and ∠ACN are vertical angles. (Given.)
8. ∠PCE = ∠ACN. (Vertical angles are equal.)
9. ∠A = ∠E. (Given.)
10. △PEC ≅ △NAC. (If there is a correspondence between the vertices of two triangles such that their corresponding sides and angles are equal, the triangles are congruent.)

Set III

The reptile at the lower right is a "mirror image" of the other three.

Chapter 4, Lesson 3

Set II

1. S. A. S.

2. Yes. S. S. S.

3. Yes. A.S.A.

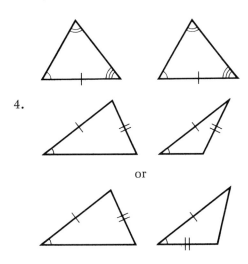

or

Set III

Frameworks a, d, and e are rigid.

Chapter 4, Lesson 4

Set II

Proof for Exercise 1.

1. FL = ET. (Given.)
2. ∠L and ∠T are right angles. (Given.)
3. ∠L = ∠T. (Right angles are equal.)
4. ∠F = ∠E. (Given.)
5. △FLU ≅ △ETU. (A.S.A. postulate.)

Proof for Exercise 2.

1. TU = UB. (Given.)
2. TA = AB. (Given.)
3. AU = AU. (Reflexive.)
4. △ATU ≅ △ABU. (S.S.S. postulate.)
5. ∠T = ∠B. (Corresponding parts of congruent triangles are equal.)

Proof for Exercise 3.

1. △IOA is equilateral. (Given.)
2. OI = OA. (All sides of an equilateral triangle are equal.)
3. ∠1 and ∠2 are a linear pair. (Given.)
4. ∠1 and ∠2 are supplementary. (If two angles are a linear pair, they are supplementary.)
5. ∠2 and ∠3 are supplementary. (Given.)
6. ∠1 = ∠3. (Supplements of the same angle are equal.)
7. PI = AN. (Given.)
8. △PIO ≅ △NAO. (S.A.S. postulate.)

Set III

1. There is not enough given information to make it possible to prove the triangles congruent.

2. Although this proof can be solved, some of the given information is unnecessary.

3. Some of the given information leads to a contradiction.

Chapter 4, Lesson 5

Set II

Proof for Exercise 1.

1. ∠1 and ∠2 are vertical angles. (Given.)
2. ∠1 = ∠2. (Vertical angles are equal.)
3. BM = MZ, EM = MN. (Given.)
4. △BEM ≅ △ZNM. (S.A.S. postulate.)
5. BE = ZN. (Corresponding parts of congruent triangles are equal.)

Proof for Exercise 2.

1. AD ⊥ UD, AD ⊥ DI. (Given.)
2. ∠3 and ∠4 are right angles. (Perpendicular lines form right angles.)
3. ∠3 = ∠4. (Right angles are equal.)
4. AD = AD. (Reflexive.)
5. ∠1 = ∠2. (Given.)
6. △AUD ≅ △AID. (A.S.A. postulate.)
7. AU = AT. (Corresponding parts of congruent triangles are equal.)

Proof for Exercise 3.

1. O is the midpoint of HN. (Given.)
2. HO = ON. (The midpoint of a line segment divides it into two equal segments.)
3. ∠HOD = ∠AON. (Given.)
4. ∠HOD = ∠1 + ∠2, ∠AON = ∠2 + ∠3. (Betweenness of rays.)
5. ∠1 + ∠2 = ∠2 + ∠3. (Substitution.)
6. ∠1 = ∠3. (Subtraction.)
7. OA = OD. (Given.)
8. △AHO ≅ △DNO. (S.A.S. postulate.)

Set III

The map contains a contradiction. It is evident that △POE ≅ △SCE by either S.A.S. or A.S.A. (PE = PE, ∠P = ∠ESC, PO = SC, and ∠POE = ∠SCE). It follows that OE = CE, since corresponding parts of congruent triangles are equal. But according to Dilcue, OE = 13 miles and CE = 15 miles.

Chapter 4, Lesson 6

Set II

Proof for Exercise 1.

1. $\angle J = \angle 1$. (Given.)
2. JU = YU. (If two angles of a triangle are equal, the sides opposite them are equal.)
3. $\angle 2 = \angle L$. (Given.)
4. YU = LY. (Same as step 2.)
5. JU = LY. (Transitive.)

Proof for Exercise 2.

1. SE = EP. (Given.)
2. $\angle 1 = \angle 3$. (If two sides of a triangle are equal, the angles opposite them are equal.)
3. ST = TP. (Given.)
4. $\angle 2 = \angle 4$. (Same as step 2.)
5. $\angle 1 + \angle 2 = \angle 3 + \angle 4$. (Addition.)
6. $\angle$ EST = $\angle 1 + \angle 2$, $\angle$ EPT = $\angle 3 + \angle 4$. (Betweenness of rays.)
7. $\angle$ EST = $\angle$ EPT. (Substitution.)

Proof for Exercise 3.

1. $\angle 1$ and $\angle 2$ are a linear pair, $\angle 3$ and $\angle 4$ are a linear pair. (Given.)
2. $\angle 1$ and $\angle 2$ are supplementary, $\angle 3$ and $\angle 4$ are supplementary. (If two angles are a linear pair, they are supplementary.)
3. $\angle 1 = \angle 4$. (Given.)
4. $\angle 2 = \angle 3$. (Supplements of equal angles are equal.)
5. EF = EB. (If two angles of a triangle are equal, the sides opposite them are equal.)
6. △FEB is isosceles. (A triangle that has two equal sides is isosceles.)

Set III

1. $\angle D = \angle E$. (Given.)
2. DE = EC. (Given.)
3. $\angle C = \angle D$. (If two sides of a triangle are equal, the angles opposite them are equal.)
4. $\angle C = \angle D = \angle E$. (Transitive.)
5. △DEC is equiangular. (A triangle that has three equal angles is equiangular.)

Chapter 4, Lesson 7

Set II

Proof for Exercise 1.

1. AE = AN. (Given.)
2. $\angle 2 = \angle 3$. (If two sides of a triangle are equal, the angles opposite them are equal.)
3. EN = EN. (Reflexive.)
4. $\angle$ WEN = $\angle$ YNE. (Given.)
5. △WEN ≅ △YNE. (A.S.A. postulate.)

Proof for Exercise 2.

1. BO = RA, OG = AG. (Given.)
2. BO + OG = RA + AG. (Addition.)
3. BG = BO + OG, RG = RA + AG. (Betweenness of points.)
4. BG = RG. (Substitution.)
5. $\angle G = \angle G$. (Reflexive.)
6. △BAG ≅ △ROG. (S.A.S. postulate.)
7. $\angle B = \angle R$. (Corresponding parts of congruent triangles are equal.)

Proof for Exercise 3.

1. $\overline{HU}$ and $\overline{NP}$ bisect each other. (Given.)
2. HB = BU, NB = BP. (If a line segment is bisected, it is divided into two equal segments.)
3. $\angle$ HBP = $\angle$ NBU. (Vertical angles are equal.)
4. △HBP ≅ △UBN. (S.A.S. postulate.)
5. $\angle H = \angle U$. (Corresponding parts of congruent triangles are equal.)
6. $\angle 1 = \angle 3$. (Same as step 3.)
7. △HBE ≅ △UBR. (A.S.A. postulate.)

Set III

1. By S.A.S. (HR = HO, $\angle H = \angle H$, and HW = HA.)

2. By S.S.S. (RW = OA, AR = WO, and AW = AW.)

3. Since $\angle$ HAW and $\angle$ RAW are a linear pair, they are supplementary; the same is true of $\angle$ HWA and $\angle$ OWA. It then follows from the fact that $\angle$ RAW = $\angle$ OWA that $\angle$ HAW = $\angle$ HWA. (Supplements of equal angles are equal.)

Chapter 4, Lesson 8

Set II

1. a)

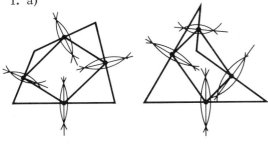

b) In each case, the quadrilateral formed seems to have two pairs of equal and parallel sides.

2. a)

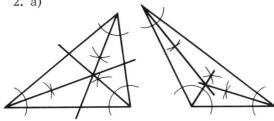

b) In each case, the bisectors of the angles seem to be concurrent.

3. a)

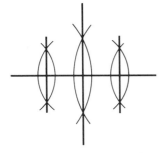

b) Eight.

Although ∡1 and ∡3 still seem to have the same measure, ∡2 seems to be larger.

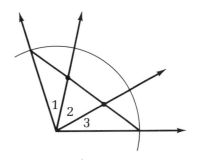

Chapter 4, Review

Set III

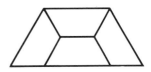

Chapter 5, Lesson 1

Set II

2.

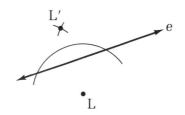

3.

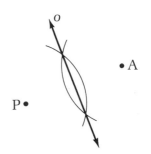

4.

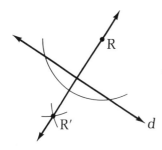

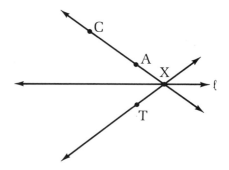

Proof for Exercise 5.

1. M is the reflection of P through $\overleftrightarrow{UA}$. (Given.)
2. $\overleftrightarrow{UA}$ is the perpendicular bisector of $\overline{PM}$. (If one point is the reflection through a line of another point, the line is the perpendicular bisector of the segment that joins the two points.)
3. $\angle$ PUA and $\angle$ MUA are right angles. (Perpendicular lines form right angles.)
4. $\angle$ PUA = $\angle$ MUA. (Right angles are equal.)
5. PU = UM. (If a line segment is bisected, it is divided into two equal segments.)
6. UA = UA. (Reflexive.)
7. $\triangle$PUA $\cong$ $\triangle$MUA. (S. A. S. postulate.)
8. PA = MA. (Corresponding parts of congruent triangles are equal.)

Set III

1. Draw $\overleftrightarrow{CX}$ and label the point in which it intersects line ℓ point X.

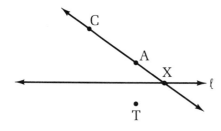

2. Draw $\overleftrightarrow{XT}$. Since C, A, and X are collinear, their reflections through line ℓ are also collinear. Points X and T are the reflections of X and A through line ℓ, so the reflection of C must lie on $\overleftrightarrow{XT}$.

3. Draw $\overleftrightarrow{CT}$ and label the point in which it intersects line ℓ point Y.

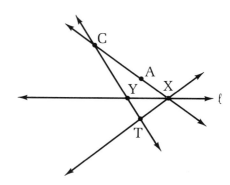

4. Draw $\overleftrightarrow{YA}$. Since C, Y, and T are collinear, their reflections through line ℓ are also collinear. Points Y and T are the reflections of Y and A through line ℓ, so the reflection of C must lie on $\overleftrightarrow{YA}$.

   Since the reflection of C lies on both $\overleftrightarrow{XT}$ and $\overleftrightarrow{YA}$, it must be the point in which they intersect.

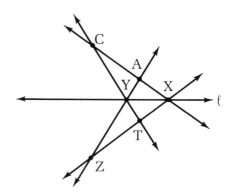

Chapter 5, Lesson 2

Set I

3.

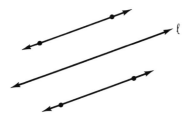

4.

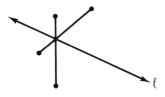

5.

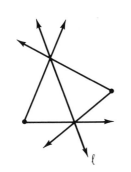

6.

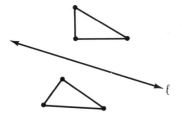

7.

8.

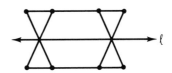

9.

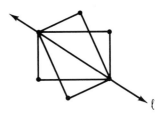

Set II

Proof for Exercise 4.

1. △SIL is the reflection of △VER through line ℓ.
2. SI = VE, IL = ER, and SL = VR. (Reflection of a set of points through a line preserves distance.)
3. △SIL ≅ △VER. (S.S.S. postulate.)

Set III

The remarkable reflection is because the word CHOICE, printed in capital letters, has a horizontal line of symmetry.

Chapter 5, Lesson 3

Set I

3. a)

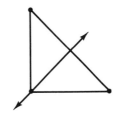

b)

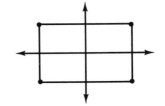

c)

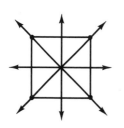

d)

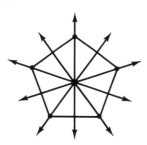

e) None.

f)

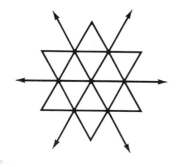

Set II

2.

3.

 ←BOOKIE→

4.

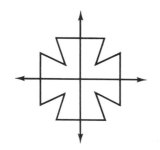

Set III

Merging the two pictures seems to result in a three-dimensional one because the two-dimensional pictures are drawn in slightly different perspectives, just as we would see the actual solid from slightly different perspectives. Line ℓ is <u>not</u> a symmetry line with respect to the pictures. If it were, merging the pictures would not create a three-dimensional illusion.

Chapter 5, Lesson 4

Set II

1. a and b)

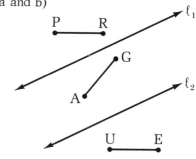

2. a, b, and c)

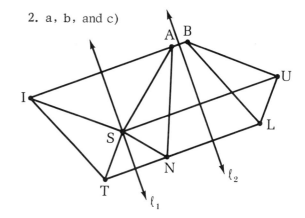

3. b and d)

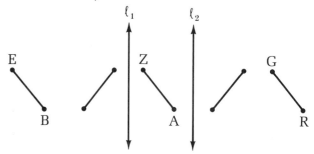

a) 1 inch.
c) ZG = AR = 2 inches.
e) ZE = AB = 2 inches.

4. a)

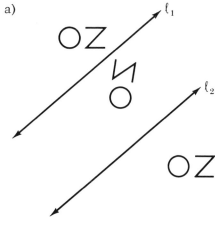

b) The translation image would be at the upper left of OZ.

5. a and b)

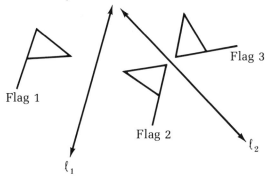

Flag 1

Flag 2

Flag 3

Set III

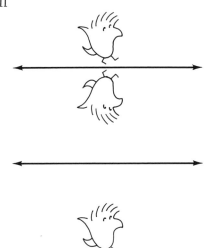

The first line can be any line that is perpendicular to the lines joining the points of the bird to the corresponding points of its translation image. The second line must be the perpendicular bisector of the segments joining the points of the bird's reflection image through the first line to the corresponding points of the bird's translation image.

Chapter 5, Lesson 5

Set I

3. Place the mirrors so that they are vertical with respect to the page and are perpendicular to each other as shown in this figure.

Set II

1. b and c)

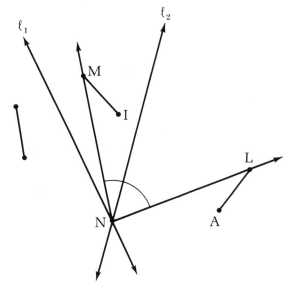

2. a, b, and c)

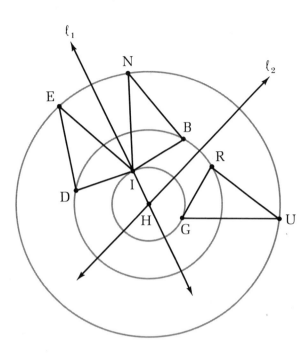

3. a)

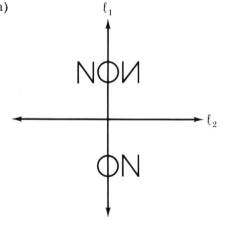

4. a and b)

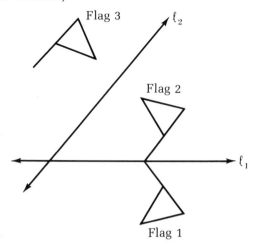

Flag 3

Flag 2

Flag 1

5. c) $\angle ASN = \angle 1 + \angle 2 + \angle 3 + \angle 4$ and
$\angle TSE = \angle 2 + \angle 3$. Since $\angle 1 = \angle 2$ and
$\angle 3 = \angle 4$,
$$\angle ASN = \angle 2 + \angle 2 + \angle 3 + \angle 3$$
$$= 2\angle 2 + 2\angle 3$$
$$= 2(\angle 2 + \angle 3).$$
Hence $\angle ASN = 2\angle TSE$.

Set III

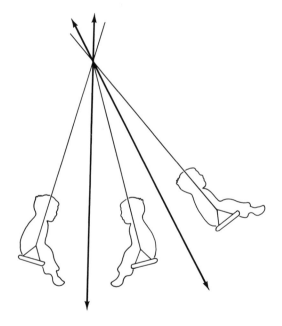

The first line can be any line that passes
through the center of the rotation (the point
in which the lines representing the swing in-

tersect.) The second line must be the perpendicular bisector of the segments joining
the points of the child's reflection image
through the first line to the corresponding
points of the child's rotation image. (Note
that this solution is comparable to that for
the exercise in Set III of Lesson 4.)

Chapter 5, Lesson 6

Set I

4. a and b)

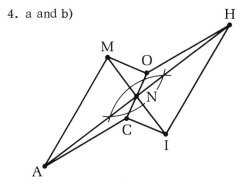

Set II

1. e) The monkey face has a line of symmetry that the fish does not have.

2.

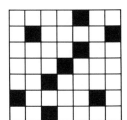

3.

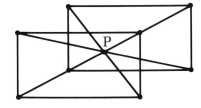

4.

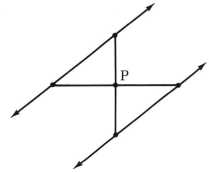

5.

Proof for Exercise 6.

1. Points X and U are the respective reflections of S and I through O. (Given.)
2. O is the midpoint of $\overline{SX}$ and $\overline{IU}$. (If one
   point is the reflection image through a
   given point of another point, the given
   point is the midpoint of the segment that
   joins the two points.)
3. SO = OX and IO = OU. (The midpoint of a
   line segment divides it into two equal segments.)
4. $\angle$ SOI = $\angle$ UOX. (Vertical angles are
   equal.)
5. $\triangle$SIO $\cong$ $\triangle$XUO. (S.A.S. postulate.)
6. $\angle$ S = $\angle$ X. (Corresponding parts of congruent triangles are equal.)

Set III

The message on the sign has point symmetry. As a result, it looks the same when
read upside down.

Chapter 6, Lesson 1

Set II

Proof for Exercise 1.

1. F-L-Y. (Given.)
2. FY = FL + LY. (Betweenness of points.)
3. FY > LY. ("Whole greater than its part"
   theorem.)

Proof for Exercise 2.

1. CR < UR and RE < RV. (Given.)
2. CR + RE < UR + RV. (Addition theorem of inequality.)
3. CE = CR + RE and UV = UR + RV. (Betweenness of points.)
4. CE < UV. (Substitution.)

Proof for Exercise 3.

1. BT = BU. (Given.)
2. ∠TUB = ∠BTU. (If two sides of a triangle are equal, the angles opposite them are equal.)
3. ∠BTN = ∠BTU + ∠UTN. (Betweenness of rays.)
4. ∠BTN > ∠BTU. ("Whole greater than its part" theorem.)
5. ∠BTN > ∠TUB. (Substitution.)

Set III

Put three bricks on one pan and three bricks on the other. If they balance, take them off and weigh the other two to see which one is heavier. If they don't balance, take two of the bricks from the heavier group and weigh them.

Chapter 6, Lesson 2

Set II

Proof for Exercise 1.

1. ∠4 is an exterior angle of △COD. (Given.)
2. ∠4 > ∠2. (An exterior angle of a triangle is greater than either remote interior angle.)
3. ∠1 > ∠4. (Given.)
4. ∠1 > ∠2. (Transitive.)

Proof for Exercise 2.

1. ∠PKE is an exterior angle of △PIK. (Given.)
2. ∠PKE > ∠I. (An exterior angle of a triangle is greater than either remote interior angle.)
3. $\overline{PI} \perp \overline{IK}$. (Given.)
4. ∠I is a right angle. (Perpendicular lines form right angles.)
5. ∠I = 90°. (A right angle has a measure of 90°.)
6. ∠PKE > 90°. (Substitution.)
7. ∠PKE is obtuse. (An angle with a measure of more than 90° is obtuse.)

Proof for Exercise 3.

1. ∠1 and ∠2 are a linear pair, ∠3 and ∠4 are a linear pair. (Given.)
2. ∠1 is an exterior angle of △AHK and ∠3 is an exterior angle of △SHR. (If an angle forms a linear pair with an angle of a triangle, it is an exterior angle of the triangle.)
3. ∠1 > ∠3 and ∠3 > ∠S. (An exterior angle of a triangle is greater than either remote interior angle.)
4. ∠1 > ∠S. (Transitive.)

Set III

1. An "inferior" angle of a triangle forms a pair of vertical angles with one of the angles of the triangle.

2. Three.

3. One possible argument: If Dilcue's Inferior Angle Theorem is true, ∠1 > ∠3 and ∠4 > ∠2. Since ∠1 = ∠2 and ∠3 = ∠4, it follows by substitution that ∠2 > ∠3 and ∠3 > ∠2. But these inequalities contradict each other, so the theorem cannot be true.

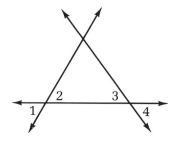

Chapter 6, Lesson 3

Set I

*4. d) The triangles cannot be congruent because the longest side of one is not equal to the longest side of the other. Corresponding parts of congruent triangles are equal.

Set II

Proof for Exercise 1.

1. MI > MW. (Given.)
2. ∠S > ∠SMW. (Given.)

3. MW > SW. (If two angles of a triangle are unequal, the sides opposite them are unequal and the longer side is opposite the larger angle.)
4. MI > SW. (Transitive.)

Proof for Exercise 2.

1. △HIK with IE = IK. (Given.)
2. ∠K = ∠2. (If two sides of a triangle are equal, the angles opposite them are equal.)
3. ∠1 > ∠K. (An exterior angle of a triangle is greater than either remote interior angle.)
4. ∠1 > ∠2. (Substitution.)

Proof for Exercise 3.

1. △SAL is equilateral. (Given.)
2. △SAL is equiangular. (An equilateral triangle is equiangular.)
3. ∠ASL = ∠L. (All angles of an equiangular triangle are equal.)
4. ∠ASL = ∠ASI + ∠ISL. (Betweenness of rays.)
5. ∠ASL > ∠ISL. ("Whole greater than its part" theorem.)
6. ∠L > ∠ISL. (Substitution.)
7. SI > IL. (If two angles of a triangle are unequal, the sides opposite them are unequal and the larger angle is opposite the longer side.)

Set III

The shortest segment would be $\overline{AC}$. $\overline{AC}$ is the shortest side of △ABC since it is opposite the smallest angle. Hence AC < BC. But $\overline{BC}$ is the shortest side of △BCD so BC < CD, etc.

of any two sides of a triangle is greater than the length of the third side.)
4. PO + ON > PD. (Substitution.)

Proof for Exercise 3.

1. CA = CE + EA. (Betweenness of points.)
2. △OCE ≅ △ANE. (Given.)
3. EO = EA. (Corresponding parts of congruent triangles are equal.)
4. CA = CE + EO. (Substitution.)
5. CE + EO > CO. (The sum of the lengths of any two sides of a triangle is greater than the length of the third side.)
6. CA > CO. (Substitution.)

Set III

Reflect the roadrunner through Road 1 and the coyote through Road 2. Draw $\overline{R'C'}$. The two points in which $\overline{R'C'}$ intersects the roads are the points to which the roadrunner should run.

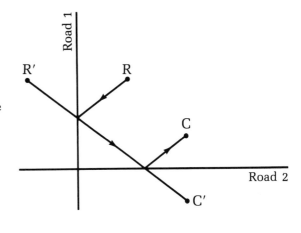

Chapter 6, Lesson 4

Set II

1. ∠1 = ∠3 because vertical angles are equal and ∠3 = ∠2 because reflection of a set of points through a line preserves angle measure. Therefore, ∠1 = ∠2 (transitive).

Proof for Exercise 2.

1. ∠ODN = ∠N. (Given.)
2. ON = OD. (If two angles of a triangle are equal, the sides opposite them are equal.)
3. PO + OD > PD. (The sum of the lengths

Chapter 7, Lesson 1

Set II

Proof for Exercise 1.

1. ∠1 + ∠2 = 180°. (Given.)
2. ∠1 = ∠3. (Vertical angles are equal.)
3. ∠3 + ∠2 = 180°. (Substitution.)
4. ∠3 and ∠2 are supplementary. (If the sum of the measures of two angles is 180°, they are supplementary.)

5. k ∥ a. (If two lines form supplementary interior angles on the same side of a transversal, the lines are parallel.)

Proof for Exercise 2.

1. WN = WD. (Given.)
2. ∠N = ∠D. (If two sides of a triangle are equal, the angles opposite them are equal.)
3. ∠WEY = ∠D. (Given.)
4. ∠N = ∠WEY. (Substitution.)
5. EY ∥ ND. (If two lines form equal corresponding angles with a transversal, the lines are parallel.)

Proof for Exercise 3.

1. JE ⊥ EN. (Given.)
2. ∠J is a right angle. (Given.)
3. JE ⊥ JA. (If two lines form a right angle, they are perpendicular.)
4. JA ∥ EN. (In a plane, two lines perpendicular to a third line are parallel to each other.)

Set III

Since the legs are attached at their midpoints, HR = RN and AR = RO. Also ∠HRA = ∠ORN because they are vertical angles. So △HRA ≅ △NRO (S.A.S.). Since ∠A = ∠O, HA ∥ ON (if two lines form equal alternate interior angles with a transversal, the lines are parallel).

Chapter 7, Lesson 2

Set I

2. Alice is right if all the lines are not confined to one plane.

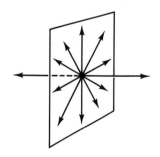

Set II

4.

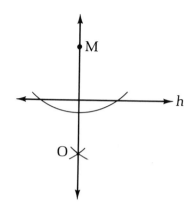

Set III

Dilcue's path is along an arc of a circle; more specifically, a semicircle.

Chapter 7, Lesson 3

Set II

1. c) (Use either perpendiculars or alternate interior angles.)

Proof for Exercise 2.

1. b ⊥ u, e ⊥ u. (Given.)
2. b ∥ e. (In a plane, two lines perpendicular to a third line are parallel to each other.)
3. b ∥ ℓ. (Given.)
4. ℓ ∥ e. (In a plane, two lines parallel to a third line are parallel to each other.)

3. Hypothesis: Line c intersects line a at point J; a ∥ k.
   Conclusion: Line c intersects line k.

   Suppose line c does not intersect line k. Then, since they lie in the same plane, c ∥ k. Since a ∥ k, it follows that c ∥ a because, in a plane, two lines parallel to a third line are parallel to each other. But this contradicts the hypothesis that lines c and a intersect. So our assumption that lines c and k do not intersect is false.

Set III

The error in the proof is the use of the reason "if two parallel lines are cut by a transversal, the corresponding angles are equal." Because we have neither assumed nor proved this previously, it cannot be used as a reason. (We have proved its converse.)

Chapter 7, Lesson 4

Set I

Proof for Exercise 1.

1. Lines r and u are cut by transversal m, r ∥ u. (Given.)
2. ∠1 = ∠3. (If two parallel lines are cut by a transversal, the corresponding angles are equal.)
3. ∠3 = ∠2. (Vertical angles are equal.)
4. ∠1 = ∠2. (Transitive.)

Set II

1. By betweenness of rays, ∠BRA = ∠1 + ∠2 and ∠NDY = ∠3 + ∠4. Since ∠BRA = ∠NDY, it follows that ∠1 + ∠2 = ∠3 + ∠4. Also, since $\overline{BR} ∥ \overline{ND}$, ∠1 = ∠3 (if two parallel lines are cut by a transversal, the corresponding angles are equal). By subtraction, ∠2 = ∠4. It follows that $\overrightarrow{RA} ∥ \overrightarrow{DY}$ because, if two lines form equal corresponding angles with a transversal, the lines are parallel.

Proof for Exercise 2.

1. $\overline{WI} ∥ \overline{EN}$. (Given.)
2. ∠IWN = ∠WNE. (If two parallel lines are cut by a transversal, the alternate interior angles are equal.)
3. WI = EN. (Given.)
4. WN = WN. (Reflexive.)
5. △WIN ≅ △NEW. (S.A.S. postulate.)

Proof for Exercise 3.

1. $\overline{PO} ∥ \overline{TR}$. (Given.)
2. ∠P and ∠T are supplementary. (If two parallel lines are cut by a transversal, the interior angles on the same side of the transversal are supplementary.)
3. ∠P and ∠R are supplementary. (Given.)
4. ∠T = ∠R. (Supplements of the same angle are equal.)

Set III

To prove that $\overline{ME} ∥ \overline{UH}$, we will show that they form equal alternate interior angles with transversal $\overline{EU}$; that is, that ∠HUE = ∠UEM. Since
$$∠1 + ∠HUE + ∠2 = 180^{\circ}$$
and
$$∠3 + ∠UEM + ∠4 = 180^{\circ},$$
$$∠1 + ∠HUE + ∠2 = ∠3 + ∠UEM + ∠4.$$

Since ∠1 = ∠2 and ∠3 = ∠4, it follows by substitution that
$$∠2 + ∠HUE + ∠2 = ∠3 + ∠UEM + ∠3.$$
Furthermore, since $\overline{VR} ∥ \overline{TO}$, ∠2 = ∠3 (if two parallel lines are cut by a transversal, the alternate interior angles are equal). So
$$∠2 + ∠HUE + ∠2 = ∠2 + ∠UEM + ∠2.$$
By subtraction, ∠HUE = ∠UEM.

Chapter 7, Lesson 5

Set II

Proof for Exercise 1.

1. $\overline{KN} \perp \overline{NE}$, $\overline{EF} \perp \overline{KF}$. (Given.)
2. ∠N and ∠F are right angles. (Perpendicular lines form right angles.)
3. ∠N = ∠F. (Right angles are equal.)
4. ∠KIN = ∠EIF. (Vertical angles are equal.)
5. ∠K = ∠E. (If two angles of one triangle are equal to two angles of another, then the third pair of angles are equal.)

Proof for Exercise 2.

1. △PIC is a right triangle (rt. ∠PIC). (Given.)
2. ∠P and ∠C are complementary. (The acute angles of a right triangle are complementary.)
3. ∠CKI and ∠P are complementary. (Given.)
4. ∠C = ∠CKI. (Complements of the same angle are equal.)
5. CI = KI. (If two angles of a triangle are equal, the sides opposite them are equal.)

Proof for Exercise 3.

1. WE = EC = CW, RN = NH = HR. (Given.)
2. △WEC and △RNH are equilateral. (If all three sides of a triangle are equal, it is equilateral.)
3. ∠HRN = 60° and ∠C = 60°. (Each angle of an equilateral triangle has a measure of 60°.)
4. ∠HRN = ∠C. (Substitution.)

Set III

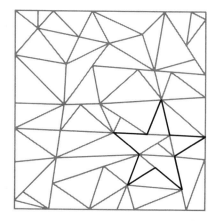

Chapter 7, Lesson 6

Set II

Proof for Exercise 1.

1. O is the midpoint of $\overline{LV}$. (Given.)
2. LO = OV. (The midpoint of a line segment divides it into two equal segments.)
3. $\angle$ C = $\angle$ E. (Given.)
4. $\angle$ LOC = $\angle$ VOE. (Vertical angles are equal.)
5. $\triangle$CLO $\cong$ $\triangle$EVO. (A.A.S. Congruence Theorem.)

Proof for Exercise 2.

1. $\angle$ A and $\angle$ E are right angles. (Given.)
2. $\triangle$SEG and $\triangle$GAS are right triangles. (A triangle with a right angle is a right triangle.)
3. SA = EG. (Given.)
4. SG = SG. (Reflexive.)
5. $\triangle$SEG $\cong$ $\triangle$GAS. (H.L. Congruence Theorem.)
6. $\angle$ ESG = $\angle$ SGA. (Corresponding parts of congruent triangles are equal.)
7. $\overline{SE} \parallel \overline{AG}$. (If two lines form equal alternate interior angles with a transversal, the lines are parallel.)

Proof for Exercise 3.

1. $\overline{MH} \perp \overline{TY}$ and $\overline{YE} \perp \overline{TM}$. (Given.)
2. $\angle$ YHM and $\angle$ MEY are right angles. (Perpendicular lines form right angles.)
3. $\triangle$YHM and $\triangle$MEY are right triangles. (A triangle with a right angle is a right triangle.)
4. MH = YE. (Given.)

5. YM = YM. (Reflexive.)
6. $\triangle$YHM $\cong$ $\triangle$MEY. (H.L. Congruence Theorem.)
7. $\angle$ TYM = $\angle$ TMY. (Corresponding parts of congruent triangles are equal.)
8. TY = TM. (If two angles of a triangle are equal, the sides opposite them are equal.)
9. $\triangle$TYM is isosceles. (If two sides of a triangle are equal, the triangle is isosceles.)

Set III

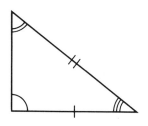

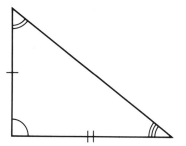

If all three sides of one triangle are equal to the sides of the other, the triangles must be congruent. Therefore, the five pairs of equal parts must be the three pairs of angles and two pairs of sides.

(Note that since the triangles are similar, their corresponding sides must be proportional. This means that

$$\frac{a}{b} = \frac{b}{c} = \frac{c}{d}.$$

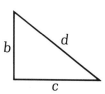

Hence, for such a pair of triangles to exist, they must be scalene and the length of one side must be the mean proportional between the lengths of the other two.)

Chapter 7, Review

Set III

Theorem. The sum of the angles of any triangle is equal to a straight angle.

Given triangle ABC, imagine a line, DE, through a vertex—for example through C—parallel to the opposite side AB. The resulting angle ACD is equal to its alternate angle CAB (with respect to parallels DE and AB and to their transversal AC) and, similarly, the resulting angle BCE is equal to its alternate angle ABC (with respect to the same parallels and to their transversal BC). Therefore, the sum of the three angles, A, B, and C, of the triangle is equal to
$$\angle\, DCA + \angle\, ACB + \angle\, BCE,$$
that is, exactly the measure of a straight angle.

Chapter 8, Lesson 1

Set I

4. a)

b) Impossible.

c)

d)

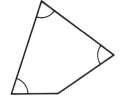

e)

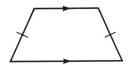

f) Impossible.

g)

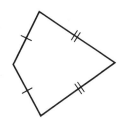

Set II

1. Since the sum of the measures of the angles of a quadrilateral is 360°,
$$\angle\, A + \angle\, R + \angle\, G + \angle\, O = 360^\circ.$$
Since $\angle$ A is a right angle and $\angle$ R and $\angle$ O are supplementary, $\angle\, A = 90^\circ$ and $\angle\, R + \angle\, O = 180^\circ$. Hence $\angle\, G = 90^\circ$. Since $\angle$ G is a right angle, $\overline{GR} \perp \overline{GO}$.

Proof for Exercise 2.

1. LY = YR, LA = AR. (Given.)
2. Draw $\overline{YA}$. (Two points determine a line.)
3. YA = YA. (Reflexive.)
4. △LYA ≅ △RYA. (S.S.S. postulate.)
5. $\angle\, L = \angle\, R$. (Corresponding parts of congruent triangles are equal.)

Proof for Exercise 3.

1. CGNS is a quadrilateral. (Given.)
2. $\angle\, C + \angle\, G + \angle\, N + \angle\, S = 360^\circ$.
   $\angle\, C + \angle\, 1 + \angle\, 2 + \angle\, S = 360^\circ$. (The sum of the measures of the angles of a quadrilateral is 360°.)
3. $\angle\, C + \angle\, G + \angle\, N + \angle\, S = \angle\, C + \angle\, 1 + \angle\, 2 + \angle\, S$. (Substitution.)
4. $\angle\, G + \angle\, N = \angle\, 1 + \angle\, 2$. (Subtraction.)
5. $\angle\, 1 = \angle\, N$. (Given.)
6. $\angle\, G + \angle\, 1 = \angle\, 1 + \angle\, 2$. (Substitution.)
7. $\angle\, G = \angle\, 2$. (Subtraction.)

Set III

Since Ollie says the slanted line segment passes through just four squares in the first figure, he evidently has noticed only the six small squares and has overlooked the two larger overlapping ones. He would probably say that the slanted segment passes through six squares in the second figure.

Alice, if she has noticed all of the larger overlapping squares in the second figure, would say the slanted segment passes through <u>fourteen</u> of them.

Chapter 8, Lesson 2

Set II

1. a) The point in which its diagonals intersect.
   b) The diagonals of a parallelogram bisect each other.
   c) A figure is symmetric with respect to a given point if the reflection of every point of the figure through the given point is also a point of the figure.

Proof for Exercise 2.

1. BRAE and EAQU are parallelograms. (Given.)
2. BR = EA and EA = UQ. (The opposite sides of a parallelogram are equal.)
3. BR = UQ. (Transitive.)

Proof for Exercise 3.

1. RB = NB. (Given.)
2. ∠N = ∠R. (If two sides of a triangle are equal, the angles opposite them are equal.)
3. $\overline{SE}$ ∥ $\overline{RU}$ and $\overline{UE}$ ∥ $\overline{RS}$. (Given.)
4. RUES is a parallelogram. (If both pairs of opposite sides of a quadrilateral are parallel, it is a parallelogram.)
5. ∠R = ∠SEU. (The opposite angles of a parallelogram are equal.)
6. ∠N = ∠SEU. (Transitive.)

Proof for Exercise 4.

1. SURT is a parallelogram. (Given.)
2. ∠S = ∠R. (The opposite angles of a parallelogram are equal.)
3. ST = UR. (The opposite sides of a parallelogram are equal.)
4. $\overline{TE}$ ⊥ $\overline{SU}$, $\overline{UA}$ ⊥ $\overline{TR}$. (Given.)
5. ∠SET and ∠UAR are right angles. (Perpendicular lines form right angles.)
6. ∠SET = ∠UAR. (Right angles are equal.)
7. △SET ≅ △RAU. (A.A.S. Congruence Theorem.)

Set III

The Escher mosaic Study of Regular Division of the Plane with <u>Fish and Birds</u>, 1938, is shown on the facing page.

Chapter 8, Lesson 3

Set II

Proof for Exercise 1.

1. SG = GT and KG = GN. (Given.)
2. $\overline{ST}$ and $\overline{KN}$ bisect each other. (If a line segment is divided into two equal segments, it is bisected.)
3. SKTN is a parallelogram. (If the diagonals of a quadrilateral bisect each other, the quadrilateral is a parallelogram.)
4. $\overleftrightarrow{SK}$ ∥ $\overrightarrow{NT}$. (The opposite sides of a parallelogram are parallel.)
5. ∠A = ∠NTI. (If two parallel lines are cut by a transversal, the corresponding angles are equal.)

Proof for Exercise 2.

1. △HOY ≅ △KEY. (Given.)
2. HO = EK. (Corresponding parts of congruent triangles are equal.)
3. K is the midpoint of $\overline{EC}$. (Given.)
4. EK = KC. (The midpoint of a line segment divides it into two equal segments.)
5. HO = KC. (Transitive.)
6. ∠H = ∠HKE. (Same as step 2.)
7. $\overline{HO}$ ∥ $\overline{KC}$. (If two lines form equal alternate interior angles with a transversal, the lines are parallel.)
8. HOCK is a parallelogram. (If two sides of a quadrilateral are both parallel and equal, the quadrilateral is a parallelogram.)

Proof for Exercise 3.

1. $\overline{GO}$ ∥ $\overline{FL}$ in quadrilateral GOLF. (Given.)
2. ∠G and ∠F are supplementary, ∠O and ∠L are supplementary. (If two parallel lines are cut by a transversal, the interior angles on the same side of the transversal are supplementary.)
3. ∠G = ∠L. (Given.)
4. ∠O = ∠F. (Supplements of equal angles are equal.)
5. GOLF is a parallelogram. (If both pairs of opposite angles of a quadrilateral are equal, the quadrilateral is a parallelogram.)

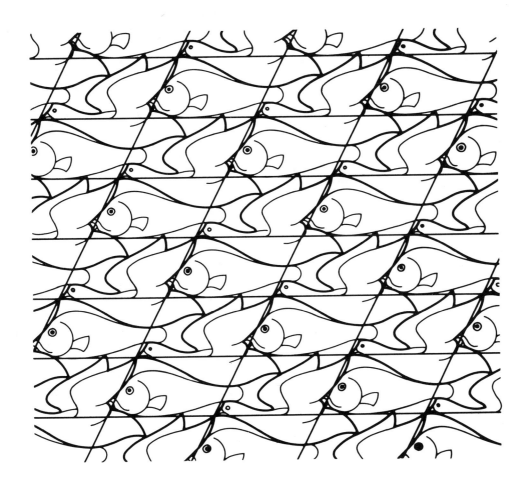

Set III

Yes. Suppose that we know that every face of the box in the figure is a parallelogram except YACH. Since the opposite sides of a parallelogram are equal, YH = TG, TG = IN, and IN = AC; also, YA = TI, TI = GN, and GN = HC. Therefore, YH = AC and YA = HC. Since both pairs of its opposite sides are equal, YACH must also be a parallelogram.)

Chapter 8, Lesson 4

Set II

Proof for Exercise 1.

1. SNOW is a kite with diagonal $\overline{NW}$. (Given.)
2. SN = NO and SW = WO. (A kite is a quadrilateral that has two pairs of equal con-

secutive sides with no side common to both pairs.)
3. NW = NW. (Reflexive.)
4. △SNW ≅ △ONW. (S.S.S. postulate.)
5. ∠ SNW = ∠ ONW. (Corresponding parts of congruent triangles are equal.)
6. $\overrightarrow{NW}$ bisects ∠ SNO. (If an angle is divided into two equal angles, it is bisected.)

Proof for Exercise 2.

1. ∠ A = ∠ L, ∠ H = ∠ I. (Given.)
2. HAIL is a parallelogram. (If both pairs of opposite angles of a quadrilateral are equal, the quadrilateral is a parallelogram.)

Study of Regular Division of the Plane with Fish and Birds by Maurits Escher is used with the permission of the Escher Foundation, Haags Gemeentemuseum, The Hague.

3. LH = AI and AH = IL. (The opposite sides of a parallelogram are equal.)
4. AI = AH. (Given.)
5. LH = AI = AH = IL. (Transitive.)
6. HAIL is a rhombus. (An equilateral quadrilateral is a rhombus.)

Proof for Exercise 3.

1. SHWR is a rhombus. (Given.)
2. SH = SR. (A rhombus is equilateral.)
3. SHWR is a parallelogram. (All rhombuses are parallelograms.)
4. ∠H = ∠R. (The opposite angles of a parallelogram are equal.)
5. $\overline{SE} \perp \overline{RW}$ and $\overline{SO} \perp \overline{WH}$. (Given.)
6. ∠SER and ∠SOH are right angles. (Perpendicular lines form right angles.)
7. ∠SER = ∠SOH. (Right angles are equal.)
8. △SER ≅ △SOH. (A.A.S. Congruence Theorem.)
9. SE = SO. (Corresponding parts of congruent triangles are equal.)

Set III

1. A quadrilateral with four equal sides is a rhombus.

2. Every rhombus is a parallelogram.

3. The diagonals of a rhombus are perpendicular to each other.

4. A quadrilateral in which two pairs of consecutive sides are equal is a kite.

5. In every kite the diagonals are perpendicular to each other.

Chapter 8, Lesson 5

Set II

1. Yes. One explanation: Suppose MAYS is a parallelogram and that ∠S is a right angle. Then ∠A is also a right angle because the opposite angles of a parallelogram are equal. Since the sum of the measures of the four angles of MAYS is 360° and ∠A = ∠S = 90°, ∠M + ∠Y = 180°. Also ∠M = ∠Y, so ∠M = 90° and ∠Y = 90°. An equiangular quadrilateral is a rectangle by definition.

Another explanation: Suppose MAYS is a parallelogram and that ∠S is a right angle. Then $\overline{MA} \parallel \overline{SY}$, $\overline{MS} \parallel \overline{AY}$, and $\overline{MS} \perp \overline{SY}$. Since, in a plane, a line per-

pendicular to one of two parallel lines is also perpendicular to the other, we can conclude, in sequence, that $\overline{MS} \perp \overline{MA}$, $\overline{MA} \perp \overline{AY}$, and $\overline{AY} \perp \overline{SY}$. Hence all four angles of MAYS are right angles and it is an equiangular quadrilateral.

Proof for Exercise 2.

1. MARI is a parallelogram. (Given.)
2. MI = AR. (The opposite sides of a parallelogram are equal.)
3. MR = AI. (Given.)
4. IR = IR. (Reflexive.)
5. △MIR ≅ △ARI. (S.S.S. postulate.)
6. ∠MIR = ∠ARI. (Corresponding parts of congruent triangles are equal.)
7. ∠IMA = ∠ARI and ∠MIR = ∠MAR. (The opposite angles of a parallelogram are equal.)
8. ∠MAR = ∠MIR = ∠ARI = ∠IMA. (Transitive.)
9. MARI is a rectangle. (An equiangular quadrilateral is a rectangle.)
10. ∠MIR is a right angle. (All four angles of a rectangle are right angles.)

Proof for Exercise 4.

1. KOFA is a rectangle. (Given.)
2. KF = OA. (The diagonals of a rectangle are equal.)
3. OUFA is a parallelogram. (Given.)
4. OA = UF. (The opposite sides of a parallelogram are equal.)
5. KF = UF. (Transitive.)
6. △KUF is isosceles. (If a triangle has two equal sides, it is isosceles.)

Set III

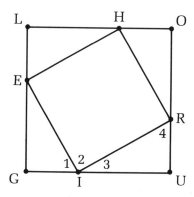

Since the four right triangles are congruent, EH = HR = RI = IE. So EHRI is equilateral. Angles 3 and 4 are complementary because they are the acute angles of right △IRU, so ∠3 + ∠4 = 90°. Also, ∠1 = ∠4 since they are corresponding parts of congruent triangles. So ∠3 + ∠1 = 90° by substitution. Since ∠1 + ∠2 + ∠3 = 180°, ∠2 = 90° by subtraction. In the same way, it can be shown that the measure of each of the other three angles of EHRI is 90°. Since EHRI is equiangular as well as equilateral, it is a square.

Chapter 8, Lesson 6

Set II

1. No. Suppose the diagonals of a certain trapezoid do bisect each other. Then that trapezoid must be a parallelogram. But a trapezoid has exactly one pair of parallel sides, whereas a parallelogram has two.

Proof for Exercise 2.

1. OLDS is an isosceles trapezoid. (Given.)
2. OL = SD. (The legs of an isosceles trapezoid are equal.)
3. ∠OLD = ∠SDL. (The base angles of an isosceles trapezoid are equal.)
4. LD = LD. (Reflexive.)
5. △OLD ≅ △SDL. (S. A. S. postulate.)
6. OD = SL. (Corresponding parts of congruent triangles are equal.)

Proof for Exercise 3.

1. ∠C = ∠VHE. (Given.)
2. CY ∥ HV. (If two lines form equal corresponding angles with a transversal, the lines are parallel.)
3. CH = YV. (Given.)
4. CHVY is an isosceles trapezoid. (If a quadrilateral has exactly one pair of parallel sides, it is a trapezoid; if its legs are equal, it is isosceles.)
5. ∠C = ∠Y. (The base angles of an isosceles trapezoid are equal.)
6. CE = YE. (If two angles of a triangle are equal, the sides opposite them are equal.)
7. △CYE is isosceles. (If two sides of a triangle are equal, the triangle is isosceles.)

Set III

A possible answer: A trapezoid is formed if a line that intersects two sides of a triangle is parallel to the third side.

Chapter 8, Lesson 7

Set II

Proof for Exercise 3.

1. UE and EA are midsegments of △BTN. (Given.)
2. UE ∥ TN and EA ∥ BT. (A midsegment of a triangle is parallel to the third side.)
3. UTAE is a parallelogram. (If both pairs of opposite sides of a quadrilateral are parallel, it is a parallelogram.)
4. ∠UEA = ∠T. (The opposite angles of a parallelogram are equal.)

Proof for Exercise 4.

1. AG = GO. (Given.)
2. ∠G = ∠O. (If two sides of a triangle are equal, the angles opposite them are equal.)
3. RN is a midsegment of △AGO. (Given.)
4. RN ∥ GO. (A midsegment of a triangle is parallel to the third side.)
5. ∠ARN = ∠G and ∠ANR = ∠O. (If two parallel lines are cut by a transversal, the corresponding angles are equal.)
6. ∠ARN = ∠ANR. (Substitution.)
7. AR = AN. (If two angles of a triangle are equal, the sides opposite them are equal.)
8. △ARN is isosceles. (If two sides of a triangle are equal, the triangle is isosceles.)

Set III

Ollie is correct even though the figure he drew, an isosceles trapezoid, illustrates a rather special case. It has been established in Exercises 1 and 2 of Set II that the quadrilateral formed by the segments connecting the midpoints of the sides of any quadrilateral in order is a parallelogram. Since the segments connecting the midpoints of the opposite sides of a quadrilateral are the diagonals of such a parallelogram, they must also bisect each other.

Chapter 8, Review

Set III

Since a ∥ b ∥ c ∥ d and ℓ_1 ∥ ℓ_2, MNRQ, NOSR, and OPTS are parallelograms. Since the trees are evenly spaced along ℓ_1, MN = NO = OP; also, QR = MN, RS = NO, and

ST = OP since the opposite sides of a parallelogram are equal. So QR = RS = ST.

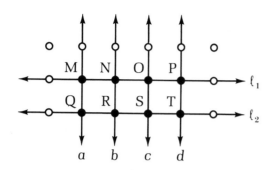

a b c d

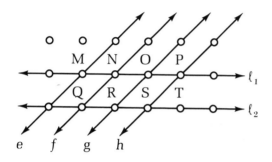

e f g h

Since QR = NO and RS = OP (substitution), NORQ and OPSR are parallelograms. (If two sides of a quadrilateral are both parallel and equal, it is a parallelogram.) Therefore, f ∥ g ∥ h.

Chapter 9, Lesson 1

Set I

1. Possible answers:
   a)

   b)

c)

Set II

Proof for Exercise 2.

1. △MIK is the reflection of △ADO through line ℓ. (Given.)
2. △MIK ≅ △ADO. (A triangle and its reflection through a line are congruent.)
3. α△MIK = α△ADO. (Congruent triangles have equal areas.)

3. Since SHEI is a rhombus, it is also a parallelogram. Therefore, SK = KE and HK = KI (the diagonals of a parallelogram bisect each other). Also SH = HE = EI = IS, since a rhombus is equilateral. So the four small triangles are congruent (S.S.S.) and have equal areas. Hence α△IKE = $\frac{1}{4}$$\alpha$SHEI.

Proof for Exercise 4.

1. HCLP and HAIP are parallelograms. (Given.)
2. CH = LP. (The opposite sides of a parallelogram are equal.)
3. $\overline{CH} \parallel \overline{LP}$ and $\overline{AH} \parallel \overline{IP}$. (The opposite sides of a parallelogram are parallel.)
4. ∠C = ∠ILP and ∠CAH = ∠I. (If two parallel lines are cut by a transversal, the corresponding angles are equal.)
5. △CAH ≅ △LIP. (A.A.S. Congruence Theorem.)
6. α△CAH = α△LIP. (Congruent triangles have equal areas.)
7. α△CAH + αHALP = α△LIP + αHALP. (Addition.)
8. αHCLP = α△CAH + αHALP; αHAIP = α△LIP + αHALP. (Area Addition Postulate.)
9. αHCLP = αHAIP. (Substitution.)

Set III

The country is Italy, whose area is 116,303 square miles. The state is New Mexico, whose area is 121,445 square miles.

Chapter 9, Lesson 2

Set II

*2. $7^2 - 5^2 = 49 - 25 = 24$ square units.

*3. $10^2 - 9(2^2) = 100 - 36 = 64$ square units.

*4. $8^2 + 6^2 - 2(4 \cdot 6) = 100 - 48 = 52$ square units.

*5. $2(1 \cdot 12 + 1 \cdot 5000) + 4(1^2) = 10,028$ square feet.

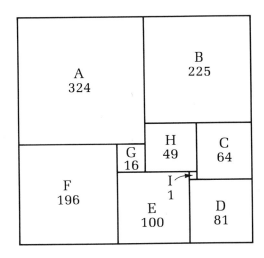

Set III

Note that this figure is not quite square; it is 33 units wide and 32 units high.

Chapter 9, Lesson 3

Set II

2. Since the legs of a right triangle are perpendicular, either one may be assumed to be its base and the other its altitude. The area of any triangle is half the product of the lengths of any base and corresponding altitude.

3. Quadrilaterals FRIE and FGTE are both parallelograms. If $\overline{FE}$ is their base, $\overline{IE}$ and $\overline{AE}$ are their corresponding altitudes. Since IE > AE, α FRIE > α FGTE.

4. Letting $\overline{AW}$ and $\overline{WL}$ be the bases of $\triangle$YAW and $\triangle$YWL, respectively, the two triangles have the same corresponding altitude (the perpendicular segment from Y to $\overleftrightarrow{LA}$.) Since W is the midpoint of side $\overline{AL}$, AW = WL. Therefore, $\alpha\triangle$YAW = $\alpha\,\triangle$YWL because triangles having equal bases and equal altitudes have equal areas.

Set III

This is a challenging problem. Here is a straightforward solution. On the basis of Exercise 4 of Set II, we can conclude that $\alpha\triangle$LCU = $\alpha\,\triangle$NCU and $\alpha\,\triangle$LAN = $\alpha\,\triangle$UAN. By the Area Addition Postulate,

$$\alpha\triangle\text{LCU} = \alpha 1 + \alpha 2,$$
$$\alpha\triangle\text{NCU} = \alpha 3 + \alpha 4,$$
$$\alpha\triangle\text{LAN} = \alpha 1 + \alpha 3, \text{ and}$$
$$\alpha\triangle\text{UAN} = \alpha 2 + \alpha 4.$$

Hence,
$$\alpha 1 + \alpha 2 = \alpha 3 + \alpha 4 \text{ and}$$
$$\alpha 1 + \alpha 3 = \alpha 2 + \alpha 4.$$
Adding,
$$2\alpha 1 + \alpha 2 + \alpha 3 = \alpha 2 + \alpha 3 + 2\alpha 4,$$
and subtracting,
$$2\alpha 1 = 2\alpha 4.$$
Hence,
$$\alpha 1 = \alpha 4.$$

Chapter 9, Lesson 4

Set I

2. c) If both bases of a "trapezoid" had the same length, it would actually be a parallelogram. If we let b = the length of each base and h = the length of the corresponding altitude,

$$A = \frac{1}{2} h(b + b) = \frac{1}{2} h(2b) = bh.$$

In other words, the trapezoid formula simplifies to that of a parallelogram.

3. b) Since the diagonals of a rhombus are perpendicular to each other (as well as bisecting each other), they form four congruent right triangles. The legs of each triangle have lengths 3 and 4 so each has an area of 6 square units. The area of the rhombus is $4 \cdot 6 = 24$ square units.

*1. $2(\frac{1}{2}9\cdot10) = 90$ square units.

*2. $12\cdot11 - (\frac{1}{2}\cdot3\cdot4 + \frac{1}{2}\cdot8\cdot5 + \frac{1}{2}\cdot3\cdot6 + \frac{1}{2}\cdot8\cdot9) = 132 - 71 = 61$ square units.

*3. $\frac{1}{2}7(8 + 2) = 35$ square units.

*6. a, c, and d)

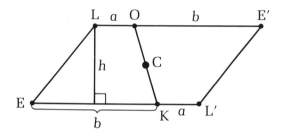

Set III

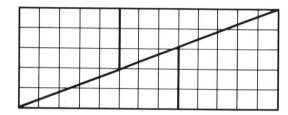

The "rectangle" is 5 units wide and 13 units long, so its area seems to be 65 square units. The area of the square is only 64 square units. Since both figures consist of the same parts, this result seems to contradict the Area Addition Postulate.

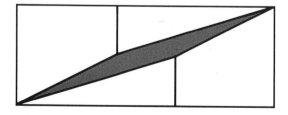

Actually, the pieces don't quite fit in the "rectangle." The exaggerated drawing shown here shows where the missing unit came from.

Chapter 9, Lesson 5

Set II

1. e) $\alpha\,AREF = \alpha\triangle ARL + \alpha\triangle LFE + \alpha\triangle RLE$

$\frac{1}{2}(a + b)^2 = \frac{1}{2}ab + \frac{1}{2}ab + \frac{1}{2}c^2$

$(a + b)^2 = ab + ab + c^2$

$a^2 + 2ab + b^2 = 2ab + c^2$

$a^2 + b^2 = c^2$

2. d) $(b - a)^2 + 4(\frac{1}{2}ab) = c^2$

e) $b^2 - 2ab + a^2 + 2ab = c^2$

$b^2 + a^2 = c^2$

3. g) Let x = the area of one of the right triangles.

$\alpha1 = a^2 + b^2 + 2x$ and

$\alpha4 = c^2 + 2x.$

Since $\alpha1 = \alpha4$,

$a^2 + b^2 + 2x = c^2 + 2x,$

so $a^2 + b^2 = c^2.$

Set III

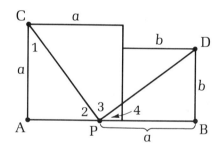

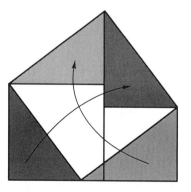

Let the lengths of the sides of the two squares be a and b as shown in the first figure. Choose point P on $\overrightarrow{BA}$ so that BP = a. Draw $\overline{PC}$ and $\overline{PD}$ and cut along them.

It is easy to see why PC = PD and ∠3 is a right angle. Since AB = a + b and PB = a, AP = b. Hence △CAP ≅ △PBD (S.A.S.). So PC = PD. Also, since ∠1 + ∠2 = 90° and ∠1 = ∠4, ∠4 + ∠2 = 90°; hence ∠3 = 90°.

Chapter 9, Lesson 6

Set I

*2. a) $\sqrt{20 \cdot 12 \cdot 5 \cdot 3}$ = 60 square units.

b) $\sqrt{25 \cdot 18 \cdot 5 \cdot 2}$ = $30\sqrt{5}$ square units.

c) $\sqrt{52 \cdot 49 \cdot 2 \cdot 1}$ = $14\sqrt{26}$ square units.

3. a) $\sqrt{10 \cdot 6 \cdot 4 \cdot 0}$ = 0 square units.

b) No triangle has sides of lengths 4, 6, and 10. Such a triangle would contradict the Triangle Inequality Theorem, since it is not true that 4 + 6 > 10.

Set II

*1. $2\sqrt{9 \cdot 2 \cdot 6 \cdot 1}$ = $12\sqrt{3}$ square units.

*2. $\frac{1}{2} \cdot 6 \cdot 8 + \sqrt{11 \cdot 1 \cdot 4 \cdot 6}$ = $24 + 2\sqrt{66}$ square units.

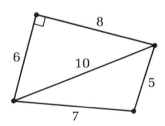

*3. $\frac{1}{2} \cdot 14 \cdot h = \sqrt{21 \cdot 8 \cdot 7 \cdot 6}$
$7h = 84$
$h = 12$.

Set III

1. A triangle.

2. Heron's Theorem.

3. a) $\sqrt{5 \cdot 9 \cdot 5 \cdot 1}$ = 15 square units.

b) $\sqrt{2 \cdot 2 \cdot 2 \cdot 2}$ = 4 square units.

4. The area of a general quadrilateral is not determined by the lengths of its sides. For example, the lengths of the

sides of the two quadrilaterals shown here are the same, yet their areas are different.

Chapter 9, Review

Set II

*1. $9 \cdot 16 - 7 \cdot 14$ = 46 square units.

*2. $6^2 - 5^2$ = 11 square units.

*3. $10^2 - \frac{10^2}{4}\sqrt{3}$ = $100 - 25\sqrt{3}$ square units.

*4. $3 \cdot 4$ = 12 square units.

*5. $\frac{1}{2}2(3 + 5) + \frac{1}{4}4(5 + 2) - \frac{1}{2}3 \cdot 2 - \frac{1}{4}4 \cdot 2$ = 15 square units.

*6. $\sqrt{27 \cdot 6 \cdot 14 \cdot 7} - \frac{1}{2}20 \cdot 4$ = $126 - 40 = 86$ square units.

Set III

The area of one of the triangular pieces is 9 square centimeters. Since there are twenty of them, the area of the square must be 180 square centimeters. The length of one of its sides is therefore $\sqrt{180}$ = $6\sqrt{5}$ centimeters.

By the Pythagorean Theorem, the length of the hypotenuse of one of the triangular pieces is $\sqrt{45}$ = $3\sqrt{5}$ centimeters.

To solve the puzzle, then, it is necessary to form each side of the square from the hypotenuses of two of the triangles. One solution is shown here.

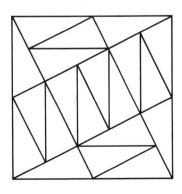

Chapter 10, Lesson 1

Set II

Proof for Exercise 3.

1. $\frac{a}{b} = \frac{c}{d}$. (Hypothesis.)
2. $ad = bc$. (The means-extremes theorem.)
3. $\frac{a}{c} = \frac{b}{d}$. (Division.)

Proof for Exercise 4.

1. $\frac{a}{b} = \frac{c}{d}$. (Hypothesis.)
2. $\frac{a}{b} + 1 = \frac{c}{d} + 1$. (Addition.)
3. $\frac{a}{b} + \frac{b}{b} = \frac{c}{d} + \frac{d}{d}$. (Substitution.)
4. $\frac{a+b}{b} = \frac{c+d}{d}$. (Substitution.)

Proof for Exercise 5.

1. $\frac{a}{b} = \frac{c}{d}$. (Hypothesis.)
2. $\frac{a}{b} - 1 = \frac{c}{d} - 1$. (Subtraction.)
3. $\frac{a}{b} - \frac{b}{b} = \frac{c}{d} - \frac{d}{d}$. (Substitution.)
4. $\frac{a-b}{b} = \frac{c-d}{d}$. (Substitution.)

Set III

The Golden Rule is a method for finding the fourth term of a proportion, given the first three.

$$\text{If } \frac{a}{b} = \frac{c}{d}, \text{ then } ad = bc, \text{ so } d = \frac{bc}{a}.$$

Chapter 10, Lesson 2

Set III

The length SA is the mean proportional between ST and SR, as shown in the following proof.

1. $\frac{TA}{ST} = \frac{ST}{SA}$. (Given.)
2. $\frac{TA + ST}{ST} = \frac{ST + SA}{SA}$. (Denominator-addition theorem.)
3. $ST = AR$. (Given.)
4. $\frac{TA + ST}{ST} = \frac{AR + SA}{SA}$. (Substitution.)

5. $TA + ST = SA$ and $AR + SA = SR$. (Betweenness of points.)
6. $\frac{SA}{ST} = \frac{SR}{SA}$. (Substitution.)
7. $\frac{ST}{SA} = \frac{SA}{SR}$. (Upsidedownable theorem.)

Chapter 10, Lesson 3

Set II

Proof for Exercise 3.

1. $\overline{LN} \parallel \overline{OI}$. (Given.)
2. $\frac{FL}{LO} = \frac{FN}{NI}$. (If a line is parallel to one side of a triangle, it divides the other two sides in the same ratio.)
3. $\overline{ON} \parallel \overline{RI}$. (Given.)
4. $\frac{FO}{OR} = \frac{FN}{NI}$. (Same as step 2.)
5. $\frac{FL}{LO} = \frac{FO}{OR}$. (Substitution.)

Proof for Exercise 4.

1. $\overline{FA}$ bisects $\angle RFN$ in $\triangle FRN$. (Given.)
2. $\angle RFA = \angle AFN$. (If an angle is bisected, it is divided into two equal angles.)
3. $FC = CA$. (Given.)
4. $\angle AFN = \angle CAF$. (If two sides of a triangle are equal, the angles opposite them are equal.)
5. $\angle RFA = \angle CAF$. (Transitive.)
6. $\overline{CA} \parallel \overline{FR}$. (If two lines form equal alternate interior angles with a transversal, the lines are parallel.)
7. $\frac{FC}{FN} = \frac{RA}{RN}$. (If a line is parallel to one side of a triangle, it cuts off segments proportional to the sides.)

Set III

Since $AB = DC$ and $AD = BC$, ABCD is a parallelogram. Therefore, $\overline{CD}$ is always parallel to $\overline{PB}$. It follows that

$$\frac{DE}{PD} = \frac{CE}{BC}$$

because a line parallel to one side of a triangle divides the other two sides in the same ratio.

Since $\overline{CE}$ and $\overline{BC}$ never change in length, the ratio $\frac{CE}{BC}$ always remains the same.

But $\frac{DE}{PD} = \frac{CE}{BC}$, so the ratio $\frac{DE}{PD}$ also always remains the same.

Chapter 10, Lesson 4

Set II

2. Since △HUX and △LEY are equilateral,
   HU = UX = HX and LE = EY = LY.
   Hence $\frac{HU}{LE} = \frac{UX}{EY} = \frac{HX}{LY}$ (division), so
   their corresponding sides are proportional. Also $\angle$ H = $\angle$ L, $\angle$ U = $\angle$ E, and
   $\angle$ X = $\angle$ Y because each angle of an equilateral triangle has a measure of 60°.
   By definition, two triangles whose corresponding sides are proportional and
   whose corresponding angles are equal are similar.

Proof for Exercise 3.

1. △UGH ~ △HGO. (Given.)
2. $\frac{UG}{HG} = \frac{GH}{GO}$. (Corresponding sides of
   similar triangles are proportional.)
3. HG is the mean proportional between UG
   and GO. (Definition of mean proportional.)

Proof for Exercise 4.

1. △SKA ~ △ASI. (Given.)
2. $\angle$ ASK = $\angle$ A. (Corresponding angles of
   similar triangles are equal.)
3. AK = SK. (If two angles of a triangle are
   equal, the sides opposite them are equal.)
4. △SKA is isosceles. (If a triangle has
   two equal sides, it is isosceles.)

Set III

1.

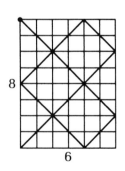 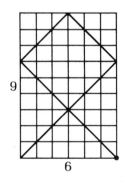

2. The path on the 9 x 6 table is like that on
   the 6 x 4 table.

3. The two tables are similar in shape.
   Their corresponding sides are proportional ($\frac{6}{4} = \frac{9}{6}$) and their corresponding
   angles are equal.

Chapter 10, Lesson 5

Set II

Proof for Exercise 1.

1. △MBI with altitudes $\overline{BL}$ and $\overline{IO}$. (Given.)
2. $\overline{BL} \perp \overline{MI}$ and $\overline{IO} \perp \overline{BM}$. (An altitude of a
   triangle is perpendicular to the line of
   the opposite side.)
3. $\angle$ BOE and $\angle$ ELI are right angles. (Perpendicular lines form right angles.)
4. $\angle$ BOE = $\angle$ ELI. (Right angles are equal.)
5. $\angle$ OEB = $\angle$ LEI. (Vertical angles are
   equal.)
6. △BOE ~ △ILE. (A. A. Similarity Theorem.)

Proof for Exercise 2.

1. SALE is a trapezoid with bases $\overline{SE}$ and
   $\overline{AL}$. (Given.)
2. $\overline{SE} \parallel \overline{AL}$. (The bases of a trapezoid are
   parallel.)
3. $\angle$ ESL = $\angle$ SLA and $\angle$ SEA = $\angle$ EAL. (If
   two parallel lines are cut by a transversal, the alternate interior angles are
   equal.)
4. △SME ~ △LMA. (A. A. Similarity Theorem.)

Proof for Exercise 3.

1. $\overline{LA}$, $\overline{LO}$, and $\overline{OA}$ are midsegments of
   △EPS. (Given.)
2. $\overline{LA} \parallel \overline{ES}$, $\overline{LO} \parallel \overline{PS}$, and $\overline{OA} \parallel \overline{EP}$. (A midsegment of a triangle is parallel to the
   third side.)
3. ELAO and OLAS are parallelograms.
   (If both pairs of opposite sides of a quadrilateral are parallel, it is a parallelogram.)
4. $\angle$ E = $\angle$ LAO and $\angle$ S = $\angle$ OLA. (The opposite angles of a parallelogram are equal.)
5. △AOL ~ △ EPS. (A. A. Similarity Theorem.)

Set III

The method will not work because the distance of the moon from the earth is so great.

It would not be possible to locate the specific point on the ground at which the moon is directly overhead.

Magritte's painting illustrates that, as an observer tries to move to different positions with respect to the moon, the moon appears to move with him.

Chapter 10, Lesson 6

Set II

Proof for Exercise 1.

1. $\angle F = \angle OAR$. (Given.)
2. $\angle R = \angle R$. (Reflexive.)
3. $\triangle FAR \sim \triangle AOR$. (A. A. Similarity Theorem.)
4. $\dfrac{FR}{AR} = \dfrac{AR}{OR}$. (Corresponding sides of similar triangles are proportional.)

Proof for Exercise 2.

1. BRID is a parallelogram. (Given.)
2. $\angle B = \angle I$. (The opposite angles of a parallelogram are equal.)
3. $\overrightarrow{RG}$ bisects $\angle BRI$. (Given.)
4. $\angle BRE = \angle GRI$. (If an angle is bisected, it is divided into two equal angles.)
5. $\triangle BER \sim \triangle IGR$. (A. A. Similarity Theorem.)
6. $\dfrac{BE}{IG} = \dfrac{ER}{GR}$. (Corresponding sides of similar triangles are proportional.)
7. $\dfrac{BE}{ER} = \dfrac{IG}{GR}$. (Interchangeable theorem.)

Proof for Exercise 3.

1. $\overline{TI} \parallel \overline{WH}$ in $\triangle WSH$. (Given.)
2. $\dfrac{WT}{WS} = \dfrac{HI}{HS}$. (If a line is parallel to one side of a triangle, it cuts off segments proportional to the sides.)
3. $\dfrac{WT}{HI} = \dfrac{WS}{HS}$. (Interchangeable theorem.)
4. $\angle WHT = \angle S$. (Given.)
5. $\angle W = \angle W$. (Reflexive.)
6. $\triangle WHT \sim \triangle WSH$. (A. A. Similarity Theorem.)
7. $\dfrac{WS}{WH} = \dfrac{HS}{HT}$. (Corresponding sides of similar triangles are proportional.)
8. $\dfrac{WS}{HS} = \dfrac{WH}{HT}$. (Interchangeable theorem.)
9. $\dfrac{WT}{HI} = \dfrac{WH}{HT}$. (Transitive.)

Set III

1. As the card is moved toward the candle, the flame's image becomes larger.

2. In the equation on page 395,
$$CD = \frac{PF \cdot AB}{PE},$$
CD is the height of the image, AB is the height of the object, PF is the distance of the image from the pinhole, and PE is the distance of the object from the pinhole.

As the card is moved toward the candle, PF becomes larger and PE becomes smaller; hence $\dfrac{PF}{PE}$ becomes larger. Since $CD = \dfrac{PF}{PE} \cdot AB$ and AB does not change, CD must also become larger.

Chapter 10, Lesson 7

Set I

*2. c) $\dfrac{x}{5-x} = \dfrac{4}{3}$, $3x = 20 - 4x$, $7x = 20$, $x = 2\dfrac{6}{7}$.

d) $\dfrac{x-2}{2} = \dfrac{7}{3}$, $3x - 6 = 14$, $3x = 20$, $x = 6\dfrac{2}{3}$.

Set II

Proof for Exercise 1.

1. $\overline{EH} \parallel \overline{AC}$. (Given.)
2. $\dfrac{BE}{EA} = \dfrac{BH}{HC}$. (If a line is parallel to one side of a triangle, it divides the other two sides in the same ratio.)
3. $\overrightarrow{AH}$ bisects $\angle BAC$. (Given.)
4. $\dfrac{BH}{HC} = \dfrac{BA}{AC}$. (An angle bisector in a triangle divides the opposite side into segments that have the same ratio as the other two sides.)
5. $\dfrac{BE}{EA} = \dfrac{BA}{AC}$. (Transitive.)

Proof for Exercise 2.

1. $\angle 1 = \angle 2$. (Given.)
2. $\overrightarrow{DA}$ bisects $\angle SDN$. (If a ray divides an angle into two equal angles, it bisects it.)

3. $\frac{SD}{DN} = \frac{SA}{AN}$. (An angle bisector in a triangle divides the opposite side into seg-
ments that have the same ratio as the
other two sides.)
4. SA = AN. (Given.)
5. $\frac{SD}{DN} = \frac{SA}{SA} = 1$. (Substitution.)
6. SD = DN. (Multiplication.)

Set III

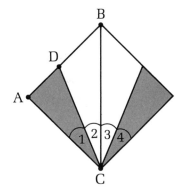

Since the figure has symmetry with respect
to $\overleftrightarrow{BC}$, the ratio of the area of the part folded over to the area of the rest of the square
is the same as

$$\frac{\alpha \triangle ACD}{\alpha \triangle BCD}.$$

Since $\overline{CA} \perp \overline{AB}$, $\overline{CA}$ is an altitude of both
$\triangle ACD$ and $\triangle BCD$. Hence

$$\frac{\alpha \triangle ACD}{\alpha \triangle BCD} = \frac{AD}{DB}$$

because, if two triangles have equal altitudes, the ratio of their areas is equal to the
ratio of the lengths of their bases.

Since $\angle 1 = \angle 2$, $\overline{CD}$ bisects $\angle ACB$. Hence

$\frac{AD}{DB} = \frac{AC}{CB}$, so that $\frac{\alpha \triangle ACD}{\alpha \triangle BCD} = \frac{AC}{CB}$. Since

$\overline{BC}$ is a diagonal of the square, $BC = \sqrt{2} \, AC$.
Therefore,

$$\frac{\alpha \triangle ACD}{\alpha \triangle BCD} = \frac{AC}{CB} = \frac{AC}{\sqrt{2} \, AC} = \frac{1}{\sqrt{2}}.$$

Chapter 10, Lesson 8

Set II

*1. c) $\frac{100}{144} = (\frac{20}{x})^2$, $\frac{10}{12} = \frac{20}{x}$, x = 24.

d) $\frac{32}{x} = (\frac{4}{6})^2$, $\frac{32}{x} = \frac{4}{9}$, x = 72.

Proof for Exercise 2.

1. $\overline{RA} \parallel \overline{UP}$ in $\triangle KUP$. (Given.)
2. $\angle KRA = \angle U$ and $\angle KAR = \angle P$. (If two
parallel lines are cut by a transversal,
the corresponding angles are equal.)
3. $\triangle KRA \sim \triangle KUP$. (A. A. Similarity Theorem.)
4. $\frac{\alpha \triangle KRA}{\alpha \triangle KUP} = (\frac{RA}{UP})^2$. (The ratio of the
areas of two similar triangles is equal to
the square of the ratio of the corresponding sides.)

Proof for Exercise 3.

1. $\triangle DAV$ and $\triangle VIS$ are equilateral. (Given.)
2. $\triangle DAV \sim \triangle VIS$. (Any two equilateral
triangles are similar.)
3. $\frac{\rho \triangle DAV}{\rho \triangle VIS} = \frac{DV}{SV}$. (The ratio of the perimeters of two similar triangles is equal
to the ratio of the corresponding sides.)
4. DV = DS + SV. (Betweenness of points.)
5. $\frac{\rho \triangle DAV}{\rho \triangle VIS} = \frac{DS + SV}{SV} = \frac{DS}{SV} + \frac{SV}{SV} = \frac{DS}{SV} + 1$.
(Substitution.)

Set III

1.

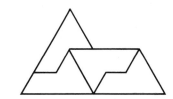

2.

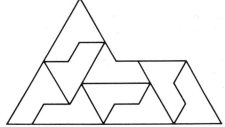

Chapter 10, Review

Set I

*2. a) $\frac{PL}{16} = \frac{9}{12}$, PL = 12.

b) $\rho \triangle PLU = 12 + 16 + 21 = 49$.

c) ΔPLU is not a right triangle because
$12^2 + 16^2 \neq 21^2$.

*3. a) Since ΔARP ~ ΔAGE,
$$\frac{RP}{GE} = \frac{AP}{AE} = \frac{8}{10} = \frac{4}{5}.$$

b) $\frac{\rho\Delta AGE}{\rho\Delta ARP} = \frac{AE}{AP}$, $\frac{\rho\Delta AGE}{24} = \frac{10}{8}$,
$\rho\Delta AGE = 30$.

c) $\frac{\alpha\Delta AGE}{\alpha\Delta ARP} = (\frac{AE}{AP})^2$, $\frac{\alpha\Delta AGE}{32} = (\frac{10}{8})^2$,
$\alpha\Delta AGE = 50$.

Set III

Here is a proof that the equilateral triangle on the hypotenuse of a right triangle is equal in area to the sum of the areas of the equilateral triangles on the two legs.

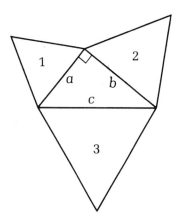

Since all equilateral triangles are similar, Δ1 ~ Δ2 ~ Δ3. Also, the ratio of the areas of two similar triangles is equal to the square of the ratio of the corresponding sides. So
$$\frac{\alpha\Delta 1}{\alpha\Delta 2} = (\frac{a}{c})^2 \text{ and } \frac{\alpha\Delta 2}{\alpha\Delta 3} = (\frac{b}{c})^2.$$
Adding,
$$\frac{\alpha\Delta 1}{\alpha\Delta 3} + \frac{\alpha\Delta 2}{\alpha\Delta 3} = (\frac{a}{c})^2 + (\frac{b}{c})^2$$
and simplifying,
$$\frac{\alpha\Delta 1 + \alpha\Delta 2}{\alpha\Delta 3} = \frac{a^2 + b^2}{c^2}.$$
Since $a^2 + b^2 = c^2$,
$$\frac{\alpha\Delta 1 + \alpha\Delta 2}{\alpha\Delta 3} = \frac{c^2}{c^2} = 1.$$
Hence, $\alpha\Delta 1 + \alpha\Delta 2 = \alpha\Delta 3$.

Chapter 11, Lesson 1

Set I

*4. a) $x = \sqrt{2\cdot 8} = 4$

b) $x = \sqrt{4\cdot 9} = 6$

c) $x = \sqrt{8\cdot 5} = 2\sqrt{10}$

d) $4 = \sqrt{10x}$, $10x = 16$, $x = 1.6$

Set II

1. b)

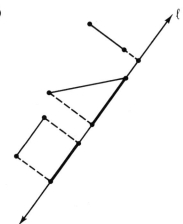

3. If the pole is horizontal, it and its shadow have the same length. As one end of the pole is raised—the other end remaining stationary—the length of the shadow decreases. The shadow has the smallest possible length when the pole is vertical.

Set III

1. a) $BC = 2$

b) $EC = \sqrt{EB^2 + BC^2} = \sqrt{5}$

c) $EF = EC = \sqrt{5}$

d) $BF = EF - EB = \sqrt{5} - 1$

e) $AF = EF + AE = \sqrt{5} + 1$

2. In rectangles ADGF and CGFB, $\overline{AD}$ corresponds to $\overline{CG}$ and $\overline{DG}$ corresponds to $\overline{GF}$.
$AD = BC = 2$
$CG = BF = \sqrt{5} - 1$
$$\frac{AD}{CG} = \frac{2}{\sqrt{5} - 1} = \frac{2(\sqrt{5} + 1)}{(\sqrt{5} - 1)(\sqrt{5} + 1)} =$$
$$\frac{2(\sqrt{5} + 1)}{5 - 1} = \frac{\sqrt{5} + 1}{2}$$

$DG = AF = \sqrt{5} + 1$

$GF = CB = 2$

$\dfrac{DG}{GF} = \dfrac{\sqrt{5}+1}{2}$

Hence $\dfrac{AD}{CG} = \dfrac{DG}{GF}$ and the corresponding dimensions of the rectangles are proportional.

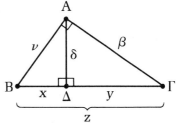

Chapter 11, Lesson 2

Set I

6. Let the three numbers of a Pythagorean triple be a, b, and c such that
$$a^2 + b^2 = c^2.$$
Suppose a, b, and c are all odd. Then a^2, b^2, and c^2 are also odd because a number is odd iff its square is odd. Since the sum of the squares of two odd numbers is even, $a^2 + b^2$ is even. Since $a^2 + b^2 = c^2$, c^2 is even. But c^2 is odd. So our supposition that a, b, and c can all be odd is false.

Set II

Proof for Exercise 2.

1. $\overline{LS} \perp \overline{AP}$ in $\triangle ALP$. (Given.)
2. $\angle ASL$ and $\angle LSP$ are right angles. (Perpendicular lines form right angles.)
3. $\triangle ASL$ and $\triangle LSP$ are right triangles. (A triangle with a right angle is a right triangle.)
4. $a^2 = c^2 + x^2$ and $b^2 = c^2 + y^2$. (In a right triangle, the square of the hypotenuse is equal to the sum of the squares of the legs.)
5. $a^2 - x^2 = c^2$ and $b^2 - y^2 = c^2$. (Subtraction.)
6. $a^2 - x^2 = b^2 - y^2$. (Substitution.)

*3. d) $\dfrac{45}{30} = \dfrac{x}{100-x}$, $\dfrac{3}{2} = \dfrac{x}{100-x}$,

$300 - 3x = 2x$, $5x = 300$, $x = 60$.

Set III

This is a challenging problem. Evidently we are to show that if $\overline{A\Delta}$ is the altitude to the hypotenuse of right $\triangle AB\Gamma$, then
$$\frac{1}{\nu^2} + \frac{1}{\beta^2} = \frac{1}{\delta^2}.$$

Let the length of the hypotenuse and its two segments be z, x, and y, respectively. Reasoning backward from the conclusion,
$$\frac{1}{\nu^2} + \frac{1}{\beta^2} = \frac{1}{\delta^2} \quad \text{if} \quad \frac{\beta^2 + \nu^2}{\nu^2\beta^2} = \frac{1}{\delta^2}$$
But $\beta^2 + \nu^2 = z^2$, so we can write
$$\frac{z^2}{\nu^2\beta^2} = \frac{1}{\delta^2}.$$
Taking square roots,
$$\frac{z}{\nu\beta} = \frac{1}{\delta}$$
and multiplying by β, $\dfrac{z}{\nu} = \dfrac{\beta}{\delta}$. But this is true because $\triangle AB\Gamma \sim \triangle \Delta BA$.

Chapter 11, Lesson 3

Set II

*2. a) $\dfrac{1}{2} 10 \cdot 2 = 10$ square units.

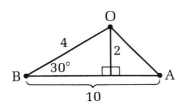

b) $\dfrac{1}{2} 10 \cdot \dfrac{4}{\sqrt{2}} = \dfrac{20}{\sqrt{2}} = 10\sqrt{2}$ square units.

c) $\frac{1}{2}10\,(2\sqrt{3}) = 10\sqrt{3}$ square units.

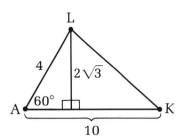

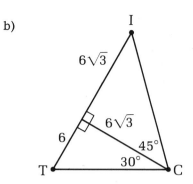

$\alpha\triangle TIC = \frac{1}{2}\,6(6\sqrt{3}) + \frac{1}{2}\,(6\sqrt{3})^2 =$
$18\sqrt{3} + 54$ square units.

*3. a)

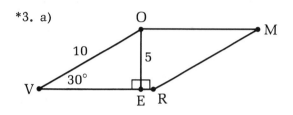

$\rho VRMO = 4(10) = 40$ units.
$\alpha VRMO = 10\cdot 5 = 50$ square units.

5.

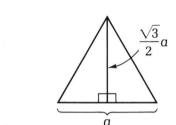

$\text{Area} = \frac{1}{2}\,a(\frac{\sqrt{3}}{2}\,a) = \frac{\sqrt{3}}{4}\,a^2 = \frac{a^2}{4}\sqrt{3}.$

b)

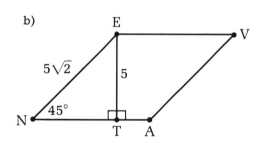

$\rho NAVE = 4(5\sqrt{2}) = 20\sqrt{2}$ units.
$\alpha NAVE = 5\sqrt{2}(5) = 25\sqrt{2}$ square
units.

Set III

A "3-4-5" triangle is a right triangle since $3^2 + 4^2 = 5^2$. If one acute angle of a right triangle has a measure of 45°, so must the other. But if two angles of a triangle are equal, the sides opposite them are equal. This proves that a "3-4-5" triangle cannot have a 45° angle.

If the object is to find how far the tree will reach when it falls, an isosceles right triangle should be used.

Chapter 11, Lesson 4

*4. a)

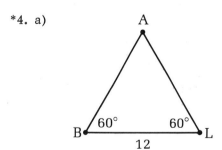

Since $\triangle BAL$ is equilateral,
$\alpha\triangle BAL = \frac{12^2}{4}\sqrt{3} = 36\sqrt{3}$ square units.

Set I

*3. a) $\tan 70^O = \frac{x}{10}$, $x = 10\tan 70^O =$
$10(2.747) = 27.47 \approx 27.5$

b) $\tan 25^O = \frac{x}{12}$, $x = 12\tan 25^O =$
$12(.466) = 5.592 \approx 5.6$

c) $\tan 35^O = \frac{14}{x}$, $x = \frac{14}{\tan 35^O} =$

$\frac{14}{.700} = 20$

*4. a) $\tan x = \frac{21}{25} = .84$, $x = 40^O$

b) $\tan x = \frac{10}{7} \approx 1.43$, $x = 55^O$

c) $\tan x = \frac{1.5}{2.6} \approx .58$, $x = 30^O$

Set II

Proof for Exercise 3.

1. In right $\triangle$PUG, $\angle$P < $\angle$U. (Given.)
2. GU < GP. (If two angles of a triangle are unequal, the sides opposite them are unequal and the longer side is opposite the larger angle.)
3. $\tan P = \frac{GU}{GP}$. (The tangent of an acute angle of a right triangle is the ratio of the length of the opposite leg to the length of the adjacent leg.)
4. $\frac{GU}{GP} < 1$. (Division.)
5. $\tan P < 1$. (Substitution.)

Set III

To find out what time it is, we can find the angle of elevation of the sun as shown in this figure.

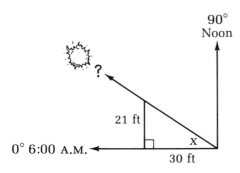

$\tan x = \frac{21}{30} = .70$, so $x = 35^O$.

The sun's angle of elevation changes at a constant rate because the earth rotates at a constant rate. Let t = the number of hours elapsed since 6:00 A.M.:

$\frac{35^O}{90^O} = \frac{t}{6}$, $\frac{7}{18} = \frac{t}{6}$, $t = \frac{7}{3} = 2\frac{1}{3}$ hours.

The time is 8:20 A.M.

Chapter 11, Lesson 5

Set I

*4. a) $\sin 32^O = \frac{x}{10}$, $x = 10 \sin 32^O =$

$10(.530) = 5.3$

b) $\cos 59^O = \frac{x}{4}$, $x = 4 \cos 59^O =$

$4(.515) = 2.060 \approx 2.1$

c) $\tan x = \frac{9}{10} = .9$, $x = 42^O$

d) $\cos x = \frac{7}{14} = .5$, $x = 60^O$

Set II

*1. $\tan 39^O = \frac{x}{100}$, $x = 100 \tan 39^O =$

$100(.810) = 81$ feet.

*2. $\sin 20^O = \frac{25}{x}$, $x = \frac{25}{\sin 20^O} = \frac{25}{.342} \approx$

73 feet.

*3. a) $\tan 14^O = \frac{x}{150}$, $x = 150 \tan 14^O =$

$150(.249) = 37.350 \approx 37$ yards.

b) $\cos 14^O = \frac{150}{x}$, $x = \frac{150}{\cos 14^O} = \frac{150}{.970} \approx$

155 yards.

4. a) Ollie is evidently assuming that $\triangle$PUN is a right triangle. It is not, because $5^2 + 5^2 \neq 8^2$.

b) Alice drew the altitude to side $\overline{PN}$ as shown in this figure.

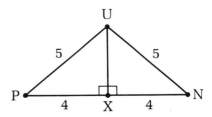

Since $\triangle$PUX $\cong$ $\triangle$NUX (H.L.), PX = XN = 4. It follows from the Pythagorean Theorem that, in right $\triangle$PUX, UX = 3;

$$\sin P = \frac{UX}{PU} = \frac{3}{5}.$$

5. $\alpha \triangle JKE = \frac{1}{2}bh$. Also, $\sin J = \frac{h}{a}$, so

$h = a \sin J$. Substituting,

$\alpha \triangle JKE = \frac{1}{2}b(a \sin J) = \frac{1}{2} ab \sin J$.

Set III

Triangle ABC is apparently a right triangle in which BC = a, CA = b, and AB = c. By the Pythagorean Theorem,

$$a^2 + b^2 = c^2.$$

Dividing by c^2,

$$(\frac{a}{c})^2 + (\frac{b}{c})^2 = 1.$$

Since $\frac{a}{c} = \sin \alpha$ and $\frac{b}{c} = \cos \alpha$, it follows that

$$(\sin \alpha)^2 + (\cos \alpha)^2 = 1.$$

You might point out to your students that it is this relationship between the sine and the cosine of an angle that is a theorem in trigonometry.

Chapter 11, Review

Set I

*1. a) $x = \sqrt{6 \cdot 3} = 3\sqrt{2}$

b) $x^2 + 21 = 121$, $x^2 = 100$, $x = 10$

c) $x = \frac{12}{2}\sqrt{3} = 6\sqrt{3}$

d) $x = 7\sqrt{2}$

e) $x = \frac{\sqrt{3}}{2} \cdot 8 = 4\sqrt{3}$

f) $x = \sqrt{12 \cdot 10} = 2\sqrt{30}$

*2. c) $\tan W = \frac{3}{4} = .75$, $\angle W = 37^o$;

$\angle X = 90^o - 37^o = 53^o$.

Set II

*1. $\tan 57^o = \frac{x}{90}$, $x = 90 \tan 57^o =$

$90(1.540) = 138.600 \approx 139$ feet.

*2. $\sin x = \frac{18}{25} = .72$, $x = 46^o$.

*3. $\tan x = \frac{7}{45} \approx .156$, $x = 9^o$.

*5. a) $\sin P = \frac{AE}{AP}$. $AE = AP \sin P =$

$6(\frac{\sqrt{5}}{3}) = 2\sqrt{5}$.

b) $\alpha PAST = PT \cdot AE = 7 \cdot 2\sqrt{5} = 14\sqrt{5}$.

c) $PE^2 + EA^2 = PA^2$, $PE^2 + (2\sqrt{5})^2 =$

6^2, $PE^2 + 20 = 36$, $PE^2 = 16$,

$PE = 4$.

d) $\alpha \triangle PEA = \frac{1}{2} PE \cdot AE = \frac{1}{2} 4(2\sqrt{5}) =$

$4\sqrt{5}$.

Set III

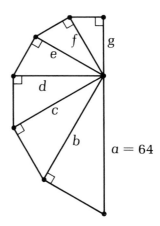

Each successive triangle is a 30°-60° right triangle. Consider the sequence of segments a, b, c, d, e, f, and g. Each successive segment is the longer leg of a right triangle in which the preceding segment is the hypotenuse. Hence each is $\frac{\sqrt{3}}{2}$ times as long as the preceding one.

In other words, $g = \frac{\sqrt{3}}{2}f$, $f = \frac{\sqrt{3}}{2}e$,

$e = \frac{\sqrt{3}}{2}d$, etc. Hence, $g = (\frac{\sqrt{3}}{2})^6 a =$

$(\frac{\sqrt{3}}{2})^6 64 = \frac{27}{64} \cdot 64 = 27$ cm.

Chapter 12, Lesson 1

Set I

1. A bicycle tire is probably better in that it does not convey the impression that a circle is a "disk," which would imply that it also consists of the points in its interior.

Set II

1. The reflection of a circle through its center is the circle itself because the center of the circle is the midpoint of every one of its diameters. This means that every point on the circle has for its reflection through the center the other endpoint of the diameter that the point and its reflection determine.

Proof for Exercise 2.

1. $\overleftrightarrow{TO}$ bisects $\overline{AG}$. (Given.)
2. NA = NG. (If a segment is bisected, it is divided into two equal segments.)
3. Draw $\overline{TA}$ and $\overline{TG}$. (Two points determine a line.)
4. TA = TG. (All radii of a circle are equal.)
5. $\overleftrightarrow{TO} \perp \overline{AG}$. (In a plane, two points each equidistant from the endpoints of a line segment determine the perpendicular bisector of the line segment.)

3. Alice is correct, because diameters are chords. Any line through the center of a circle bisects every diameter of the circle, yet is perpendicular to only one of them.

Proof for Exercise 4.

1. $\overleftrightarrow{IE}$ is the perpendicular bisector of $\overline{MN}$. (Given.)
2. $\overleftrightarrow{IE}$ passes through the center of the circle. (The perpendicular bisector of a chord passes through the center of the circle.)
3. $\overline{MN} \parallel \overline{UT}$. (Given.)
4. $\overleftrightarrow{IE} \perp \overline{UT}$. (In a plane, a line perpendicular to one of two parallel lines is perpendicular to the other.)
5. $\overleftrightarrow{IE}$ bisects $\overline{UT}$. (If a line through the center of a circle is perpendicular to a chord, it also bisects it.)

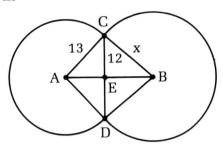

This figure represents a cross section through the centers of the intersecting spheres. Since A and B are each equidistant from C and D, $\overleftrightarrow{AB}$ is the perpendicular bisector of $\overline{CD}$. AB = 14 cm, EC = 12 cm, and AC = 13 cm. Triangle ACE is evidently a 5-12-13 right triangle, with AE = 5 cm. So EB = AB - AE = 14 cm - 5 cm = 9 cm. Since the legs of right △BCE are 9 cm and 12 cm long, its hypotenuse, BC, is 15 cm long.

Chapter 12, Lesson 2

Set I

3.

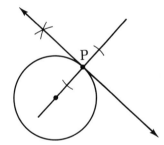

Set II

1. $\overline{HO} \perp \overline{JO}$ and $\overline{HN} \perp \overline{JN}$ because, if a line is tangent to a circle, it is perpendicular to the radius drawn to the point of contact. So $\angle O$ and $\angle N$ are right angles. Since $\angle J + \angle O + \angle H + \angle N = 360°$ and $\angle O = \angle N = 90°$, $\angle J + \angle H = 180°$. Therefore, $\angle J$ and $\angle H$ are supplementary.

Proof for Exercise 2.

1. $\overline{AE}$ is tangent to circle J at A and to circle S at E. (Given.)

2. $\overline{AE} \perp \overline{JA}$ and $\overline{AE} \perp \overline{ES}$. (If a line is tangent to a circle, it is perpendicular to the radius drawn to the point of contact.)
3. $\overline{JA} \parallel \overline{ES}$. (In a plane, two lines perpendicular to a third line are parallel to each other.)
4. $\angle J = \angle S$. (If two parallel lines are cut by a transversal, the alternate interior angles are equal.)

Proof for Exercise 3.

1. M is the center of both circles and $\overline{AK}$ is tangent to the smaller circle at R. (Given.)
2. Draw $\overline{MR}$. (Two points determine a line.)
3. $\overline{MR} \perp \overline{AK}$. (If a line is tangent to a circle, it is perpendicular to the radius drawn to the point of contact.)
4. $\overline{MR}$ bisects $\overline{AK}$. (If a line is perpendicular to a radius at its outer endpoint, it is tangent to the circle.)
5. AR = RK. (If a segment is bisected, it is divided into two equal segments.)

4. Since $\overline{UK}$ is tangent to circle L, $\overline{UK} \perp \overline{LU}$. Therefore, $\triangle LUK$ is a right triangle. Since LU = LE (all radii of a circle are equal) and UE = LU, LU = LE = UE and $\triangle LUE$ is equilateral. Hence $\angle L = \angle LUE = 60°$. So $\angle K = 30°$ (the acute angles of a right triangle are complementary) and $\angle EUK = 30°$ ($\angle EUK = 90° - \angle LUE$). Since $\angle K = \angle EUK$, UE = EK (if two angles of a triangle are equal, the sides opposite them are equal). Finally, LE = EK since both are equal to UE. So $\overline{UE}$ bisects $\overline{LK}$.

Set III

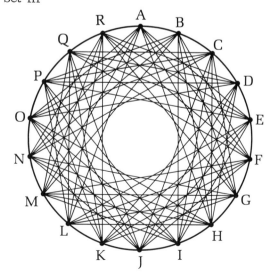

The figure seems to contain several concentric circles. If these circles were actually drawn, the chords would be tangent to them.

Chapter 12, Lesson 3

Set II

Proof for Exercise 1.

1. Draw $\overline{AK}$, $\overline{AO}$, $\overline{AR}$, and $\overline{AE}$. (Two points determine a line.)
2. AK = AE and AO = AR. (All radii of a circle are equal.)
3. $m\overset{\frown}{KO} = m\overset{\frown}{RE}$. (Hypothesis.)
4. $\angle KAO = \angle EAR$. (In a circle, two central angles are equal if their minor arcs are equal.)
5. $\triangle KAO \cong \triangle EAR$. (S. A. S. postulate.)
6. KO = RE. (Corresponding parts of congruent triangles are equal.)

Proof for Exercise 2.

1. MO = XI in circle O. (Given.)
2. $m\overset{\frown}{MO} = m\overset{\frown}{XI}$. (In a circle, if two chords are equal, their minor arcs are equal.)
3. $m\overset{\frown}{MO} + m\overset{\frown}{OI} = m\overset{\frown}{XI} + m\overset{\frown}{OI}$. (Addition.)
4. $m\overset{\frown}{MO} + m\overset{\frown}{OI} = m\overset{\frown}{MI}$ and $m\overset{\frown}{XI} + m\overset{\frown}{OI} = m\overset{\frown}{XO}$. (Arc Addition Postulate.)
5. $m\overset{\frown}{MI} = m\overset{\frown}{XO}$. (Substitution.)
6. MI = XO. (In a circle, if two minor arcs are equal, their chords are equal.)

Proof for Exercise 3.

1. $\overline{CA} \parallel \overline{HN}$. (Given.)
2. $\angle C = \angle NHI$. (If two parallel lines are cut by a transversal, the corresponding angles are equal.)
3. Draw $\overline{AH}$. (Two points determine a line.)
4. $\angle CAH = \angle AHN$. (If two parallel lines are cut by a transversal, the alternate interior angles are equal.)
5. CH = HA. (All radii of a circle are equal.)
6. $\angle C = \angle CAH$. (If two sides of a triangle are equal, the angles opposite them are equal.)
7. $\angle NHI = \angle AHN$. (Substitution.)
8. $m\overset{\frown}{AN} = m\overset{\frown}{NI}$. (In a circle, if two central angles are equal, their minor arcs are equal.)

Set III

1. The photograph is a time exposure. The stars seem to travel in circles about a point directly above the South Pole because of the earth's rotation on its axis.

2. Although the lengths of the arcs increase as their distances from the center of the circle increase, all of the arcs have the same measure. This is because they all have equal central angles (the angle through which the earth rotated during the time exposure).

Chapter 12, Lesson 4

Set I

2. Since $\angle Y$ is inscribed in a semicircle, it intercepts a semicircle. $\angle Y = \frac{1}{2}m\stackrel{\frown}{NX}$. But $m\stackrel{\frown}{NX} = 180°$, so $\angle Y = 90°$. Hence $\angle Y$ is a right angle.

Set II

Proof for Exercise 1.

1. $\overline{TA}$ is a diameter of circle O. (Given.)
2. $\stackrel{\frown}{APT}$ and $\stackrel{\frown}{AZT}$ are semicircles. (A semicircle is the set of points of a circle that lie on or on one side of a diameter.)
3. $\angle P$ and $\angle Z$ are right angles. (An angle inscribed in a semicircle is a right angle.)
4. $\angle P = \angle Z$. (Right angles are equal.)
5. $m\stackrel{\frown}{PA} = m\stackrel{\frown}{AZ}$. (Given.)
6. $\angle PTA = \angle ATZ$. (Inscribed angles that intercept equal arcs are equal.)
7. $TA = TA$. (Reflexive.)
8. $\triangle PAT \cong \triangle ZAT$. (A.A.S. Congruence Theorem.)

Proof for Exercise 2.

1. DIAN is a parallelogram. (Given.)
2. $\angle I = \angle N$. (The opposite angles of a parallelogram are equal.)
3. $\angle N = \angle M$. (Inscribed angles that intercept the same arc are equal.)
4. $\angle I = \angle M$. (Transitive.)
5. $DM = DI$. (If two angles of a triangle are equal, the sides opposite them are equal.)

Proof for Exercise 3.

1. BL = ER. (Given.)
2. $m\stackrel{\frown}{BL} = m\stackrel{\frown}{ER}$. (In a circle, if two chords are equal, their minor arcs are equal.)
3. Draw $\overline{BR}$. (Two points determine a line.)
4. $\angle EBR = \angle BRL$. (Inscribed angles that intercept equal arcs are equal.)
5. $\overline{BE} \parallel \overline{LR}$. (If two lines form equal alternate interior angles with a transversal, the lines are parallel.)

Set III

This time both Ollie and Alice are wrong. (Ollie thinks $m\stackrel{\frown}{AH} > m\stackrel{\frown}{MY}$ because $\stackrel{\frown}{AH}$ looks longer than $\stackrel{\frown}{MY}$. Alice thinks $m\stackrel{\frown}{AH} = m\stackrel{\frown}{MY}$ because they are both intercepted by $\angle T$. However, $\angle T$ is not inscribed in the smaller circle.)

Since $\angle T$ is inscribed in the larger circle, $\angle T = \frac{1}{2}m\stackrel{\frown}{AH}$. Draw $\overline{MS}$. Angle MSY is an inscribed angle in the smaller circle, so $\angle MSY = \frac{1}{2}m\stackrel{\frown}{MY}$. Since $\angle MSY$ is an exterior angle of $\triangle MST$, $\angle MSY > \angle T$. Substituting,

$$\frac{1}{2}m\stackrel{\frown}{MY} > \frac{1}{2}m\stackrel{\frown}{AH},$$

and multiplying,

$m\stackrel{\frown}{MY} > m\stackrel{\frown}{AH}$. So $m\stackrel{\frown}{AH} < m\stackrel{\frown}{MY}$.

Chapter 12, Lesson 5

Set I

Proof for Exercise 2.

1. Secant $\angle AKT$ with K outside circle O. (Hypothesis.)
2. Draw $\overline{ET}$. (Two points determine a line.)
3. $\angle AET = \angle AKT + \angle KTE$. (An exterior angle of a triangle is equal in measure to the sum of the measures of the two remote interior angles.)
4. $\angle AKT = \angle AET - \angle KTE$. (Subtraction.)
5. $\angle AET = \frac{1}{2}m\stackrel{\frown}{AT}$ and $\angle KTE = \frac{1}{2}m\stackrel{\frown}{EN}$. (An inscribed angle is equal in measure to half its intercepted arc.)
6. $\angle AKT = \frac{1}{2}m\stackrel{\frown}{AT} - \frac{1}{2}m\stackrel{\frown}{EN} = \frac{1}{2}(m\stackrel{\frown}{AT} - m\stackrel{\frown}{EN})$. (Substitution.)

*1. a) A central angle is a secant angle whose vertex is inside a circle.

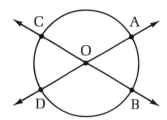

$$\angle AOB = \frac{1}{2}(m\,\widehat{AB} + m\,\widehat{CD}).$$

Since $\angle AOB = \angle COD$, $m\,\widehat{AB} = m\,\widehat{CD}$ (in a circle, if two central angles are equal, their minor arcs are equal).

So $\angle AOB = \frac{1}{2}(m\,\widehat{AB} + m\,\widehat{AB}) = \frac{1}{2}(2\,m\,\widehat{AB}) = m\,\widehat{AB}.$

c) An inscribed angle intercepts only one arc on a circle and its vertical angle does not intercept an arc at all.

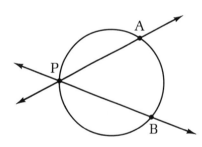

If we let $m\,\widehat{CD} = 0$ in the formulas

$$\angle APB = \frac{1}{2}(m\,\widehat{AB} + m\,\widehat{CD}) \text{ and}$$
$$\angle APB = \frac{1}{2}(m\,\widehat{AB} - m\,\widehat{CD}),$$

we get
$$\angle APB = \frac{1}{2}\,m\,\widehat{AB}.$$

Proof for Exercise 2.

1. $\overline{CA}$ and $\overline{PH}$ are chords of the larger circle. (Given.)
2. In the smaller circle, $\angle PIA = \frac{1}{2}m\,\widehat{LN}.$

   (An inscribed angle is equal in measure to half its intercepted arc.)

3. In the larger circle, $\angle PIA = \frac{1}{2}(m\,\widehat{PA} + m\,\widehat{CH})$. (A secant angle whose vertex is inside a circle is equal in measure to half the sum of the arcs intercepted by it and its vertical angle.)
4. $\frac{1}{2}m\,\widehat{LN} = \frac{1}{2}(m\,\widehat{PA} + m\,\widehat{CH})$. (Substitution.)
5. $m\,\widehat{LN} = m\,\widehat{PA} + m\,\widehat{CH}$. (Multiplication.)
6. $m\,\widehat{LN} > m\,\widehat{CH}$. (The "whole greater than its part" theorem.)

Proof for Exercise 3.

1. $\angle C$ is a secant angle of the circle. (Given.)
2. $\angle C = \frac{1}{2}(m\,\widehat{AS} - m\,\widehat{HE})$. (A secant angle whose vertex is outside a circle is equal in measure to half the positive difference of its intercepted arcs.)
3. $m\,\widehat{AS} = 2\,m\,\widehat{HE}$. (Given.)
4. $\angle C = \frac{1}{2}(2\,m\,\widehat{HE} - m\,\widehat{HE}) = \frac{1}{2}m\,\widehat{HE}$. (Substitution.)
5. $\angle A = \frac{1}{2}m\,\widehat{HE}$. (An inscribed angle is equal in measure to half its intercepted arc.)
6. $\angle C = \angle A$. (Substitution.)
7. $\overline{AE} = \overline{CE}$. (If two angles of a triangle are equal, the sides opposite them are equal.)
8. $\triangle ACE$ is isosceles. (If two sides of a triangle are equal, the triangle is isosceles.)

Set III

As the king walks toward the statue, the angle becomes larger until he gets to point B. Beyond this point, the angle becomes smaller again.

The angle is at its largest at B because it is an inscribed angle that intercepts just the arc of the circle corresponding to the statue. All other viewing angles are secant angles whose vertices are outside the circle; therefore, each is measured by half the difference of the statue arc and another arc of the circle.

Chapter 12, Lesson 6

Set I

*1. b) $x^2 + 6^2 = (6 + 4)^2$, $x^2 + 36 = 100$, $x^2 = 64$, $x = 8$.

Set II

Proof for Exercise 1.

1. $\overline{JE}$ and $\overline{JS}$ are tangent segments from point J to circle T. (Given.)
2. JE = JS. (The tangent segments to a circle from an external point are equal.)
3. Draw $\overline{TE}$ and $\overline{TS}$. (Two points determine a line.)
4. TE = TS. (All radii of a circle are equal.)
5. JT = JT. (Reflexive.)
6. $\triangle$JET $\cong$ $\triangle$JST. (S.S.S. postulate.)
7. $\angle$ EJT = $\angle$ SJT. (Corresponding parts of congruent triangles are equal.)
8. $\overrightarrow{JT}$ bisects $\angle$ EJS. (If a ray divides an angle into two equal angles, it bisects it.)

Proof for Exercise 2.

1. The sides of $\triangle$OBN are tangent to the circle and BO = BN. (Given.)
2. BO = BR + RO and BN = BS + SN. (Betweenness of points.)
3. BR + RO = BS + SN. (Substitution.)
4. BR = BS. (The tangent segments to a circle from an external point are equal.)
5. RO = SN. (Subtraction.)
6. OW = RO and WN = SN. (Same as step 4.)
7. OW = WN. (Substitution.)

Proof for Exercise 3.

1. Circle S with diameter $\overline{CF}$ and tangents $\overline{CH}$, $\overline{HE}$, and $\overline{EF}$. (Given.)
2. $\overline{CH} \perp \overline{CF}$ and $\overline{FE} \perp \overline{CF}$. (If a line is tangent to a circle, it is perpendicular to the radius drawn to the point of contact.)
3. $\overline{CH} \parallel \overline{FE}$. (In a plane, two lines perpendicular to a third line are parallel to each other.)
4. CHEF is a trapezoid. (A quadrilateral with exactly one pair of parallel sides is a trapezoid.)
5. $\overline{CF}$ is an altitude of trapezoid CHEF. (A segment that joins the bases of a trapezoid and is perpendicular to both of them is an altitude of the trapezoid.)
6. αCHEF = $\frac{1}{2}$CF(CH + FE). (The area of a trapezoid is half the product of its altitude and the sum of the lengths of its bases.)
7. CH = HI and FE = IE. (The tangent segments to a circle from an external point are equal.)

8. αCHEF = $\frac{1}{2}$CF(HI + IE). (Substitution.)
9. HE = HI + IE. (Betweenness of points.)
10. αCHEF = $\frac{1}{2}$CF$\cdot$HE. (Substitution.)

Set III

Since the tangent segments to a circle from an external point are equal, the lengths of the segments of the quadrilateral can be labeled as shown.

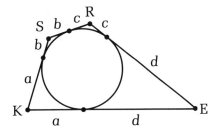

It is evident from this that, if a circle can be inscribed in a quadrilateral, the sum of the lengths of the opposite sides of the quadrilateral are equal:

$$KS + RE = KE + SR,$$
so
$$24 + 40 = KE + 14,$$
and
$$KE = 50.$$

This method cannot be applied to the triangle because the lengths of two sides of a triangle in which a circle has been inscribed do not determine the length of the triangle's third side. We will prove in the next chapter that a circle can be inscribed in <u>every</u> triangle.

Chapter 12, Lesson 7

Set I

*3. a) $3x = 2\cdot6$, $x = 4$.

   b) $x^2 = 3\cdot8$, $x = \sqrt{24} = 2\sqrt{6}$.

   c) $8\cdot3 = (2 + x)2$, $4 + 2x = 24$, $x = 10$.

   d) $20\cdot7 = x\cdot4$, $x = 35$.

Set II

Proof for Exercise 1.

1. $\overline{IE}$ and $\overline{IN}$ are secants to circle O. (Given.)

2. $IE \cdot ID = IN \cdot IS$. (If two secant segments are drawn to a circle from an external point, the product of the lengths of one secant segment and its external part is equal to the product of the lengths of the other secant segment and its external part.)
3. $IE = IN$. (Given.)
4. $ID = IS$. (Division.)

Proof for Exercise 2.

1. Chords $\overline{WS}$ and $\overline{IH}$ intersect at G. (Given.)
2. $WG \cdot GS = IG \cdot GH$. (If two chords intersect in a circle, the product of the lengths of the segments of one chord is equal to the product of the lengths of the segments of the other.)
3. $\dfrac{WG}{IG} = \dfrac{GH}{GS}$. (Division.)
4. $\overrightarrow{RT}$ bisects $\angle WGI$ and $\angle HGS$.
5. $\dfrac{WR}{RI} = \dfrac{WG}{IG}$ and $\dfrac{HT}{TS} = \dfrac{GH}{GS}$. (An angle bisector of a triangle divides the opposite side into segments having the same ratio as the other two sides.)
6. $\dfrac{WR}{RI} = \dfrac{HT}{TS}$. (Substitution.)

Set III

The problem seems to say something to the effect that in $\triangle ABC$, the bisector of $\angle BAC$ intersects $\overline{BC}$ in point D and the circle in point E.

1. In $\triangle ABE$ and $\triangle ADC$, $\angle BAE = \angle DAC$ (it seems to be given that $\angle BAC$ is bisected) and $\angle E = \angle C$ (inscribed angles that intercept the same arc are equal). So $\triangle ABE \sim \triangle ADC$ (A.A. Similarity Theorem).

2. $\dfrac{AB}{AD} = \dfrac{AE}{AC}$ (corresponding sides of similar triangles are proportional), so $AB \cdot AC = AD \cdot AE$ (means-extremes theorem).

3. Since $AE = AD + DE$ (betweenness of points), $AB \cdot AC = AD(AD + DE)$ (substitution). Hence $AB \cdot AC = AD^2 + AD \cdot DE$. Subtracting, $AD^2 = AB \cdot AC - AD \cdot DE$. But $AD \cdot DE = BD \cdot DC$ (the Intersecting Chords Theorem), so $AD^2 = AB \cdot AC - BD \cdot DC$ (substitution).

Chapter 12, Lesson 8

Set I

4. a)

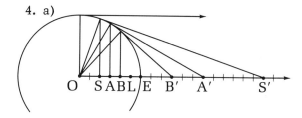

b) After the radius at point O has been drawn perpendicular to the inverse line, it is evident that the tangent at its outer endpoint is parallel to the inverse line. Hence they do not intersect, which is consistent with the fact that O has no inverse.

Set II

3. The inverse of line ℓ is, except for the center of the inversion circle, line ℓ itself.

4. The inverse of $\overline{AB}$ seems to be an arc of a circle as shown in this figure.

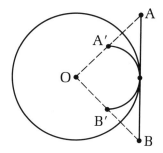

Set III

The eyes and smile of the happy face invert into eyes above and a smile below, as shown here. The nose does not have an inverse.

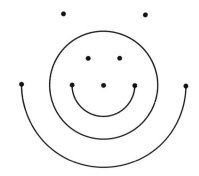

Chapter 12, Lesson 9

Set I

2. d) As the line moves toward O, the center of the inversion circle, its inverse is, except for O, a circle through O that becomes larger and larger. When the line makes it to O, its inverse becomes, except for O, the line itself.

Set II

*1. a)

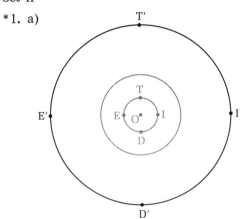

b)

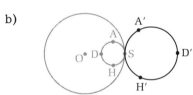

c)

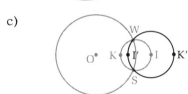

d)

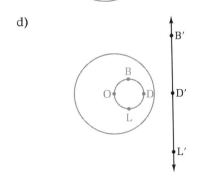

2. The inverse of a circle that does not pass through the center of the inversion circle is a circle. If a circle passes through the center of the inversion circle, its inverse is a line.

Set III

1. Points X, A, and C are collinear because they are each equidistant from B and D and hence lie on the perpendicular bisector of $\overline{BD}$.

2. Since quadrilateral ABCD is a rhombus, it is also a parallelogram. The diagonals of a parallelogram bisect each other.

3. The diagonals of a rhombus are perpendicular to each other.

4. The Pythagorean Theorem, since △XOB and △AOB are right triangles.

5. Subtraction.

Chapter 12, Review

Set I

*2. b) $8x = 11 \cdot 12$, $x = 16.5$.

c) $x = \frac{1}{2}(95^o + 105^o) = 100^o$.

e) $(5 + x) \cdot 5 = 10 \cdot 4$, $25 + 5x = 40$, $x = 3$.

f) $(5 + x) \cdot 4 = 5^2$, $20 + 4x = 25$, $x = 1.25$.

g) $x = \frac{1}{2}(330^o - 10^o) = 160^o$.

*Set III

This figure shows the astronaut's apparent path, starting at A and ending at C.

Since ∠B is an inscribed right angle, m $\overset{\frown}{AC}$ = 180°. So $\overset{\frown}{AC}$ is a semicircle and $\overline{AC}$ is a diameter. $AC^2 = AB^2 + BC^2$, $(2r)^2 = 14^2 + 48^2$, $r^2 = 625$, $r = 25$.

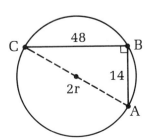

Chapter 13, Lesson 1

Set I

2.

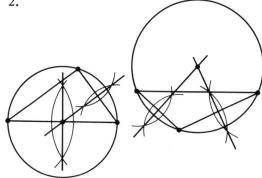

4. a)

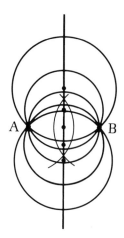

Set II

Proof for Exercise 3.

1. △STA with circumcircle R. (Given.)
2. $\overline{TA}$ is a diameter of circle R. (A chord that contains the center of a circle is a diameter of the circle.)
3. $\overset{\frown}{TSA}$ is a semicircle. (A set of points of a circle that lie on or on one side of a line containing a diameter is a semicircle.)
4. ∠S is a right angle. (An angle inscribed in a semicircle is a right angle.)
5. ∠S = 90°. (A right angle has a measure of 90°.)
6. ∠TWA > ∠S. (An exterior angle of a triangle is greater than either remote interior angle.)
7. ∠TWA > 90°. (Substitution.)

8. ∠TWA is obtuse. (An angle with a measure greater than 90° is obtuse.)
9. △WTA is obtuse. (A triangle with an obtuse angle is obtuse.)

Set III

The first diagram shown here suggests that Ollie's path is along an arc of a circle.

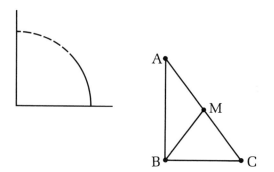

In the second diagram, $\overline{AC}$ represents the ladder, $\overline{BA}$ the wall, and $\overline{BC}$ the floor. Ollie is at M, the midpoint of the hypotenuse of right △ABC.

From the assumption that the midpoint of the hypotenuse of a right triangle is its circumcenter, it follows that M must be equidistant from A, B, and C. In other words, MA = MB = MC. But since $\overline{MA}$ and $\overline{MC}$ do not change in length as the ladder slides down the wall, this means that $\overline{MB}$ does not change either. Since for every position of the ladder Ollie remains the same distance from B, his path is along an arc of a circle.

Chapter 13, Lesson 2

Set II

Proof for Exercise 1.

1. Quadrilateral DRKE is cyclic. (Given.)
2. ∠D and ∠RKE are supplementary. (The opposite angles of a cyclic quadrilateral are supplementary.)
3. ∠AKR and ∠RKE are supplementary. (If two angles are a linear pair, they are supplementary.)
4. ∠D = ∠AKR. (Supplements of the same angle are equal.)
5. ∠A = ∠A. (Reflexive.)
6. △ARK ~ △AED. (A.A. Similarity Theorem.)

Proof for Exercise 2.

1. MTEF is a parallelogram. (Given.)
2. ∠F and ∠E are supplementary. (The consecutive angles of a parallelogram are supplementary.)
3. MNRF is a cyclic quadrilateral. (A quadrilateral is cyclic if there exists a circle that contains all of its vertices.)
4. ∠F and ∠MNR are supplementary. (The opposite angles of a cyclic quadrilateral are supplementary.)
5. ∠E = ∠MNR. (Supplements of the same are equal.)
6. ∠MNR and ∠RNT are supplementary. (If two angles are a linear pair, they are supplementary.)
7. ∠MNR + ∠RNT = 180°. (If two angles are supplementary, the sum of their measures is 180°.)
8. ∠E + ∠RNT = 180°. (Substitution.)
9. ∠E and ∠RNT are supplementary. (If the sum of the measures of two angles is 180°, they are supplementary.)
10. NTER is cyclic. (A quadrilateral is cyclic if a pair of its opposite angles are supplementary.)

Set III

Each of these lines is perpendicular to the opposite side of the quadrilateral.

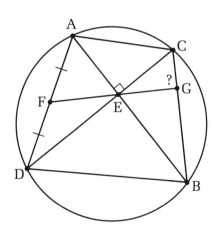

In the figure shown here, we are claiming that, if $\overline{AB} \perp \overline{CD}$ and F is the midpoint of $\overline{AD}$, then $\overline{FG} \perp \overline{CB}$. The proof of this is based upon the fact that the midpoint of the hypotenuse of a right triangle is its circumcenter (suggested by Exercise 3a in Set I of Lesson 1).

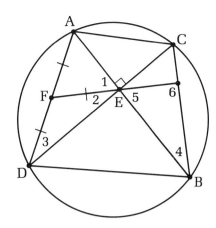

Because △AED is a right triangle and F is its circumcenter, FA = FE = FD. Since FE = FD, ∠2 = ∠3; also ∠3 = ∠4 (inscribed angles that intercept the same arc are equal), so ∠2 = ∠4. Furthermore, ∠1 = ∠5. Since ∠1 + ∠2 = 90°, it follows that ∠5 + ∠4 = 90° (substitution). Since ∠4 + ∠5 + ∠6 = 180°, ∠6 = 90°, so $\overline{FG} \perp \overline{CB}$.

Chapter 13, Lesson 3

Set I

2. b)

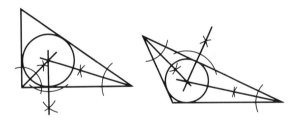

Set II

1. If SNEA is a rhombus, AS = AE because all four sides of a rhombus are equal. Also SD = DE because all rhombuses are parallelograms and the diagonals of a parallelogram bisect each other. Furthermore, AD = AD. So △SDA ≅ △EDA (S.S.S.). Since ∠SAD = ∠EAD, $\overrightarrow{AN}$ bisects ∠SAE.

Proof for Exercise 3.

1. Quadrilateral NCLU has a circle inscribed in it. (Given.)

2. $\overline{NC}$, $\overline{CL}$, $\overline{LU}$, and $\overline{UN}$ are tangent to the circle. (If a circle is inscribed in a quadrilateral, each side of the quadrilateral is tangent to the circle.)
3. NI = NS, IC = CK, KL = AL, and UA = SU. (The tangents to a circle from an external point are equal.)
4. NC = NI + IC, UL = UA + AL, NU = NS + SU, and CL = CK + KL. (Betweenness of points.)
5. NC + UL = NI + IC + UA + AL. (Addition.)
6. NC + UL = NS + CK + SU + KL = NS + SU + CK + KL = NU + CL. (Substitution.)

Set III

Circle O is inscribed in right △ABC and radii have been drawn to the points of tangency. Since the tangents to a circle from an external point are equal, we can label their lengths as shown in the figure. Since AMON is a square (it can be proved both equiangular and equilateral), OM = c. So 2OM = 2c and AB + AC - BC = (c + b) + (a + c) - (a + b) = 2c. Hence 2OM = AB + AC - BC.

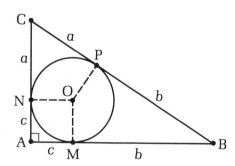

Chapter 13, Lesson 4

Set II

2. Since $\overline{WD}$, $\overline{NO}$, and $\overline{SI}$ are concurrent, $\dfrac{WI}{IN} \cdot \dfrac{ND}{DS} \cdot \dfrac{SO}{OW} = 1$. Also, since I and D are the midpoints of $\overline{WN}$ and $\overline{NS}$, respectively, WI = IN and ND = DS. Hence $\dfrac{WI}{WI} \cdot \dfrac{ND}{ND} \cdot \dfrac{SO}{OW} = 1$ (substitution). So $\dfrac{SO}{OW} = 1$ and SO = OW (multiplication). Therefore, O is the midpoint of $\overline{SW}$.

Proof for Exercise 3.

1. Cevians $\overline{EA}$, $\overline{MT}$, and $\overline{HL}$ in △HEM are concurrent. (Given.)
2. $\dfrac{MA}{AH} \cdot \dfrac{HT}{TE} \cdot \dfrac{EL}{LM} = 1$. (Ceva's Theorem.)
3. TE = 2HT and LM = 3EL. (Given.)
4. $\dfrac{MA}{AH} \cdot \dfrac{HT}{2HT} \cdot \dfrac{EL}{3EL} = 1$, $\dfrac{MA}{AH} \cdot \dfrac{1}{2} \cdot \dfrac{1}{3} = 1$. (Substitution.)
5. MA = 6AH. (Multiplication.)

Set III

Gergonne's proof is based upon Ceva's Theorem and the fact that the tangent segments to a circle from an external point are equal. According to Ceva's Theorem, if $\dfrac{VE}{ER} \cdot \dfrac{RO}{ON} \cdot \dfrac{NA}{AV} = 1$, then $\overline{VO}$, $\overline{RA}$, and $\overline{NE}$ are concurrent. Since $\overline{VR}$, $\overline{RN}$, and $\overline{NV}$ are tangent to the circle, VE = VA, RE = RO, and NA = NO. Substituting for VE, RE, and NA in the product $\dfrac{VE}{ER} \cdot \dfrac{RO}{ON} \cdot \dfrac{NA}{AV}$, we get $\dfrac{VA}{RO} \cdot \dfrac{RO}{ON} \cdot \dfrac{NO}{AV}$. Since this product is equal to 1, the three cevians are concurrent.

Chapter 13, Lesson 5

Set I

1. a)

c)

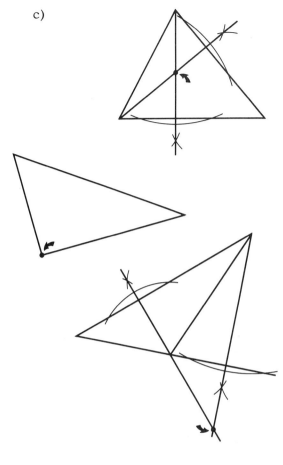

2. a)

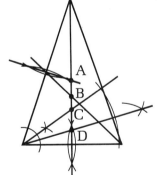

A: Circumcenter
B: Centroid
C: Incenter
D: Orthocenter

2. Since $\overline{RU}$ and $\overline{TO}$ are medians of $\triangle RPT$, O and U are midpoints of its sides and $\overline{OU}$ is a midsegment of the triangle.

Hence $\overline{OU} \parallel \overline{RT}$ and OU = $\frac{1}{2}$RT (a mid-

segment of a triangle is parallel to the third side and half as long). Further-more, since A and L are the midpoints of $\overline{RG}$ and $\overline{TG}$, $\overline{AL}$ is a midsegment of $\triangle RGT$, so that

$$\overline{AL} \parallel \overline{RT} \text{ and } AL = \frac{1}{2}RT.$$

Therefore, $\overline{OU} \parallel \overline{AL}$ (in a plane, two lines parallel to a third line are parallel to each other) and OU = AL (substitu-tion).

Hence ALUO is a parallelogram; AG = GU because the diagonals of a parallelogram bisect each other. Final-ly, RA = AG = GU (transitive).

Set III

1. MNOP looks like a parallelogram.

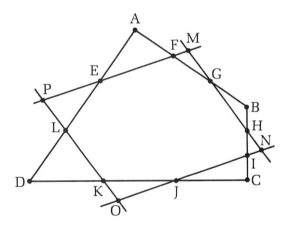

2. The point in which the diagonals of the parallelogram intersect (which is its point of symmetry). (This point was discovered by F. Wittenbauer and is mentioned in an exercise in Introduc-tion to Geometry, 2nd ed., by H.S.M. Coxeter, Wiley, 1969, p. 216.)

Set II

1. c) $\dfrac{GU}{GA} \cdot \dfrac{IN}{IU} \cdot \dfrac{EA}{EN} = \dfrac{GE}{GI} \cdot \dfrac{IG}{IE} \cdot \dfrac{EI}{EG}$ (multipli-

cation). $\dfrac{GU}{UI} \cdot \dfrac{IN}{NE} \cdot \dfrac{EA}{AG} = 1$ (substitution).

$\overleftrightarrow{GN}$, $\overleftrightarrow{IA}$ and $\overleftrightarrow{EU}$ are concurrent.
(Ceva's Theorem.)

Chapter 13, Lesson 6

Set I

4.

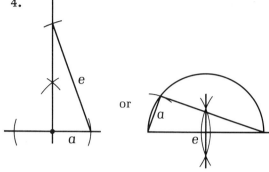

5.

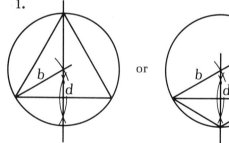

Set II

1.

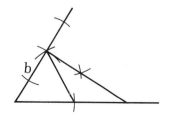

or

2.

3.

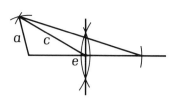

4.

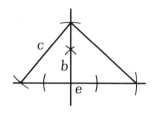

or

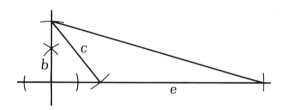

Set III

The fifth triangle seems also to be equilateral. (A proof of this is in a section titled "Napoleon triangles" in Geometry Revisited, by H. S. M. Coxeter and S. L. Greitzer, Random House, 1967, pp. 60-65.)

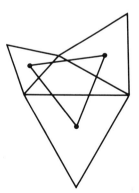

Chapter 13, Review

Set II

*4. $\dfrac{3}{6} \cdot \dfrac{8}{x} \cdot \dfrac{4}{5} = 1$, $5x = 16$, $x = 3.2$.

*5. (Since S is the incenter of △PEA, it lies on the bisector of each angle of the triangle.)

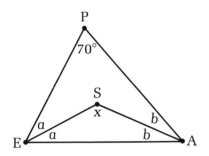

In △PEA, $\angle P + \angle PEA + \angle PAE = 70° + 2a + 2b = 180°$. Hence $2a + 2b = 110°$ and $a + b = 55°$. In △SEA, $\angle S + \angle SEA + \angle SAE = x + a + b = 180°$. Since $a + b = 55°$, $x = 125°$.

*Set III

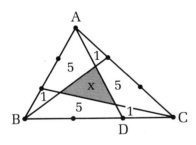

Choosing $\overline{BD}$ and $\overline{DC}$ as the bases of △ABD and △ADC, we see that they have the same altitude (a perpendicular segment from A to $\overleftrightarrow{BC}$). Hence

$$\frac{\alpha \triangle ABD}{\alpha \triangle ADC} = \frac{BD}{DC}.$$

(If two triangles have equal altitudes, the ratio of their areas is equal to the ratio of their bases.)

Since D is a point of trisection of $\overline{BC}$, BD = 2DC. So

$$\frac{\alpha \triangle ABD}{\alpha \triangle ADC} = \frac{2DC}{DC} = 2 \text{ and}$$

$$\alpha \triangle ABD = 2\,\alpha \triangle ADC.$$

But $\alpha \triangle ABD = 11 + x$ and $\alpha \triangle ADC = 7$, so
$$11 + x = 2(7) \text{ and } x = 3.$$
Since the new farm has an area of 3 acres and the original one had an area of 21 acres, the new farm has one-seventh the area of the original one.

(This problem is based upon the following theorem, discovered by E.J. Routh.

"If the sides $\overline{BC}$, $\overline{CA}$, $\overline{AB}$ of △ABC are divided at X, Y, Z in the ratios
$$\frac{a}{1}, \frac{b}{1}, \frac{c}{1},$$
respectively, the cevians $\overline{AX}$, $\overline{BY}$, $\overline{CZ}$ form a triangle whose area is
$$\frac{(abc - 1)^2}{(ab + a + 1)(bc + b + 1)(ca + c + 1)}$$
times that of △ABC."

It is discussed in Introduction to Geometry, 2nd ed., by H.S.M. Coxeter, Wiley, 1969, p. 211.)

Chapter 14, Lesson 1

Set I

2. a)

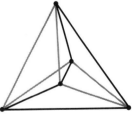

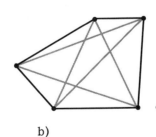

b)

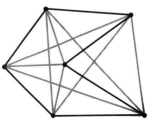

In Exercise 1 of Set II, we found that the sum of the measures of the angles of a convex n-gon seems to be $(n - 2)180°$. Hence the sum for a convex hexagon would be $(6 - 2)180° = 720°$.

The hexagon in Washington's map, however, is concave. Because of this, there is a problem with the measure of $\angle B$. If we consider it to have a measure of $360° - 100° = 260°$, then the sum of the six angles would be $260° - 100° = 160°$ larger than the sum found.

Chapter 14, Lesson 2

Set I

1. b) An example:

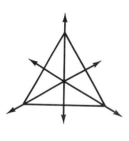

*4.

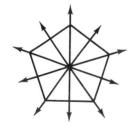

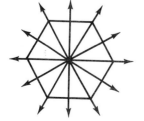

2. a)

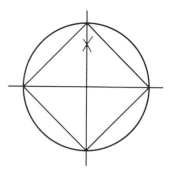

b)

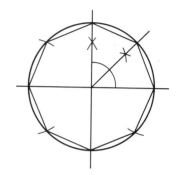

c)

Proof for Exercise 3.

1. NOUGA is a regular polygon with central angles 1 and 2. (Given.)
2. Circumscribe circle T about NOUGA. (Every regular polygon is cyclic.)
3. AN = GU. (A regular polygon is equilateral.)
4. $\overline{TN}$, $\overline{TA}$, $\overline{TG}$, and $\overline{TU}$ are radii. (A central angle of a regular polygon is formed by radii drawn to two consecutive vertices.)
5. TN = TG and TA = TU. (All radii of a circle are equal.)
6. $\triangle TNA \cong \triangle TGU$. (S.S.S. postulate.)
7. $\angle 1 = \angle 2$. (Corresponding parts of congruent triangles are equal.)

Set III

Dissection puzzles:

1.

2.

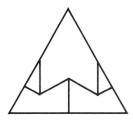

3.

Chapter 14, Lesson 3

Set II

*2. a) $\rho_{triangle} = 2(3 \sin 60^{\circ})10 = 60(.866) = 51.96.$

b) $\rho_{hexagon} = 2(6 \sin 30^{\circ})10 = 120(.500) = 60.$

c) $\rho_{dodecagon} = 2(12 \sin 15^{\circ})10 = 240(.259) = 62.16.$

*3. $\rho_{polygon} = 2(180 \sin 1^{\circ}) = 180(.0175) = 3.15.$

Set III

1. As the turtle draws the polygon, it turns through 360°. Since each side of the polygon corresponds to a change in direction of $1"$, and $1^{\circ} = 3600"$, the turtle would draw a regular $360(3600) = 1,296,000$-gon.

2. The perimeter of this polygon would be $1,296,000$ feet, since each side is one foot long.

$$\frac{1,296,000 \text{ ft}}{5280 \text{ ft/mi}} \approx 245.5 \text{ mi}$$

The turtle would travel almost 246 miles.

Chapter 14, Lesson 4

Set II

*1. a) $\rho_{decagon} = 2(10 \sin 18^{\circ})11 = 220(.309) = 67.98 \approx 68$ units.

b) $\alpha_{decagon} = (10 \sin 18^{\circ}) \cos 18^{\circ} (11)^2 = 1210(.2939) = 355.619 \approx 356$ square units.

*2. a) $\alpha_{regular\ 30\text{-gon}} = (30 \sin 6^{\circ}) \cos 6^{\circ} r^2 = 30(.1040) r^2 = 3.12r^2.$

b) $\alpha_{regular\ 90\text{-gon}} = (90 \sin 2^{\circ}) \cos 2^{\circ} r^2 = 90(.03488) r^2 = 3.1392 r^2.$

c) Although a regular 90-gon has three times as many sides as a regular 30-gon, the two polygons look very much alike because they both look circular. It follows that, if they have the same radius, their areas should be almost the same.

Set III

To compare the amounts of light let in by the two windows, we need to compare their areas.

It is easy to show that the right triangle formed by the two radii shown in this figure is a 30°-60° right triangle.

If we label the length of its short leg x, the lengths of its hypotenuse and longer leg must be 2x and $x\sqrt{3}$, respectively. We showed in Exercise 3 of Set I that the ratio of the areas of two regular polygons that have the same number of sides is equal to the square of the ratio of their radii. Since the ratio of the radii of the two windows (comparing smaller with larger) is $\frac{x\sqrt{3}}{2x}$, the ratio of their areas is $(\frac{x\sqrt{3}}{2x})^2 = \frac{3}{4}$.

The smaller window lets in three-fourths of the light let in by the larger.

Chapter 14, Lesson 5

Set III

The stack of elephants would have a finite height.

The height of the stack of

the first two elephants

$$10 + \frac{1}{2}10 = 1\frac{1}{2}(10); =$$

the first three elephants =

$$10 + \frac{1}{2}10 + \frac{1}{4}10 = 1\frac{3}{4}(10);$$

the first four elephants =

$$10 + \frac{1}{2}10 + \frac{1}{4}10 + \frac{1}{8}10 = 1\frac{7}{8}(10);$$

the first five elephants =

$$10 + \frac{1}{2}10 + \frac{1}{4}10 + \frac{1}{8}10 + \frac{1}{16}10 = 1\frac{15}{16}(10).$$

It seems that, as the number of elephants in the stack increases, the height of the stack gets closer and closer to 2(10) = 20 feet. It seems to approach 20 feet as its limit.

Chapter 14, Lesson 6

Set I

*5. $\pi = 3.1415926\ldots$, $\frac{355}{113} = 3.1415929\ldots$.

Set II

*2. a) $\pi 6^2 - \pi 3^2 = 36\pi - 9\pi = 27\pi$ square units.

b) $8^2 - \pi 4^2 = 64 - 16\pi$ square units.

c) $\pi 5^2 - 6 \cdot 8 = 25\pi - 48$ square units.

*3. $c = 2\pi r$, so $r = \frac{c}{2\pi}$. $r = \frac{47}{2(3.14)} \approx$ 7.5 inches.

*4. a) $\rho_{hexagon} = 6(5) = 30$ centimeters.

b) $c_{circle} = 2\pi(5) = 10(3.14) \approx 31.4$ centimeters.

c) $\alpha_{hexagon} = (6\sin 30^o)\cos 30^o(5^2) =$ 150(.4330) = 64.95 $\approx$ 65 square centimeters.

d) $\alpha_{circle} = \pi 5^2 = 25(3.14) \approx 78.5$ square centimeters.

*5. In one year the earth moves about $2\pi(93)$ million miles. In one day it moves about $\frac{2\pi(93)}{365}$ million miles ≈ 1.6 million miles.

Set III

If the wheel-creature assumes a circular shape with a radius of $\frac{1}{6}$ foot, it travels $2\pi(\frac{1}{6}) = \frac{\pi}{3}$ feet in one revolution. To travel 100 feet, it must make $\frac{100}{\frac{\pi}{3}} = \frac{300}{\pi}$ revolutions. (This is about 95.5 revolutions.) In each revolution, a point on the rim of the creature travels along one arc of the cycloid. Since one arc of the cycloid has a length of $4(2 \cdot \frac{1}{6}) = \frac{4}{3}$ feet, a point on the rim must travel about $\frac{300}{\pi}(\frac{4}{3}) = \frac{400}{\pi} \approx 127$ feet.

Chapter 14, Lesson 7

Set II

*1. a) $\frac{40}{360}\pi 5^2 = \frac{25}{9}\pi \approx 8.7$, or approximately 9 square inches.

b) $\frac{320}{360}\pi 5^2 = \frac{200}{9}\pi \approx 69.8$, or approximately 70 square inches.

*2. $\frac{1}{4}\pi 2^2 - \frac{1}{2}2^2 = \pi - 2$ square units.

*3. $\frac{1}{60} 2\pi 30 = \pi \approx 3$ inches.

*4. a) $\frac{1}{3}(\pi 10^2 - \frac{(10\sqrt{3})^2}{4}\sqrt{3}) =$

$\frac{1}{3}(100\pi - \frac{300}{4}\sqrt{3}) = \frac{100}{3}\pi - 25\sqrt{3}$

square units.

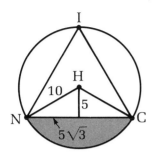

b) $\pi(\sqrt{10})^2 - 5\cdot 2^2 = 10\pi - 20$ square units.

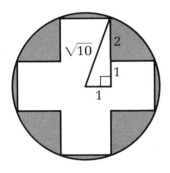

c) $2(\frac{1}{4}\pi 4^2 - \frac{1}{2}4^2) = 8\pi - 16$ square units.

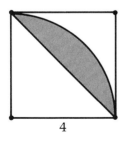

Set III

The area within biting distance is $\frac{1}{4}\pi 3^2 +$

$\frac{3}{4}\pi 15^2 + \frac{1}{4}\pi 5^2 = \frac{9}{4}\pi + \frac{675}{4}\pi + \frac{25}{4}\pi = \frac{709}{4}\pi$

square feet. (This is approximately 560 square feet.)

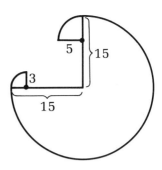

Chapter 14, Review

Set I

*5. b) $\alpha_{nonagon} = 9\sin 20^o(\cos 20^o)10^2 =$
900(.3214) = 289.26 ≈ 289 square units.

$\alpha_{decagon} = 10\sin 18^o(\cos 18^o)10^2 =$
1000(.2939) = 293.9 ≈ 294 square units.

Set II

*2. b) $\frac{1}{6} 2\pi 3 = \pi \approx 3.14$ units.

c) 3.14 - 3 = 0.14 units.

d) $\frac{2(60\sin 3^o)30}{60} = 60(.052) = 3.12$ units.

e) $\frac{1}{60} 2\pi 30 = \pi \approx 3.14$ units.

f) 3.14 - 3.12 = 0.02 units.

*3. a) $\pi 3^2 - \pi 2^2 = 9\pi - 4\pi = 5\pi$ square units.

b) $\frac{\sqrt{3}}{4}(10\sqrt{3})^2 - \pi 5^2 = 75\sqrt{3} - 25\pi$ square units.

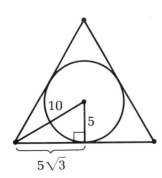

*3.

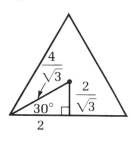 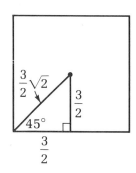

$r_{\text{triangle}} = \dfrac{4}{\sqrt{3}} = \dfrac{4\sqrt{3}}{3} \approx 2.3$ units.

$\alpha_{\text{triangle}} = \dfrac{\sqrt{3}}{4}\,4^2 = 4\sqrt{3} \approx 6.9$ square units.

$r_{\text{square}} = \dfrac{3}{2}\sqrt{2} \approx 2.1$ units.

$\alpha_{\text{square}} = 3^2 = 9$ square units.

Chapter 15, Lesson 1

Set II

1. Since V ∥ O, planes V and O do not intersect (if two planes are parallel, they do not intersect). Since $\overleftrightarrow{ER}$ and $\overleftrightarrow{NT}$ lie in V and O, respectively, this implies that they do not intersect either. But $\overleftrightarrow{ER}$ and $\overleftrightarrow{NT}$ both lie in plane M. Hence $\overleftrightarrow{ER} \parallel \overleftrightarrow{NT}$ (two lines that lie in the same plane and do not intersect are parallel).

Proof for Exercise 2.

1. $\overline{TX} \perp S.$ (Given.)
2. $\overline{TX} \perp \overline{XE}$ and $\overline{TX} \perp \overline{XA}.$ (If a line and plane are perpendicular, the line is perpendicular to every line in the plane that passes through the point of intersection.)
3. ∠TXE and ∠TXA are right angles. (Perpendicular lines form right angles.)
4. △TXE and △TXA are right triangles. (A triangle having a right angle is a right triangle.)
5. TE = TA. (Given.)

6. TX = TX. (Reflexive.)
7. △TXE ≅ △TXA. (H.L. Congruence Theorem.)
8. ∠E = ∠A. (Corresponding parts of congruent triangles are equal.)

3. a) Suppose planes M and I intersect in a line and E is a point on this line. Since $\overleftrightarrow{AN}$ is perpendicular to planes M and I, $\overleftrightarrow{AN} \perp \overleftrightarrow{AE}$ and $\overleftrightarrow{AN} \perp \overleftrightarrow{NE}$ (if a line and plane are perpendicular, the line is perpendicular to every line in the plane that passes through the point of intersection).

   This means that through point E, there are two lines, $\overleftrightarrow{EA}$ and $\overleftrightarrow{EN}$, both perpendicular to $\overleftrightarrow{AN}.$ But through a point not on a line, there is exactly one perpendicular to the line.

   b) This contradiction implies that our original supposition that the planes are not parallel is false. Hence M ∥ N.

Set III

The impossibility is in the way in which the first floor columns are connected to the second floor. As a result, someone climbing the ladder starts inside the building but ends up outside upon reaching the top.

Chapter 15, Lesson 2

Set II

1. a) This figure shows the closet as seen through the door. By the Pythagorean Theorem, $x^2 = 6^2 + 2^2 = 40$, so $x = \sqrt{40} = 2\sqrt{10} \approx 2(3.16) = 6.32$ feet. But the skis are $6\frac{10}{12} \approx 6.83$ feet long.

b) Dilcue could put the skis in the closet so that they fall along one of its diagonals.

$$d = \sqrt{2^2 + 3^2 + 6^2} = \sqrt{49} = 7 \text{ feet.}$$

2. Suppose the diagonals of a cube were perpendicular to each other. Then, since they are concurrent in the center of the cube, there would be four lines through a common point in space that are all perpendicular to each other. This is equivalent to saying that space has four dimensions. Since it has only three, our original assumption is false; the diagonals of a cube cannot be perpendicular.

3. Yes! It can be considered to be the silhouette of a cube, as this figure shows.

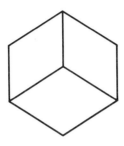

Set III

A tesseract seems to have 16 vertices, 32 edges, 24 "square faces" (of course, they are distorted in the shadow), and 8 "cubical faces."

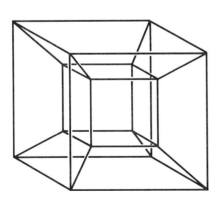

Chapter 15, Lesson 3

Set II

*2. $6(\frac{1}{8})(\frac{29}{4}) = \frac{87}{16} \approx 5.4$ square inches.

*3. $2 \cdot 3 + 2 \cdot 4 + 2 \cdot 5 + 2(\frac{1}{2}3 \cdot 4) = 36$ square inches.

Set III

1. There are two possible solutions.

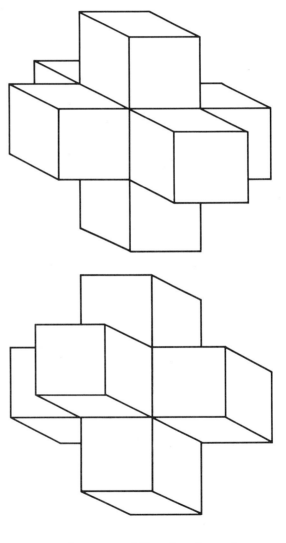

2. Two-dimensional line drawings of three-dimensional solids in which every edge is shown can be interpreted in two different ways. Many optical illusions are based upon this fact.

Chapter 15, Lesson 4

Set I

*4. b) $\frac{\sqrt{3}}{4}4^2 = 4\sqrt{3}$ square units.

d) $(4\sqrt{3})4 = 16\sqrt{3}$ cubic units.

Set II

*1. c)

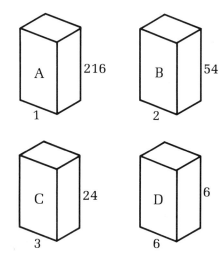

A. $4(1 \cdot 216) + 2(1^2) = 866$ square units.
B. $4(2 \cdot 54) + 2(2^2) = 440$ square units.
C. $4(3 \cdot 24) + 2(3^2) = 306$ square units.
D. $4(6 \cdot 6) + 2(6^2) = 216$ square units.

*2. $B = \frac{1}{2}2(14 + 10) = 24$, h = 2.

$V_{prism} = Bh = 48$ cubic feet.

*3. $V_{one\ step} = \frac{1}{2}(6 \cdot 8)30 = 720$ cubic inches.

$V_{staircase} = \frac{24(720)}{12^3} = 10$ cubic feet.

Set III

To find which wedge is larger, we will compare their volumes.

The area of a base of the first wedge is $\sqrt{15}$ square units and its altitude is 3 units. So its volume is $3\sqrt{15}$ cubic units.

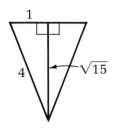

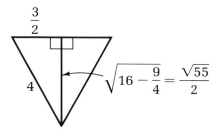

The area of a base of the second wedge is $\frac{3\sqrt{55}}{4}$ square units and its altitude is 2 units. So its volume is $\frac{3}{2}\sqrt{55}$ cubic units.

To find out which of these volumes is larger without referring to a table of square roots, we might do the following:

	First wedge	Second wedge
Volume	$3\sqrt{15}$	$\frac{3}{2}\sqrt{55}$
Divide by $3\sqrt{5}$	$\sqrt{3}$	$\frac{\sqrt{11}}{2}$
Square	3	$\frac{11}{4}$

Since $3 > \frac{11}{4}$, $\sqrt{3} > \frac{\sqrt{11}}{2}$ and $3\sqrt{15} > \frac{3}{2}\sqrt{55}$. The first wedge is larger.

Chapter 15, Lesson 5

Set II

*1. a) $\frac{1}{3}5^2 \cdot 9 = 75$ cubic units.

b) $\frac{1}{3}(\frac{1}{2}3 \cdot 8) \cdot \frac{1}{2} = 2$ cubic units.

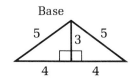

Base

c) $\frac{1}{3}(6 \cdot \frac{\sqrt{3}}{4} \cdot 2^2)14 = 28\sqrt{3}$ cubic units.

Base

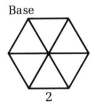

2

*2. b) Since $\overline{EN} \perp \overline{NO}$, $EO^2 = EN^2 + NO^2$.
$EO^2 = 7^2 + 4^2 = 65$, $EO = \sqrt{65}$ units.

c) Since $\overline{NO} \perp \overline{OR}$, $NR^2 = NO^2 + OR^2$.
$NR^2 = 4^2 + 4^2 = 32$, $NR = 4\sqrt{2}$ units.

d) Since $\overline{EN} \perp \overline{NR}$, $ER^2 = EN^2 + NR^2$.
$ER = 7^2 + (4\sqrt{2})^2 = 81$, $ER = 9$ units.

*3. One way: Since the six pyramids that make up the cube are identical, the volume of one of them is one-sixth the volume of the cube.
$$\frac{1}{6}(6^3) = 36 \text{ cubic units.}$$

Another way: The base of one of the pyramids is a square whose area is $6^2 = 36$ square units. Its altitude, half the altitude of the cube, is 3 units.
$$\frac{1}{3}36 \cdot 3 = 36 \text{ cubic units.}$$

*4. a) We can find the additional lengths shown in this figure by means of the Pythagorean Theorem.

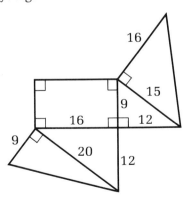

The lateral area is the sum of the areas of the four triangular faces.
$\frac{1}{2}9 \cdot 20 + \frac{1}{2}12 \cdot 16 + \frac{1}{2}9 \cdot 12 + \frac{1}{2}15 \cdot 16 = $
360 square units.

b) The base of the pyramid is a rectangle having the dimensions 16 and 9. The altitude of the pyramid is 12.
$$\frac{1}{3}(16 \cdot 9)12 = 576 \text{ cubic units.}$$

Set III

This is a trick question because it implies that a set of identical regular tetrahedra can be put together to form a larger one. Any student who has tried it knows that it can't be done. Although space can be filled with identical cubes, it cannot be filled with identical regular tetrahedra.

Chapter 15, Lesson 6

Set I

*1. a) $\pi 4^2 \cdot 111 = 1776\pi$ cubic units.

b) $\frac{1}{3}\pi 2^2 \cdot 1119 = 1492\pi$ cubic units.

c) $151 \cdot 12 = 1812$ cubic units.

*4. a) $\pi 3^2 \cdot 5 = 45\pi$ cubic units.

b) $\pi 5^2 \cdot 3 = 75\pi$ cubic units, so the answer is no.

c)

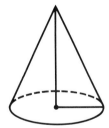

d) $\frac{1}{3}\pi 4^2 \cdot 9 = 48\pi$ cubic units.

e) $\frac{1}{3}\pi 9^2 \cdot 4 = 108\pi$ cubic units.

Set II

*1. a) $2(\frac{1}{3}\pi 2^2 \cdot 3) = 8\pi$ cubic inches.

b) $\pi 2^2 \cdot 6 - 8\pi = 24\pi - 8\pi = 16\pi$ cubic inches.

*2. $c = 2\pi r$, $31.4 = 2(3.14)r$, $r = 5$.
$\frac{1}{3}\pi 5^2 \cdot 9 - 35.5 = 75\pi - 35.5 \approx$
$235.5 - 35.5 = 200$ cubic inches.

*3. $\pi(4.2)^2 \cdot 20 - \pi 4^2 \cdot 20 = 20\pi(4.2^2 - 4^2) =$
$20\pi(17.64 - 16) = 20\pi(1.64) \approx 103$ cubic inches.

Set III

The point to which the flea walks does not matter. Every path from A to a point on the ellipse to B has the same length.

Chapter 15, Lesson 7

Set I

*3. a) $4\pi 4000^2 \approx 201,000,000$ square miles.

b) $\frac{4}{3}\pi 4000^3 \approx 268,000,000,000$ cubic miles.

Set II

*2. a)

Radius of sphere	10	20	30
Surface area	$4\pi 10^2$ = 400π	$4\pi 20^2$ = 1600π	$4\pi 30^2$ = 3600π
Volume	$\frac{4}{3}\pi 10^3$ $\approx$ 1333π	$\frac{4}{3}\pi 20^3$ $\approx$ 10667π	$\frac{4}{3}\pi 30^3$ $\approx$ 36000π

b) Ollie's conclusion is wrong, as a simple counterexample illustrates. Suppose the radius of a sphere is 1 inch. Then its volume is $\frac{4}{3}\pi 1^3 = \frac{4}{3}\pi$ cubic inches and its surface area is $4\pi 1^2 = 4\pi$ square inches. But $4\pi > \frac{4}{3}\pi$.

*3. a) $4\pi r^2 = 36\pi$, $r^2 = 9$, $r = 3$ units.

b) $\frac{4}{3}\pi 3^3 = 36\pi$ cubic units.

c) We are to show that if the surface area and the volume of a sphere are the same number, then its radius is 3 units.

If $4\pi r^2 = \frac{4}{3}\pi r^3$, then $1 = \frac{1}{3}r$ (division by $4\pi r^2$) and $r = 3$ (multiplication by 3).

*4. Since the radius of the ball of string was 18 inches, its volume was
$\frac{4}{3}\pi 18^3 \approx 24,400$ cubic inches.

(24,400 cubic inches)(0.03 pound per inch) ≈ 730 pounds.

Set III

The first exercise of Set I implies that, if the radius of a sphere is doubled, its volume is multiplied by 8. If the balloon is blown up at a steady rate, 8 times the volume should require 8 times as much time.
$8 \cdot 5 - 5 = 35$ seconds.
It would take 35 more seconds.

Chapter 15, Lesson 8

Set I

Proof for Exercise 2.

1. $A_1 = 4\pi r_1^2$ and $A_2 = 4\pi r_2^2$. (The surface area of a sphere is $4\pi r^2$, where r is its radius.)

2. $\frac{A_1}{A_2} = \frac{4\pi r_1^2}{4\pi r_2^2}$. (Division.)

3. $\frac{A_1}{A_2} = (\frac{r_1}{r_2})^2$. (Substitution.)

Set II

*2. a) If the Athenians doubled the edges of the original cube, its volume would be multiplied by 8. (All cubes are similar.) The ratio of the volumes of two similar solids is equal to the cube of the ratio of any pair of corresponding segments: $(\frac{2}{1})^3 = \frac{8}{1}$.

b) Since the ratio of the volumes is $\frac{2}{1}$, the ratio of the edges would be $\frac{\sqrt[3]{2}}{\sqrt{1}} = \frac{\sqrt[3]{2}}{1}$. Hence the length of an edge of the larger cube is $\sqrt[3]{2}$ times the length of an edge of the smaller one.

*3. a) Since the cans are similar in shape, the ratio of their volumes is
$$(\frac{12}{8})^3 = (\frac{3}{2})^3 = \frac{27}{8}.$$

The colossal can is more than three times larger than the large one $(\frac{27}{8} > 3)$, but it costs only three times as much $(\frac{72}{24} = 3)$. Therefore the colossal can is the better buy.

b) If the walls of the two cans have the same thickness, the ratio of the amount of metal in the cans is equal to the ratio of their surface areas.
$$\frac{x}{4} = (\frac{3}{2})^2, \quad \frac{x}{4} = \frac{9}{4}, \quad x = 9.$$
The metal in the colossal can costs 9¢.

c) The ratio of the amounts of dog food in the cans is equal to the ratio of their volumes.
$$\frac{x}{8} = (\frac{3}{2})^3, \quad \frac{x}{8} = \frac{27}{8}, \quad x = 27.$$
The dog food in the colossal can costs 27¢.

d)

	Selling price	Cost of metal		Cost of dog food		Total cost
Large can	24¢	4¢	+	8¢	=	12¢
Colossal can	72¢	9¢	+	27¢	=	36¢

The selling price is twice the cost of the material in each can.

Set III

We will assume that the clams are similar and that the ratio of their weights is equal to the ratio of their volumes.
$$\frac{x}{1} = (\frac{48}{2.4})^3;$$
$$x = 20^3 = 8000.$$
The larger clam would weigh 8000 ounces, or 500 pounds.
   The 1974 edition of the Guinness Book of World Records states that a clam weighing 579.5 pounds was found in the Great Barrier Reef in 1917.

Chapter 15, Lesson 9

Set II

3. g) If $F + V = E + 2$, then $F + V + n = E + 2 + n$. (Addition.) If $F + V + n = E + 2 + n$, then $(F + n - 1) + (V + 1) = (E + n) + 2$. (Substitution.)

4. g) If $F + V = E + 2$, then $F + V + n = E + 2 + n$. (Addition.) If $F + V + n = E + 2 + n$, then $(F + 1) + (V + n - 1) = (E + n) + 2$. (Substitution.)

Set III

The truncated cube and truncated octahedron have the same number of faces, edges, and corners.
   This table shows the numbers for all five polyhedra.

Polyhedron	Faces	Edges	Corners
Cube	6	12	8
Truncated cube	14	36	24
Cuboctahedron	14	24	12
Truncated octahedron	14	36	24
Octahedron	8	12	6

Chapter 15, Review

Set I

*1.

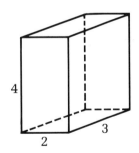

a) $3 \cdot 2 \cdot 4 \cdot 12^3 = 41,472$ cubic inches.

b) $2(2 \cdot 4 + 3 \cdot 4 + 2 \cdot 3) = 52$ square feet.

c) $\sqrt{2^2 + 3^2 + 4^2} = \sqrt{29}$ feet.

*2. b) $\frac{1}{3} \pi 4^2 \cdot 9 = 48\pi$ cubic centimeters.

c) $\pi 4^2 = 16\pi$ square centimeters.

Set II

*2. a) $V_{cylinder} = \pi r^2(2r) = 2\pi r^3$.

$V_{sphere} = \frac{4}{3}\pi r^3$.

The ratio of their weights would be equal to the ratio of their volumes.

$$\frac{V_{cylinder}}{V_{sphere}} = \frac{2\pi r^3}{\frac{4}{3}\pi r^3} = \frac{2}{\frac{4}{3}} = \frac{6}{4} = \frac{3}{2}.$$

The cyclindrical can would be 1.5 times as heavy as the spherical can.

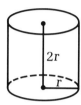 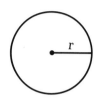

b) $A_{cylinder} = 2\pi r(2r) = 4\pi r^2$.

$A_{sphere} = 4\pi r^2$.

The amount of paint would be the same for both cans.

*3. Since the wire is 36 inches long and a cube has 12 equal edges, each edge of the cube would be 3 inches long.

$V_{cube} = 3^3 = 27$ cubic inches.

*4. As shown in the figure, each of the eight segments of ribbon is 5 inches long, so the ribbon is 40 inches long.

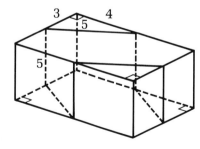

*Set III

When the wire is stretched out straight, it is a cylinder having bases with a radius of $\frac{1}{200}$ inch.

Wound up into a ball, it is a sphere having a radius of 12 inches.

Either way, its volume is the same. Letting x = the total length of the wire (the height of the cylinder),

$$\pi(\frac{1}{200})^2 x = \frac{4}{3}\pi 12^3.$$

Dividing by π and solving for x,

x = 92,160,000.

The wire would be 92,160,000 inches long. (This is about 1455 miles, not nearly long enough to reach to the moon, which is about 230,000 miles away.)

Chapter 16, Lesson 1

Set III

1. Obtuse.

2. No.

3. No.

4. Trapezoids.

Chapter 16, Lesson 2

Set II

1. a) Since $\overline{EZ} \perp \overline{ZR}$ and $\overline{AR} \perp \overline{ZR}$, $\overline{EZ} \parallel \overline{AR}$ (in a plane, two lines perpendicular to a third line are parallel to each other). Also, EZ = AR, so EZRA is a parallelogram (if two sides of a quadrilateral are both parallel and equal, it is a parallelogram).

b) Since a Saccheri quadrilateral in Euclidean geometry is a parallelogram, its opposite sides are equal.

2. In Euclidean geometry, a Saccheri quadrilateral is a parallelogram. Since the opposite angles of a parallelogram are equal, each summit angle is equal to the base angle opposite it. The base angles are right angles, so the summit angles are right angles also.

3. a) $\overline{JU}$ and $\overline{SU}$ are corresponding sides of $\triangle JAU$ and $\triangle SHU$. $\triangle JAU \cong \triangle SHU$ because JA = SH, $\angle A = \angle H$, and AU = UH (S.A.S.).

b) In a plane, two points equidistant from the endpoints of a line segment determine the perpendicular bisector of the line segment.

c) JA = SH, $\angle J = \angle S$ (the summit angles of a Saccheri quadrilateral are equal), and JO = OS. So $\triangle JOA \cong \triangle SOH$ (S.A.S.).

d) Since OA = OH (they are corresponding parts of $\triangle JOA$ and $\triangle SOH$) and UA = UH, points O and U are equidistant from the endpoints of $\overline{AH}$. Hence $\overline{OU} \perp \overline{AH}$.

Set III

Nasir Eddin assumed that, if $\overline{DI} \perp \ell$, $\overline{AE} \perp \ell$, $\angle 1$ and $\angle 3$ are acute, and $\angle 2$ and $\angle 4$ are obtuse, then DI < AE.

Quadrilateral DAEI is biperpendicular and its summit angles are unequal. Since $\angle 2$ is obtuse and $\angle 3$ is acute, $\angle 2 > \angle 3$.

Hence AE > DI (if the two summit angles of a biperpendicular quadrilateral are unequal, then the legs are unequal and the longer leg is opposite the larger angle), so DI < AE.

Chapter 16, Lesson 3

Set II

2.

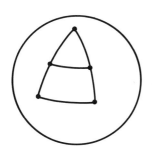

a) In Riemannian geometry, a midsegment of a triangle is more than half as long as the third side.

b) No, because there are no parallel lines in Riemannian geometry.

Set III

Although the situation described in this exercise would be impossible in Euclidean geometry, it is possible in Lobachevskian geometry. All of the conditions named are consistent with KERN being a Saccheri quadrilateral in Lobachevskian geometry because the summit of such a quadrilateral is longer than its base.

Chapter 16, Lesson 4

Set I

*3. Draw CR. Since $\angle 1 + \angle 4 + \angle P < 180^{\circ}$ and $\angle 2 + \angle 3 + \angle A < 180^{\circ}$ (in Lobachevskian geometry, the sum of the measures of the angles of a triangle is less than 180°), $\angle 1 + \angle 4 + \angle P + \angle 2 + \angle 3 + \angle A < 360^{\circ}$ (addition).

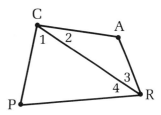

Since $\angle 1 + \angle 2 = \angle PCA$ and $\angle 3 + \angle 4 = \angle ARP$, $\angle PCA + \angle A + \angle ARP + \angle P < 360^{\circ}$ (substitution).

Set II

3. a)

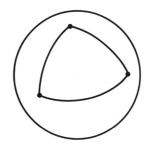

b) Yes. Since the measure of each angle must be less than 180°, the sum of the measures of the three angles of a triangle in Riemannian geometry must be less than 540°.

Set III

In Lobachevskian geometry, $\angle 1 + \angle 2 + \angle EOS < 180°$ and $\angle EOL + \angle 3 + \angle 4 < 180°$. Therefore, $\angle 1 + \angle 2 + \angle EOS + \angle EOL + \angle 3 + \angle 4 < 360°$. Since $\angle EOS$ and $\angle EOL$ are a linear pair, $\angle EOS + \angle EOL = 180°$. Subtracting,

$$\angle 1 + \angle 2 + \angle 3 + \angle 4 < 180°.$$

Furthermore, since OS = OE and OE = OL (all radii of a circle are equal), $\angle 1 = \angle 2$

and $\angle 3 = \angle 4$. Substituting,
$$\angle 2 + \angle 2 + \angle 3 + \angle 3 < 180°$$
so
$$2\angle 2 + 2\angle 3 < 180°.$$
Dividing by 2,
$$\angle 2 + \angle 3 < 90°.$$
Since $\angle SEL = \angle 2 + \angle 3$, $\angle SEL < 90°$.

We have shown that in Lobachevskian geometry, an angle inscribed in a semicircle is acute. A similar proof can be given that, in Riemannian geometry, an angle inscribed in a semicircle is obtuse.

List of Transparency and Worksheet Masters

The following transparency and worksheet masters are available in book form from W. H. Freeman and Company. The pages are perforated so that they may be removed and used to make projection transparencies and duplicating masters with a thermographic reproduction machine. The transparencies are numbered consecutively with respect to each chapter of the text and are referred to by these numbers in the lesson plans contained in this guide. There are 363 transparencies—many have overlays—and 11 worksheets in all. Some of them are to be used with particular exercises in the text, in which case the chapter, lesson, set, and exercise are given in parentheses.

0-1	Map around Mediterranean	1-11	Sugar ad
0-2	Title page of Euclid's <u>Elements</u>	1-12	If a soft drink does not contain sugar
0-3	Equilateral triangle	Ov. A	Crummy Cola
0-4	Surfer and spotter cartoon	Ov. B	Sparkle Soda
1-1	General Electric flashcube ad	1-13	A proof that a cow has nine legs
		1-14	Lewis Carroll quotation: Seeing nobody
1-2	Test question: Going by plane	1-15	Lewis Carroll quotation: Nobody walks slower
Ov.	Corrected version		
1-3	Avis ad	1-16	Fuzzy
1-4	Two-circle Euler diagram	1-17	Some basic geometric terms
1-5	A Grant for today's geometry lesson	1-18	Klutzes and inept blockheads
Ov.	Portrait of U. S. Grant	Ov.	Converse
1-6	When it rains, it pours	1-19	Euler diagram: Klutzes and inept blockheads
1-7	If all pelicans have enormous beaks	1-20	The presidential parade
1-8	Electric circuit	1-21	Five and six points and the lines they determine (1-8-III: 1 and 2)
1-9	Avis ad		
1-10	If you're not the biggest, you have to try harder	1-22	Ten points and the lines they determine (1-8-III: 3)
Ov. A	Avis is No. 2		
Ov. B	Avis has to try harder	1-23	Arthur Conan Doyle quotation: A series of inferences
Ov. C	Hertz is No. 1		
Ov. D	Hertz doesn't have to try harder	1-24	Emerson, Lake, and Palmer